Drugs from A to Z:
A Dictionary

Drugs
from A to Z:
A Dictionary
Richard R. Lingeman

McGraw-Hill Book Company

New York   St. Louis   San Francisco   London   Sydney   Toronto   Mexico   Panama

Library of Congress Catalog Card Number 68-30559
121314151617 MUMU 765432

ISBN 07-037910-6 pbk - 37911-4 cl

Grateful acknowledgment is hereby made to the authors and publishers
for permission to quote from the following (which are also cited within
this text):

Tom Alexander, "Drugs and the Law." Reproduced from *The Drug Takers.*
Copyright 1965, Time, Inc., New York.

Jack Altman and Marvin Ziporyn, M.D., *Born to Raise Hell: The Untold
Story of Richard Speck.* Reprinted by permission of Grove Press, Inc. Copyright © 1967 by Jack Altman and Marvin Ziporyn, M.D.

Charles Baudelaire, *Les Paradis Artificiels* (translated by Norman Cameron),
Weidenfeld and Nicolson Ltd., London, 1860.

Claude Brown, *Manchild in the Promised Land,* The Macmillan Company,
New York, 1965.

Tom Buckley, "The LSD Trigger," *The New Republic,* © 1966, Harrison-
Blaine of New Jersey, Inc.

William Burroughs, *Junkie,* Ace Books, New York, 1953.

William Burroughs, *Naked Lunch.* Reprinted by permission of Grove Press,
Inc. Copyright © 1959 by William Burroughs.

John Cashman, *The LSD Story,* Fawcett Publications, Inc., Greenwich,
Connecticut, 1966.

"The Cheapest Turn-On in Town," *World Journal Tribune,* November 6,
1966.

Desoxyn (Manufacturer's Statement), Abbott Laboratories, Chicago, 1967.

Havelock Ellis, "Mescal: A New Artificial Paradise," *The Contemporary
Review,* January, 1898, by permission of Leonard Scott Publication Co.

"Everybody's Turning On," *Look,* August 8, 1967.

Seymour Fiddle, *Portraits from a Shooting Gallery,* Harper & Row, Publishers, Incorporated, New York, 1967.

Paul J. Fink, Morris J. Goldman, and Irwin Lyons, "Morning Glory Seed
Psychosis," *Archives of General Psychiatry,* Vol. 15, August, 1966.

Theophile Gautier, *Revue des Deux Mondes,* 1846. Translation by Polly
Kraft for David Ebin (ed.), *The Drug Experience,* The Orion Press, New
York, 1961.

Allen Ginsberg, *Kaddish and Other Poems.* Copyright © 1961 by Allen Ginsberg. Reprinted by permission of City Lights Books.

Louis S. Goodman and A. Z. Gilman (eds.), *The Pharmacological Basis of Therapeutics,* The Macmillan Company, New York, 1965.

Richard Goldstein, *One in Seven: Drugs on Campus.* Reprinted by permission of Walker and Company. Copyright © 1966 by Richard Goldstein.

Albert Hofmann, in H. J. DeShon, M. Rinkel and H. C. Solomon, "Mental Changes Experimentally Produced by LSD," *Psychiatric Quarterly,* Vol. 57, 1952.

M. Hoffman, *Comprehensive Psychology,* Vol. 5, 1964.

Helen MacGill Hughes (ed.), *The Fantastic Lodge,* Houghton Mifflin Company, Boston, 1961.

Aldous Huxley, *The Doors of Perception,* Harper & Row, Publishers, Incorporated, New York, 1954.

"Iceberg Slim," *Pimp. The Story of My Life,* Holloway House Publishing Company, Los Angeles, 1967.

Alexander King, *Mine Enemy Grows Older.* Copyright © 1958 by Alexander King. Reprinted by permission of Simon & Schuster, Inc.

Heinz Kusel, "Ayahuasca Drinkers among the Chama Indians," *Psychedelic Review,* No. 6, 1964.

Jeremy Larner and Ralph Tefferteller, *The Addict in the Street.* Reprinted by permission of Grove Press, Inc. Copyright © 1964 by Grove Press, Inc.

Peter Laurie, *Drugs,* Penguin Books, Ltd., Harmondsworth, England, 1967.

Louis Lewin, *Phantastica: Narcotic and Stimulating Drugs.* Translated by P. H. A. Wirth. Copyright, ©, 1964 by Routledge & Kegan Paul, Ltd. Reprinted by permission of E. P. Dutton & Co., Inc.

Dr. Donald Louria, *Nightmare Drugs.* Copyright, ©, 1966 by Mel Sokolow Associates. Reprinted by permission of Simon & Schuster, Inc.

Don McNeill, "Green Grows the Grass on the Lower East Side," *Village Voice,* December 1, 1966.

Don McNeill, "Is Acid Obsolete? The New Initials Are STP," *Village Voice,* April 13, 1967.

B. Manzini and Saraval, in *Delysid (LSD-25), Annotated Bibliography Addendum No. 3,* Sandoz Pharmaceuticals, Hanover, New Jersey, 1961.

The Marihuana Problem in the City of New York, by The Mayor's Committee on Marihuana. Copyright 1944, The Ronald Press Company, New York.

The Marijuana Newsletter, Peace Eye Press (Ed Sanders, Publisher), 1965. Reprinted by permission of William Beckman.

Mezz Mezzrow and Bernard Wolfe, *Really the Blues.* Copyright 1946 by Mezz Mezzrow and Bernard Wolfe. Reprinted by permission of Harold Matson Co., Inc.

James Mills, "Karen and John: Two Young Lives Lost to Heroin." Reproduced from *The Drug Takers.* Copyright 1965, Time Inc., New York.

James Mills, *The Panic in Needle Park.* Reprinted with the permission of Farrar, Straus & Giroux, Inc. Copyright © 1965, 1966 by James Mills.

Ed Sanders, *Coming Down,* United International Copyright Representatives, Ltd., New York © 1966.

Richard E. Schultes, "Botanical Sources of the New World Narcotics," *Psychedelic Review,* No. 2, 1964.

Hubert Selby, Jr., *Last Exit to Brooklyn.* Reprinted by permission of Grove Press, Inc. Copyright © 1957, 1960, 1961, 1964, by Hubert Selby, Jr.

J. S. Slotkin, "Menomini Peyotism," *Transactions of the American Philosophical Society,* Vol. 42, Part 4, 1952.

Howard Smith, "Scenes" (Column), *Village Voice,* 1966.

Richard B. Stolley, "Synanon: The Open Door and the Blunt Truth," Reproduced from *The Drug Takers.* Copyright 1965, Time, Inc.

Piri Thomas, *Down These Mean Streets.* © Copyright 1967 by Piri Thomas. Reprinted by permission of Alfred A. Knopf, Inc.

Hunter S. Thompson, *Hell's Angels.* © Copyright 1966, 1967 by Hunter S. Thompson. Reprinted by permission of Random House, Inc.

Alexander Trocchi, *Cain's Book.* Reprinted by permission of Grove Press, Inc. Copyright © 1960 by Grove Press, Inc.

R. Gordon Wasson, "Rite of the Magic Mushroom." Reproduced from *The Drug Takers.* Copyright 1965, Time Inc., New York.

Abraham Wikler, *Opiate Addiction. Psychological and Neurophysiological Aspects in Relation to Clinical Practice,* Charles C Thomas, Publisher, Springfield, Ill., 1953.

Warren R. Young and Joseph R. Hixon (eds.), *LSD on Campus,* Dell Publishing Co., Inc., New York, 1966.

To Anthea

Preface

When I was in college, drugs were things you bought at the drugstore. Oh, there was a small benzedrine scene on campus around exam time, and one read about marijuana in Jack Kerouac, who was then in vogue, but an offer of marijuana probably would have been turned down without the slightest compunction. In those benighted days, in the early fifties, our "trip," if we indeed had one, was Ortlieb's beer. LSD had been discovered, but if someone had mentioned it, we would probably have thought he meant an honorary degree.

The fact that in recent years drug use, or more correctly abuse, has radically changed is, of course, the *raison d'être* of this book. My maiden entry into the new drug scene came a couple of years ago, when I wrote an article for the *New York Times Sunday Magazine* on the then infant subculture of hallucinogenic-drug users. For an innocent user of nicotine, caffeine, and alcohol, it was a case of what the anthropologists call "cultural shock." New York's "East Village" (known to Harry Golden fans as the lower East Side) was just opening itself up to a new wave of immigrants—young people who were knowledgeable about "trips"; who talked of "burn artists," "narcs," and "fuzz"; who patronized "head shops" and had Timothy Leary as their idol and LSD as their sacrament. In the course of the article I did considerable research in the excellent New York County Medical Society Library and interviewed such students of the field as Dr. Jerome Jaffe and Mr. Leon Brill, of Albert Einstein Medical College; Dr. Donald B. Louria, of Bellevue Hospital; and Mr. George Belk, District Supervisor of the federal Bureau of Narcotics.

So when the opportunity arose to do a book about drugs in dictionary format, I was immediately intrigued—not only because, as a thrifty writer, I would have an opportunity to employ some of the research which was necessarily omitted from *The Times* article—but because the subject itself had become a fascinating one to me.

I must express my gratitude to Dr. Herbert Berger for reading the manuscript and pointing out the inevitable errors of a layman and for writing an introduction to the book. The views expressed and any present errors are, of course, the author's responsibility. Dr. Berger has a distinguished record of public service in the drug-addiction field and in the treatment of drug addicts—an act of courage for a physician in view of our rigid narcotics laws, which have transformed narcotics abuse from a medical into a penal problem. (In his comments on the manuscript, Dr. Berger remarked *en passant*: "Note—addict is really self-destructive. He is consciously committing suicide slowly! One once described drugs as 'Having all the advantages of death without its permanence.' ") Because of the high relapse rate and the low economic level of the typical addict, it is also rather unrewarding both emotionally and financially.

A word about the purpose and format of this book. It is primarily intended for laymen, especially those who through occupation or association have become concerned about drugs. The approach is two-pronged. Drugs are discussed from both a pharmacological and sociological point of view. It might be appropriate here to define what we mean by a "drug" in the context of this book. Generally speaking, a drug is any substance, synthetic or naturally occurring, with a more or less predictable effect on the human physiology. We here are concerned with the so-called "mind" drugs, that is, drugs which alter consciousness, mood, affect, and emotions, which intoxicate and induce pleasurable sensations, and which have been used for extramedical purposes by persons seeking these effects. A "drug" really has five facets: (*1*) its chemistry or molecular structure; (*2*) its pharmacological action, that is, its effects upon mind and body; (*3*) its clinical use, that is, the selective employment of these effects in medical therapy; (*4*) its sociopsychological context, that is, who takes it and by what methods, their motives, the subcultures they form, and so on; and finally, (*5*) its implications to society, that is, how it is used in medicine (if it is used) and with what implications, how society regards its extramedical use, what the moral attitude toward it is, what legal controls exist for it, and how society defines its "abuse," in other words, what uses the culture sanctions and what uses it considers abnormal.

Tying in with the last two categories, since language is a social gesture, is the slang, argot, or cant employed by drug users. It is part of the mystique of drugs to give them special names, different from their common or medical names. It provides a kind of code for the drug subculture in carrying out illegal transactions, and it serves to forge loose fraternal bonds among them and keep the "square" world on the outside. There are probably deeper, more primitive motives at work, too, as well as the desire to be "hip," "in," or easily colloquial. Cocaine is called "coke," and it is easy to understand the abbreviating process. But why is it also called "girl"? And why is heroin called "junk" or "shit" or "crap"? I have attempted, whenever possible, to go into these origins, both psychological and etymological. In doing so, I have found Eric Partridge's work in the field of slang of great help. Two of his books which were of particular assistance are *A Dictionary of Slang and Unconventional English, 6th ed.* (The Macmillan Company, New York, 1967) and *A Dictionary of the Underworld, rev. ed.* (The Macmillan Company, New York, 1961).

Drug slang changes, and some words pass out of vogue as others come along. New drugs demand new words, and there is even a form of technological change at work in that new drugs sometimes replace other drugs in favor, making the slang that grew up around them obsolete. The discovery of heroin, a highly potent narcotic easily trafficked, meant that the use of opium declined, at least in the United States. Nevertheless, as Partridge points out, much underworld argot is conservative in its development. For example, "junk" for narcotics has been with us since at least the turn of the century. New classes of drug users (college students, for example) also adopt many of the old words from the addict underworld, sometimes altering their meanings, sometimes taking them over intact. Some of the words in this book are admittedly what Partridge calls "cliquisms and ephemerides"; they are included, nevertheless, because of the light they cast upon the drug user's world. Similarly, some words which are probably obsolete (so indicated, whenever possible) are also included for the same reason and because they may be lineal relatives of current terms.

A word on the form of this dictionary. Slang and drug names are intermixed. All entries are in alphabetical order, dictionary style; that is, *AMT* follows *amphetamines*. A word is often followed by brackets enclosing the derivation; the chemical composition, or the chemical, generic, and manufacturer's names of a drug; or the meaning of foreign words. There are two abbreviations used to credit source for derivations of entries, i.e., EP for Eric Partridge, and MM for Mezz Mezzrow. The other less frequently appearing sources are not abbreviated. Cross-references are indicated by SMALL CAPITALS. In the body of an entry on a drug the cross-reference generally refers to specific kinds of drugs, such as particular brands of amphetamines, e.g., BENZEDRINE, or, conversely, to a more general discussion of a specific drug; that is, in the entry for Seconal, a brand name of a barbiturate, the reader is referred to the general discussion of BARBITURATES or else to a term, such as WITH-DRAWAL SYMPTOMS, discussed at greater length as a separate entry. With some slang words, related terms are referred to for purposes of comparison. An entry is cross-referenced only once in a given article. Words are generally not marked for cross-reference if they are merely synonyms. With *compare,* however, small capitals are used for such entries. When an entry is followed by a word or words in small capitals, it is a synonym for that main entry. When such a cross-reference is preceded by *see,* the second term is not a synonym but an entry where more information can be found.

Quotations that follow the definitions are intended to illustrate how a slang term is used or its implications or to provide a subjective description of the effects of a drug. Such accounts, it should be noted, represent one man's experience, and thus are not necessarily typical.

A final caveat: this book is not intended to be a guide to drug taking. As practically all the drugs in this book should be taken only under the direction of a physician (if at all), only his advice, and not the amounts set down herein, should be heeded.

R.R.L.
New York City

Contents

Introduction

Communication begins with words—and words can bring understanding only when their connotations are the same for those who are communicating.

I can recall with humor a third-year class in medical school when the professor of obstetrics asked me how to repair a tear such as a woman might suffer in giving birth to a large infant.

Said he, "Describe every step of your procedure."

I started to recite, "I would grasp the injured edge of the tissue with a pair of forceps in my left hand and—"

He interrupted sarcastically, "Why not use a shovel?"

The word "forceps," to an obstetrician, was the large two-handled device used to grasp the head of an infant when it cannot be born spontaneously. To me the term meant the kind of tweezers a woman might use to pull an unsightly hair from her chin.

This shattering experience, of which some of my classmates still like to remind me, had one salutary effect that has somewhat healed my wounded ego: it made me profoundly aware of the need for precise definitions.

When Richard Lingeman's pioneer and monumental effort to compile a lexicon of terms from the world of drug abuse first came to my attention, I greeted it with ambivalence—first, with enthusiasm, for it was long overdue; second, with remorse, for why didn't I think of doing this myself?

Over the last twenty years, I have taken part in many symposia in which experts representing various disciplines explored the problems of narcotic addiction. Here were police officials, pharmacologists, public prosecutors, judges, teachers, guidance counsellors, clergymen, and physicians. A good part of our time had to be spent in defining terms to everyone's satisfaction; we could not simply say "I mean what I mean and not what I say."

Since our efforts would help various legislatives bodies draft laws to combat drug addiction, we were acutely aware of the need for precise definitions: ambiguity in the meaning of the law would result in confusion and even chaos in its enforcement. We therefore compiled a glossary of terms. But our definitions were necessarily arbitrary, because there was no standard reference work that adequately covered the subject. Most of the terms used by addicts are slang, and they increase and change too rapidly for most dictionaries to cope with them.

Not too many years ago the students of addiction were concerned only with the opiates—tinctures and infusions prepared from powdered opium. Some addicts smoke the product of the poppy directly. Then the various alkaloids, the active principles, of opium were isolated, and we were faced with addiction to much more potent materials, such as morphine. Still later, heroin was introduced as a nonaddictive substitute for morphine. Unfortunately heroin did indeed replace its predecessor, only to produce the much more complicated addiction problem which faces us today.

As time went on, many new synthetic drugs appeared—demarol, methadone, and laterine, to name a few—whose formulas were very different from those of morphine, heroin, and the other alkaloids of opium. But their effects were almost identical with those of the opium derivatives. These new drugs, too, were looked upon as panaceas which one day would cure addictions, but they proved to be as dangerous and as habit-forming as their precursors.

Then came the barbiturates—the sleeping pills and sedatives. Still more recently, the tranquilizers have appeared on the scene, and at the other end of the spectrum stimulants like the amphetamines have been introduced.

The drug group now receiving the widest publicity is the psychedelics, or hallucinogens. New hallucinogens are being synthesized almost daily. Others, such as marijuana, have been in use for centuries. Chemicals like psilocybin and fly agaric have been used by primitive peoples to produce trances as a part of religious rituals. There seems never to have been a single race of man that has not felt the need to escape from reality through the medium of drugs!

We cannot help but reflect on this truth as we blame our present preoccupation with drugs on the pressures of modern society. It is quite probable that the contemporary American is less subject to stress than was any predecessor. Our society will not let him starve; it will not permit him to suffer untreated when he falls ill. It insists on housing him. At no time in history were his basic needs met so adequately. Yet modern man, like his neanderthal forebear, is beset by frustration. Sometimes he responds by running away from his problem. Physical flight is the often-attempted means of escape; drug taking is another.

As pharmaceutical chemists continue to synthesize new drugs, many of which find their way onto the market both licitly and illicitly, the narcotics problem multiplies exponentially. Until recently most addicts used heroin or barbiturates or stimulants such as amphetamine. Today multiple addictions are the rule rather than the exception. A variety of materials is used because one drug or the other is not obtainable at the time, or because the addict hopes to overcome different kinds of discomfort with different kinds of drug. Several years ago a cartoon appeared in the *New Yorker* magazine which depicted a man standing before a vending machine. Across the top was the legend "Start the Day Right." The machine buttons had such labels as "Tired–Benzedrine"; "Nervous–Phenobarbital." It was difficult for me to smile at this piece of humor; too many of my patients could have posed as the bewildered man reaching for a coin to insert in the machine. For it is all too true that the multiple addict often starts his day with amphetamine and keeps using it all day long in order to be "the life of the party." However, when night time approaches, he is still hopped up and thus unable to sleep. He then turns to a barbiturate sedative for relief. In the morning he has such a hangover from the massive dose of barbiturate he needed to bring on sleep that he must have still larger amounts of his stimulant.

Multiple addictions are also found in the world of sports. Some boxers, for example, take a combination of heroin and amphetamine in the hope that the former will keep them from suffering too much from the blows while the latter will keep them from tiring. This is often specious reasoning in the extreme, but it tends to further complicate the study of addictions.

How many addicts are there? No one knows. Laws which drive these people underground obscure the answer, but some figures are available. Over thirty thousand narcotic addicts were registered in New York City in a two-year period. Names are obtained primarily from police records; some addicts voluntarily come to physicians' offices or clinics. Most impoverished addicts must eventually come to the attention of the authorities because the cost of narcotics usually exceeds their earning capacity. Addicts are often unemployable. They are not dependable, often steal from their employers, and are narcotized—largely incapacitated—much of the time, so they usually lose their jobs. Most become addicted too young to acquire a salable skill, so they must steal to support the enormous cost of their habits. The District Attorney of New York County tells me that fences pay only about one-fifth the retail price for stolen goods. Thus, a $50-a-day addict must steal about $250 worth of merchandise daily. Most addicts cannot maintain this scale of theft without getting caught eventually. Thus, for this class of addict, the police figures are fairly accurate.

The wealthy addict, however, doesn't have to break laws to buy drugs and therefore rarely becomes a police statistic. Recently the public has become aware of something which physicians have known for some time: There are as many addicts on Fifth Avenue as there are on First. Addiction is no longer a disease afflicting just the subcultures of our great cities. It has become an urgent problem for all segments of society.

To these addicts must be added the 6 million homeless alcoholics. This is not the total figure, for only some 5 percent of these addicts are female. Females are just as prone to addiction as males, but they are hidden and protected by their families—often sequestered in upstairs bedrooms with "sick headaches," "female troubles," and the like.

How much does addiction cost? Several years ago I was commissioned with some others by Mayor Robert F. Wagner to find the cost of drug addiction in New York City. The figure we arrived at—$5 billion— seemed so large that we reviewed it by various accounting methods. All yielded similar answers—narcotic addiction cost $625 per person per year. This included the cost of apprehending, trying, and jailing addicts and pushers; welfare costs for addicts and their dependents; and—the largest sum of all—the value of the stolen goods. Yet neither the number of registered addicts nor the material cost of addiction tells the whole story. The real immeasurable price is paid in threatened lives, wasted potential, broken homes, and misery. Is narcotic addiction increasing? This, too, is hard to evaluate. There are many more arrests today—but this may indicate more police activity rather than more addiction. For whatever this figure is worth, arrests have increased over 1,000 percent in the past ten years. Significantly, such distressing figures are found not only in a known addiction center like New York City but also in a prosperous suburban area like Westchester County. Such data certainly suggest that addiction is increasing.

It is no secret that drugs have become a problem on college campuses. A Harvard survey suggests that over 25 percent of the student body has experimented with drugs and that over half of the experimenters continue to use them. Although these figures are obtained through questionnaires with guaranteed anonymity, they are inaccurate, as are all estimates of the incidence of drug abuse.

Addiction is no respecter of class, race, education, or geography. It has become imperative that our ignorance of its causes and consequences be dispelled as rapidly as possible. Richard Lingeman's *Drugs from A to Z* is a signal contribution to the understanding of this problem.

Herbert Berger, M.D.
New York Medical College

**Drugs from A to Z:
A Dictionary**

A. AMPHETAMINES.

A-bomb. [since the 1940s—*EP*] a mixture of MARIJUANA and HEROIN smoked in a cigarette (a practice also called DUSTING). Both word and practice may be rare. More preferred are the combinations OPIUM and HASHISH and PALL MALL AND PAREGORIC.

Acapulco gold. [from the golden brown color] also called gold and golden leaf. A kind of MARIJUANA considered especially potent by users, grown near Acapulco, Mexico (potency of marijuana varies with its origin; see CANNABIS SATIVA). It is priced from 15 to 60 percent higher than the lowest "grades." Compare MEXICAN GREEN.

> This is a special grade of pot growing only in the vicinity of Acapulco. The color is either brownish gold or a mixture of gold and green. This grade has a potency surpassed by few of the green varieties and usually comes at slightly higher prices or in short weights.
> —*The Marijuana Newsletter No. 1* (Jan. 30, 1965)

ace. [from *ace,* highest card in the deck; unparalleled, number one; since the 1940s] a MARIJUANA cigarette. *Obsolete?*

1-acetyl-*d*-lysergic acid diethylamide. a chemical congener of LSD-25.

acid. [from a shortening of *d*-lysergic *acid* diethylamide; since around 1960] LSD-25.

acid freak. [from *acid,* LSD-25, and FREAK, suggested by bizarre behavior and states of consciousness induced by a HALLUCINOGEN, and *to freak,* to be under the influence of LSD-25] *1.* a user of LSD-25. *2.* one who exhibits the dress, behavior patterns, etc., of the LSD cult and whose behavior is bizarre.

acid head. [compare HEAD] frequent, habitual, often exclusive user of LSD-25; similar to ACID FREAK, except that the term connotes a subjective state of choice as much as a characteristic pattern of behavior.

acid rock. also FREAK ROCK. A kind of rock and roll music emphasizing electronically produced sounds, songs with surrealist imagery and loud, monotonous, sometimes atonal sound, or a primitive, pounding, coarse blues sound, considered to be inspired by, and compatible with, LSD-induced states of consciousness. The music originated mainly in San Francicso and was performed by groups with such concrete impersonal names as Jefferson Airplane, Dow-Jones and the Industrials, and The Grateful Dead. The music was initially associated with ACID TESTS and with the use of HALLUCINOGENS in general, though it does not follow that it is composed or played under the influence of those drugs. More famous groups such as the Beatles and the Rolling Stones have exhibited this style in some of their music. It is an oversimplification, however, to say that such music consists solely of sly encoded signals in the form of esoteric drug slang flashed among the drug cognoscenti, for this ignores the musical and poetic values sometimes expressed.

acid test. [from *acid,* LSD-25, and *test* in the sense of a psychic trial by fire] party at which guests wear bizarre, colorful costumes and clown makeup and dance randomly to the accompaniment of raga music or ACID ROCK, while slides and stroboscopic lights are flashed on the walls, the intention being to mimic and/or enhance the LSD experience. (Studies have shown that the stroboscope and variable-speed shutter enhance the MESCALINE experience.) A punch containing LSD, called ELECTRIC KOOL-ADE, is often served, sometimes to the discomfiture of participants, who unwittingly take a large amount and undergo the drug's adverse effects.

active principle. the chemical substance (or alkaloid) in a plant which produces mind-altering and toxic effects; e.g., MESCALINE, isolated from the PEYOTE cactus, has been identified as its active principle.

A.D. [initials reversed to avoid confusion with district attorney; addicts' term—H. J. Anslinger; since the 1930s] drug addict. *Obsolete.*

addiction. an overwhelming involvement with, and craving for, a substance, often accompanied by PHYSICAL DEPENDENCE, which motivates continuing usage, resulting in a syndrome of identifiable symptoms appearing when the drug is suddenly withdrawn. The addict's use of the substance becomes compulsive, so that he feels he cannot exist without it, orients his life around acquiring it, at whatever the personal and social cost, and is subjectively preoccupied with repeating his intake, in quantities that are excessive for his culture. Addiction is also characterized by a high rate of relapse after the addict has been withdrawn from the substance. Although, in common parlance, addiction refers to such compulsive, excessive use of narcotic drugs, the term properly encompasses any substance so used. As the World Health Organization says:

> There is scarcely any agent which can be taken into the body to which some individuals will not get a reaction satisfactory or pleasurable to them, persuading them to continue its use even to the point of abuse—that is, to excessive or persistent use beyond medical need.

Of course some drugs, because of their pharmacological effects and the severe disapprobation with which a culture regards their use, wreak greater harm than other drugs. The opium user in nineteenth-century China was regarded with the same tolerance as that extended by many Americans to heavy social drinking as long as it does not result in destructive behavior, while a narcotic addict in this country generally must resort to desperate criminality to support his addiction. Because the social problems of addiction are more precisely defined in terms of a specific drug, the WHO has recommended that its use be abandoned in favor of the formula "drug DEPENDENCE of the [name of drug] type," further differentiating between PHYSICAL DEPENDENCE and PSYCHIC DEPENDENCE, the latter referring to a compulsive need for the drug's mental effects such that the user feels his well-being depends upon continuing its use.

The three leading approaches to treatment of addiction are (1) treating the specific drug dependence by addicting the patient to another drug (compare METHADONE, CYCLAZOCINE); (2) treating the character structure through intensive group therapy directed by cured addicts who serve as discussion leaders and authority figures (see SYNANON); and (3) incarceration and compulsory withdrawal.

adrenochrome. one of the components of "pink adrenaline," a derivative of the epinephrine produced in the body. It has an indole nucleus, identical to that in the HALLUCINOGENS, and for this reason was thought to be a chemical cause of schizophrenia, since some of the effects of that disease are similar to those produced by the hallucinogens (see SEROTONIN). When injected, adrenochrome will cause immediate physical pain unless it is mixed with the subject's own blood. Mixed or not, it produces certain abnormal and unpredictable mental effects in the subject, including changes in color and texture of the environment, distorted visual patterns, vague paranoia, and irritability with those not participating in the experience.

A-head. [from *A,* AMPHETAMINES, and HEAD, a frequent drug user] a frequent, habitual, often exclusive user of amphetamines.

a la canona. [Puerto Rican addicts' slang] abruptly stopping HEROIN and undergoing WITHDRAWAL SYMPTOMS without medication. Compare COLD TURKEY.

> He was gonna let me make it—cold turkey—*a la canona.*
> —Piri Thomas, *Down These Mean Streets* (1967)

alcohol. See ETHYL ALCOHOL.

alley. inmates' name for a dormitory corridor at the U.S. Public Health Service (Narcotics) Hospital, Lexington, Kentucky.

alphaprodine. a synthetic compound similar in its effects to MORPHINE, though a larger dosage (40 to 60 milligrams) is necessary to produce the ANALGESIC (pain-relieving) effect of the standard 10-milligram dose of morphine. Its duration (one to two hours) is somewhat less than that of morphine. Prolonged use of the drug results in PHYSICAL DEPENDENCE. WITHDRAWAL SYMPTOMS are not so severe as those associated with morphine. Alphaprodine is sold commercially as Nisentil, Nisintil, and Prisiliden. Compare MEPERIDINE.

Amanita muscaria. FLY AGARIC.

amphetamines. synthetic amines which act with a pronounced stimulant effect on the central nervous system. They are thought to POTENTIATE the effects of norepinephrine, a neurohormone which activates parts of the sympathetic nervous system. Chemically there are three types; salts of racemic amphetamines, dextro amphetamines, and methamphetamines, which vary only in the degree of control over peripheral effects and potency. The dextro amphetamines have the least peripheral activity and in general use produce fewer side effects, e.g., decrease in saliva, alteration in blood pressure, tremors, and faster heartbeat, while continuing to stimulate the brain. The amphetamines are used medically in postencephalitic parkinsonism, sometimes in manic-depressive or schizoid psychoses, and to aid in dieting by depressing appetite (perhaps by acting on the appetite control center in the hypothalamus, lessening the sense of taste and smell and, by providing a feeling of euphoria, providing a substitute pleasure for the self-indulgence of eating).

TOLERANCE to the pleasurable euphoric effects of the amphetamines develops, however, necessitating an increased dose to achieve the same effect of a lesser dose; hence, there is a temptation to increase the dose and to take by injection, and for this reason many doctors prefer that other methods of dieting be employed. The amphetamines also have some value in counteracting mild, temporary states of depression, such as caused by a bereavement, and in breaking the alcoholic's vicious circle, in which he drinks to relieve the depression caused by his previous hangover.

Amphetamines are not effective in treating deep-seated or psychotic depressions. Psychotherapists have employed them to make a reticent patient more talkative. They are also used to combat narcolepsy (involuntary sleep) and other forms of central nervous system depression, i.e., drug-induced because of their stimulant effects. Usual prescribed dosages range from 15 to 30 milligrams per day up to (by gradually increasing the daily dose) 50 milligrams in narcolepsy. As tolerance to the stimulant's effects develops and the user increases his daily dosage beyond recommended limits, he suffers loss of appetite, chronic insomnia, marked restlessness, acute paranoia, delusions, irritability, and combativeness. A single dose of 50 milligrams (ten 5-milligram BENZEDRINE tablets) when there is no tolerance to the drug may produce in some persons a toxic psychosis, with hallucinations and paranoid delusions.

Fatalities due to an overdose of amphetamine are fairly rare but have occurred. The lethal dose is not known and varies among individuals. A dose of 120 milligrams was fatal in one case, while a dose of 500 milligrams was survived in another. Based on experiments with monkeys, the lethal dose in human adults would be around 20 to 25 milligrams per kilogram of body weight (or 780 to 890 milligrams in a 150-pound man), and for children, about one-fourth to one-fifth of this amount. If prolonged use has produced tolerance to the drug, larger amounts could be consumed; a habitual user probably ingests anywhere from 200 to 1,000 milligrams a day, although not all at one time.

Amphetamines are hazardous in any amounts to people with high blood pressure or heart trouble. Overdosages may also be followed by chills, collapse, and loss of consciousness. Whatever the single dosage that will trigger a psychotic reaction, if usage is continued over a long period of time accompanied by ever-increasing dosages as tolerance to the drug's effects increases (some users increase their dosage to the point where they are taking 1,000 pills a week), a severe psychosis and possibly brain damage frequently result. Upon withdrawal and treatment, severe depression may follow, sometimes resulting in suicide. Prolonged use of amphetamines to counter fatigue is a form of PSYCHIC DEPENDENCE. The truck drivers who take amphetamines to stay awake risk severely impaired judgment, psychoses, and accompanying hallucinations, which have been the proximate cause of serious accidents. Deaths from heart failure have occurred among athletes who use them to increase alertness and endurance—most prominently long-distance bicycle racers—and this group includes a comparatively high number of abusers.

Although psychic dependence upon amphetamines does occur, PHYSICAL DEPENDENCE does not, and there are no specific WITHDRAWAL SYMPTOMS. On the other hand, the hyperexcitability and masking of fatigue they produce will take their toll: upon withdrawal the user will experience massively his accumulated fatigue and suffer from general depression, weakness, tremors, gastrointestinal disturbances, and a long, exhausted sleep, sometimes lasting days. The heavy use of amphetamines can be determined by laboratory tests on the blood or urine. The amphetamine user often has dilated pupils, dry mouth and nasal passages; exhibits excited, aggressive behavior; and talks incessantly.

Amphetamines are often used by students and persons engaged in highly cerebral work to stimulate their mental processes and promote alertness, retention, and wakefulness. Such users commonly take one or two tablets and use the drug only when they want added mental energy to cope with a task, or simply to keep awake for purposes of completing a large amount of work. Apparently amphetamines do not improve performance (errors may be increased); they do stimulate the initiative to undertake and keep on with the task. Such use, if it becomes frequent, may slide over into a mild to severe psychic dependence in which the drug becomes a prerequisite for work. The danger of sustained wakefulness over a period of time followed by relapse and exhaustion, irritability, improper eating, paranoia, and aggressiveness, or possibly acute temporary psychosis, is thus not to be discounted, even though the drug may enable the user to accomplish a specific task.

As several writers have noted, the sustained use of amphetamines to mask fatigue and produce a continuous state of stimulation is overdrawing one's account at one's energy bank, and one may have to pay up later in the form of an unpleasant mental state. Unlike foods, amphetamines do not create energy; they mobilize energy already in being. Further, amphetamines, when used in large amounts, can have bizarre effects upon the operation of the mind and indeed be inimical to systematic intellectual work. The heavy amphetamine user often compulsively engages in some grotesque parody of a mechanical task; he will start to repair something then find himself staring for hours at the object to be repaired before taking the simplest step; he may repeat an operation, or a form of physical activity, such as flipping a coin or dancing, over and over and over—an action known as *hypomania;* and though his mind may be full of brilliant ideas and verbal energy he may be unable to apply these in any way other than dissipating them in a talking jag or singing the same song repeatedly.

Amphetamines, then, appeal not only to those who seek euphoria, KICKS, sexual excitation or, simply, wakefulness but also to intellectuals, who sometimes become heavy, regular users simply because they seek to explore and savor the accelerated mental activities unleashed by the drug.

Specific commercial preparations most commonly taken by drug abusers include BENZEDRINE, DEXEDRINE, METHEDRINE, DESBUTAL, DESOXYN, and DEXAMYL. Amphetamine and amphetamine-BARBITURATE preparations are subject to the DRUG ABUSE CONTROL AMENDMENT OF 1965. Compare MAO INHIBITORS. Slang names: ups, thrusters, forwards, A, speed, etc.

Georgette twisted her face with pain, not too much though, and they wondered and thrilled. Goldie handed her half a dozen bennie and she swallowed them, gulped hot coffee and sat silent . . . trying to think the bennie into her mind . . . not wanting to wait for it to dissolve and be absorbed by the blood and pumped through her body; wanting her heart to pound *now;* wanting the chills *now;* wanting the lie *now;* Now!!! . . . Goldie sent Rosie, a demented female who acted as sortofa housemaid for gin, cigarettes and another gross of bennie. They made a small pot of bouillon and danced around it dropping tablets in and chanting *ben*nie in the *bouil*lon, *ben*nie in the *bouil*lon, whirling away the fear and boredom, gibbling, popping bennie, drinking gin, toasting Georgette. . . .

But the boys were having a ball, not too sure what they were laughing about, but really digging the bennie scene, enjoying the cold chills and the strange feeling in their jaws as they clenched and ground their teeth. . . .

Goldie opened the box of bennie slowly and proffered it to Georgette. She took two, just two thank you, smiled and laid them on her tongue and sipped her gin. They spoke quietly, smiling, sipping their drinks, at peace with all and Georgette leaned back in her chair speaking softly with Vinnie, and the others when addressed, all her movements; smoking, drinking, nodding, soft and regal; feeling extremely human; looking upon her world (kingdom) with kindness, softness; waiting, excitedly yet not nervously, for the time, soon for her to nod to her lover. . . . Goldie kept glancing at her watch and listening to hear Sheila and her john leaving, wanting to get out of this ugly room and upstairs with the boys before the light brought them down and they lost what Georgette had given them; afraid if a bennie depression set in that the boys would simply become rough and not trade. . . .

—Hubert Selby, Jr., *Last Exit to Brooklyn* (1964)

AMT. [perhaps a play on the nickname of HALLUCINOGEN DMT] AMPHETAMINES.

amyl nitrite. an inhalant dilator of the small blood vessels, which also acts to lower high blood pressure; the drug relaxes the smooth (involuntary) muscles of the body.

Amyl nitrite was discovered by Sobrero in 1847; its first medical use was in the treatment of angina pectoris. The drug is active only when inhaled; hence, it is sold as a clear, yellow, volatile liquid in glass ampuls, which are broken open, usually in a handkerchief, and inhaled. It has a fruity odor and a pungent, aromatic taste. The ampuls are called *pearls* in the medical profession; a slang name is *snapper*. Each contains 2/10 milliliter.

Amyl nitrite is still used to relieve the pain of angina pectoris and to prevent seizures, which it does by dilating the blood vessels leading to the heart. Amyl nitrite is very quick acting, taking effect within thirty seconds, hence its value in such seizures. The effects last only two to three minutes. Sometimes unpleasant side effects, such as headaches, nausea, vomiting, and flushing of the face, are experienced; the drug may also cause temporary visual disorders, e.g., halos of yellow or blue surrounding dark objects seen against a light background.

Among illicit users, the drug is prized for its alleged sexual stimulation or prolongation of orgasm as well as the perceptual and consciousness distortions it produces. In most states it is sold without prescription. TOLERANCE develops to the effects of drugs of the nitrite family. Deaths from nitrite poisoning are rare.

amys. also called pearls and snappers. Small glass vials containing AMYL NITRITE.

Amytal. [amobarbital, Eli Lilly and Company] an intermediate-acting BARBITURATE hypnotic and sedative, which acts in fifteen to thirty minutes and lasts three to six hours. The sedative dose is 20 to 50 milligrams, two to three times daily. The hypnotic (sleep-inducing) dose is 100 to 200 milligrams. Amytal comes in capsule-shaped scored tablets inscribed "Lilly," in different colors, depending on the amount of the drug:

color	milligrams	grains
light green	15	¼
yellow	30	½
orange	50	¾
pink	100	1½

Amytal Sodium. more frequently the choice of drug abusers than AMYTAL, this form comes in pale blue capsules, with a darker band of blue where the upper and lower parts join, in 60- and 180-milligram (1- and 3-grain) sizes. Prolonged heavy use, i.e., 600 milligrams per day, will result in PHYSICAL DEPENDENCE and severe WITHDRAWAL SYMPTOMS and convulsions if abruptly stopped. Subject to the DRUG ABUSE CONTROL AMENDMENT OF 1965. Slang names: blue heavens, bluebirds.

analgesic. [from the Greek *an-*, without, and *algesia,* pain] a drug producing relief from pain without loss of consciousness (although the more potent narcotics, such as MORPHINE, in large doses will produce sedation).

angel off. [police term; from [?] *angel,* a person easily victimized, like a theatrical angel, who puts up money for a show, or one who puts up the money for a criminal venture—*EP*] to arrest the customers of a peddler who is under surveillance.

> . . . but we figure we'll go up and *angel off* some of his customers. Angeling off is when you know someone's dealing and you lay back some place and bust the customers coming out. Sometimes you do it to get information on exactly where the dealer is and sometimes you do it, like this time, just to make business rough for him.
>
> —narcotics detective in James Mills, in
> *The Panic in Needle Park* (1966)

anileridine. a synthetic compound similar in effects to MORPHINE, anileridine is also very similar to MEPERIDINE, another SYNTHETIC OPIATE, in chemical structure and pharmacological actions. It is not so constipating as morphine but otherwise has similar side reactions, e.g., vomiting, nausea, feelings of warmth, faintness, and dizziness. Injections of 30 to 40 milligrams will produce analgesia equal to that of 10 milligrams of morphine with a shorter duration (two to three hours) than morphine. Like morphine, overdosage can cause respiratory depression and death. PHYSICAL DEPENDENCE results from long-term usage with WITHDRAWAL SYMPTOMS similar to those of morphine in severity. Commercial preparations are Lerinol and LERITINE. Compare DEMEROL.

antihistamines. drugs which block the action of histamine on effector cells in the nerves. A large number of commercial preparations are marketed but there is little difference among them, except in potency. The drugs are most effective in alleviating various allergies and mitigating symptoms such as sneezing, runny nose, itching of the eyes and throat, and skin conditions. Some are also useful in preventing motion sickness, and because of the drugs' sedative effects, they are used in certain nonprescription sleeping tablets. Drug abusers mainly use them either mixed with CODEINE and terpin hydrate elixir (BLUE VELVET) or as found in commercial cough syrups such as Robitussin A-C, which contains codeine, pheniramine maleate (the antihistamine), and glyceryl guaiacolate (a muscle relaxant). The effects sought are probably sedation and some euphoria. Alcohol (of which there is a high percentage in terpin hydrate elixir) acts synergistically with antihistamines, thus magnifying the sedative effects of both and possibly lowering the toxic dose of the antihistamine. Toxic doses engender excitation, restlessness, and convulsions followed by central nervous system depression; death, if it occurs, is a result of respiratory arrest. In these effects, the antihistamines resemble ATROPINE and SCOPOLAMINE. Antihistamines can also generate various unpleasant side effects among approximately 20 percent of the population. Abuse of antihistamine combinations is a fairly recent (1968) phenomenon.

anywhere. possessing drugs, as in "are you *anywhere?*", meaning "do you have any drugs?" Compare HOLDING.

army disease. MORPHINE addiction among soldiers. During the Civil War the hypodermic needle was first employed to inject the drug and was used widely and indiscriminately. Because only soldiers were so widely affected, the addiction became known as the army disease. After the war, the number of addicts in the United States was estimated at 400,000, or 1 percent of the population.

Asthmador. an obsolete asthma cigarette containing 50.4 percent STRAMONIUM and 4.5 percent BELLADONNA, both of which are toxic in large amounts and produce hallucinations. Three cases of experiments with this drug by teen-agers with resultant hallucinations have been reported, even though it is no longer dispensed.

ataraxic drug. [from Greek, *ataraxia,* perfect peace of mind] also called ataractic drug. A drug that acts as a TRANQUILIZER.

atropine. [from *Atropos,* one of the three Fates; so named because BELLADONNA was used in the Middle Ages as a poison] an alkaloid found in deadly nightshade, *Atropa belladonna,* henbane, *Hyoscyamus niger,* and other plants of the potato family (Solanaceae). It is also synthesized.

The drug is used mainly as an antispasmodic (in parkinsonism, gastrointestinal upset, peptic ulcer, vomiting, etc.), because it acts to block the action of acetylcholine, a neural activator, on the parasympathetic nerves, thus tranquilizing the smooth muscles and glands. The average dose of atropine is 0.5 milligram. Such small doses do not depress the central nervous system or inhibit normal bodily activity.

As it does not depress the central nervous system or cause sedation to the extent that SCOPOLAMINE, a related alkaloid, does, atropine is preferred as an antispasmodic. In massive doses, atropine can cause death through medullary paralysis and respiratory failure. The lethal dose is not known, and fatalities in adults are rare. Dosages of 1,000 milligrams have been survived; however, toxic reactions usually occur in doses of 10 milligrams or more. Atropine is considered less toxic than scopolamine. Fatalities among children from atropine poisoning (mainly due to eating the plants containing it) are much more common, in doses as small as 10 milligrams. Doses above 1 milligram will result in stimulation; those above 10 milligrams will be toxic, producing in adults rapid weak pulse; enlargement of the pupil so that the iris is almost obliterated (thus it may induce or aggravate glaucoma); blurred vision; flushed hot dry skin; loss of motor control; restlessness, excitement, wakefulness and hallucinations and delirium (the "belladonna jag"); followed by paralysis and coma.

Atropine acts as an antidote to the deadly poison MUSCARINE, found in the mushrooms *Amanita muscaria,* FLY AGARIC, and *A. pantherina.* It is also an antidote to certain poisons used as insecticides and in chemical warfare.

ayahuasca. [Peruvian Indian word] also called caapi and yage. A hallucinogenic beverage brewed from various species of the tropical liana *Banisteriopsis,* especially BANISTERIOPSIS CAAPI, by the Chama Indians of northeastern Peru. Sometimes the beverage is prepared with the vine alone, and sometimes in conjunction with other leaves, especially *Haemadictyon amazonica,* a member of the family Apocynaceae.

When ill, the Indians take the beverage in the belief that the plants they see in their hallucinations are those which will cure them. They also take it before an important enterprise, in the hope that their visions will foretell the future, and for pleasure and escape from the harsh reality of their life. The drug is little known among North Americans, though there is evidence that it is appearing now on college campuses.

> The first visual experience was like fireworks. . . . There were patterns that consisted of twining repeats, and others geometrically organized with rectangles or squares that were like Maya designs or those decorations which the Chamas paint on their thin, ringing pottery. . . . At times snake-like stems of plants were growing profusely in the depths, at others these were covered with arrangements of myriads of lights that like dewdrops or gems adorned them. . . . A big ship with many flags appeared in one of these flashes, a merry-go-round with people dressed in highly colored garments in another. . . . The color scheme became a harmony of dark browns and greens. . . . Naked dancers appeared turning slowly in spiral movements. Spots of brassy lights played on their bodies which gave them the texture of polished stones. . . .
>
> —Heinz Kusel, *Psychedelic Review* (1964)

B b

baby. MARIJUANA.

backwards. [certain TRANQUILIZERS will reverse panic reactions caused by LSD-25 or may be used to dampen overexcitability induced by AMPHETAMINES; i.e., they will "bring you *back*"] tranquilizers. Compare DOWNIES, UPS, and UPPERS.

bador. [Aztec, little children] Aztec name for the hallucinogenic seed from *Rivea corymbea*. See MORNING GLORY SEEDS.

bad seed. [probably a pun based upon the appearance of the cactus buds and the common phrase meaning ill-fated offspring] PEYOTE.

bad trip. a panic reaction or temporary or chronic psychosis after taking a HALLUCINOGEN, especially LSD.

bag. *1.* a measure of HEROIN diluted with MILK SUGAR or quinine and packed in the small glassine envelopes used by stamp collectors or folded paper. The proportion of heroin ranges from 1 to 80 percent, and the addict is never certain of the strength of the dose he he is taking. The usual bag contains about 5 grains of diluted material containing about 1 to 5 percent pure heroin. This is the equivalent of 3 to 15 milligrams of heroin with the analgesic potency of 9 to 45 milligrams of MORPHINE, the latter amount being used medically in very severe pain. Often referred to as a FIVE-DOLLAR BAG or THRUPENCE BAG. *2.* a measure of MARIJUANA, usually called a NICKEL ($5) BAG, containing 1/7 to 1/5 ounce of marijuana. *3.* a way of life; sometimes the bag is by choice, sometimes it represents an enclosed mode of doing that which one would like to break out of. Also, style of life, habitual way of looking at things, a closed mind due to a rigid set of beliefs, assumptions, as in "he was in the paranoia *bag*." *4.* style of music, as in "blues *bag*."

bagman. [from BAG; since the 1950s] a narcotics peddler.

bale. a pound of MARIJUANA.

bam. [from *bombita*] amphetamine pill, or amphetamine for injection.

banana smoking. a fad (1966) with overtones of *épater l'établisse-ment.* In the most favored way of preparation the fibrous skin cling-ing to the inside of the banana peel is scraped off and dried out for several hours in a slow oven. The resultant material is smoked as a cigarette or in a pipe. Although federal authorities have called the alleged hallucinogenic benefits a hoax, users claim that the amount extracted from four bananas gives a mild HIGH comparable to that from half a MARIJUANA cigarette. A New York botanist has said that the banana peels contain SEROTONIN, which heat converts to BUFOTENINE.

Inhaled in sufficient amounts, banana smoke probably does pro-duce a mild, drowsy, fuzzy mental state which users equate with a high. No hallucinations have been reported; however, the inhalation of large amounts of corn-silk smoke would probably produce a similar state of mind. In any case, the fact that bananas are a com-mon product unlikely to be made illegal gives the drug user a rationale for the legalization of all hallucinogenic drugs. Compare JACKSON ILLUSION PEPPER, MELLOW YELLOW.

bang. [from pun on *shoot* or *shot*] *1.* an injection of narcotics, as in "I had a *bang.*" *2.* to inject narcotics, as in "I was *banging* heroin."

Banisteriopsis caapi. a species of jungle liana belonging to the fam-ily Malpighiaceae and known to the Chama Indians of northeastern Peru as the vine of death. The entire vine or the more tender inner part is used by South American Indians to prepare a beverage with hallucinogenic effects under the names yage, AYAHUASCA, or CAAPI.

The Indians used it simply as an intoxicant, to get in touch with the spirits of their ancestors, for divination, in religious ritual, and for anesthesia during painful initiation ceremonies. In small doses it reportedly produces a powerful stimulation of the genital organs, causing erection in the male and engorgement of the clitoris ac-companied by vaginal spasm in the female. Enhancement of the visual powers so that the user sees lights too dim for ordinary vision and enhanced auditory acuity so that the user hears sounds too faint for normal hearing have also been reported. Other effects include blue flashes before the eyes, sensations of heat alternating with sen-sations of cold; wild bravado alternating with fear; vertigo; and intensification of colors and hallucinations of ornamental objects.

The drug has a fast onset, taking effect within five minutes; a profound sleep, accompanied by dreams full of forms fluctuating between the microscopic and the megascopic, is said to complete the hallucinatory cycle. The drug is thought to act as an excitant upon the central nervous system. The lethal dose for human beings is not known, but the lethal dose in dogs has been experimentally determined as 200 milligrams per kilogram of body weight. Death results from respiratory paralysis, while toxic doses produce muscle incoordination and convulsions. The active alkaloid extracted from the vine is HARMINE.

bank bandit pills. BARBITURATES or other sedative pills.

bar. a solid block of MARIJUANA, stuck together with honey or sugar water. Compare BRICK.

barbiturates. hypnotic and sedative derivatives of barbituric acid (malonylurea), which in itself does not have these effects. The first hypnotic barbiturate was issued in 1903 under the trade name VERONAL. Its basis was barbital (diethylbarbituric acid), and it is still used today. In 1912 came LUMINAL, a phenobarbital, and since its appearance over 2,500 barbituric acid derivatives have been synthesized; some fifty commercial brands are presently on the market, although, according to the American Medical Association, five or six types are sufficient for most clinical purposes.

The barbiturate derivatives act to depress the central nervous system, which is profoundly sensitive to their action. In small doses ("daytime sedation") they are effective in relieving tension and anxiety and, like TRANQUILIZERS, do not cause excessive drowsiness. In larger doses, their selective activity is lost, while their depressant actions spread to all parts of the central nervous system and the spinal cord, causing drowsiness, loginess, and sleep under normal circumstances. A barbiturate-induced sleep resembles natural sleep but is not precisely the same (experiments have shown that the rate of eye movement is slower, for example).

In addition to producing sedation or sleep, certain of the barbiturate derivatives are useful as anticonvulsants, e.g., in epilepsy, as analgesics when minor pain is preventing sleep (though in severe pain they cannot induce sleep and may produce excitation), and as preoperative anesthetics, or anesthetics for minor surgery.

The various barbiturates are eliminated through the kidney and the liver at varying rates of speed. By this criterion they are subdivided into three categories: *long-acting barbiturates,* which move slowly through the blood to the brain and hence are slow in taking effect but which produce a more profound and prolonged sleep because they are slow in passing through the kidney; *short- to intermediate-acting barbiturates,* which have a faster onset and do not last so long because they are more rapidly metabolized, thus tending to eliminate "barbiturate hangover," the morning-after drowsiness caused by barbiturates still in the system, and making them preferable for persons who have difficulty in falling asleep but, once asleep, tend not to wake up; and *very fast-acting barbiturates,* which take effect in approximately ten minutes when administered intravenously, producing hypnosis for about fifteen minutes, and are thus useful in inducing a rapid onset of vapor anesthetics such as nitrous oxide.

In the presence of severe pain or psychological disturbance, the barbiturates in clinical doses may produce delirium; rashes, nausea, diarrhea, anxiety, nervousness, and other undesirable side effects sometimes occur. If for some reason ingestion of a hypnotic dose is not followed by sleep, the patient may show signs of mental confusion and euphoria, even stimulation, closely resembling intoxication with alcohol. Hence, the abuse of the drug (often in combination with alcohol or HEROIN or as a substitute for them) by persons seeking this intoxication, which deteriorates eventually into slurred speech, excessive drowsiness, and unconsciousness.

TOLERANCE to the sedative effects of the drug will develop after prolonged heavy use because the rate of elimination from the system increases, necessitating a larger dose to achieve the original effect. Tolerance does not significantly increase the lethal dose, as is the case with the OPIUM derivatives; there is a maximum dose, varying widely among individuals, beyond which the barbiturate user, no matter how tolerant to the drug, cannot go and live. Since the long-acting barbiturates achieve their effects more slowly, yet more profoundly and longer, an overdose is more likely to be fatal, because there is less chance that it will be discovered in time for medical attention.

The lethal dose is generally assumed to be something more—varying with the individual—than ten times the hypnotic dose, or 1,000 to 2,000 milligrams. With such a dosage severe poisoning will occur, producing deep coma, respiratory and kidney failure, complications, and death. A person who has taken an overdose develops a typical shock syndrome, including a weak, rapid pulse, cold sweaty skin, and breathing that is either slow or rapid and shallow. The large medical armamentarium available is usually effective if treatment is undertaken in time, barring complications.

Nevertheless, barbiturates are a leading mode of suicide (over 3,000 a year in the U.S.). Further, since the insomnia states for which they are prescribed are often symptomatic of an underlying depression that may be in itself suicidal, they tend to be available to the suicide-prone individual. DRUG AUTOMATISM, the state of mental confusion in which the barbiturate user forgets how many doses he has taken, is another potential cause of overdose. On the other hand, overdosage is usually deliberate. The person who, out of impatience because his usual dose has not brought sleep, repeats the dose several times usually falls asleep before he can take a sufficient amount to cause death. Used under proper supervision (avoiding indiscriminate, open-ended prescriptions), the barbiturates are perhaps not so sinister as depicted by the press and popular fiction.

At the usual therapeutic dose (100 to 200 milligrams a day) no PHYSICAL DEPENDENCE develops. Dependence upon barbiturates to sleep is another milder form of PSYCHIC DEPENDENCE but, if unaccompanied by excessive dosage, not an abuse of the drug. In the matter of barbiturate dependence among those who do not use large amounts or seek frequent, chronic barbiturate intoxication, Dr. Henry L. Price and Dr. Robert D. Dripps say:

> The danger of *severe* physical dependence and addiction is over-emphasized; more pertinent is the question whether regular use of barbiturates and other hypnotics may not tend to obscure or exacerbate the condition underlying the insomnia, thus establishing a vicious cycle in which the patient becomes psychologically dependent on, or habituated to the drug.
>
> —In L. S. Goodman and A. Z. Gilman (eds.),
> *The Pharmacological Basis of Therapeutics* (1965)

Yet, since it is difficult for the average physician to ascertain his patient's underlying neuroses, or prevent him from obtaining prescriptions elsewhere, it seems that when prolonged or excessive barbiturate use comes to light, the patient should be hospitalized, if possible, and the underlying causes of his dependence treated. When barbiturate use is heavy (upward of 400 milligrams a day), prolonged physical dependence develops.

When the drug is suddenly withdrawn, severe, sometimes fatal,

WITHDRAWAL SYMPTOMS ensue. Indeed, these can be more dangerous than those of the HEROIN addict, especially since the latter often has a milder physical dependence due to the diluted nature of the heroin he has been taking. (Upward of a third of heroin addicts also use barbiturates, and when they are detoxified, their barbiturate addiction is a greater problem than the heroin addiction.) Withdrawal symptoms include weakness, violent tremors, anxiety, rise in temperature, rapid pulse, and violent epileptic seizures, which are sometimes fatal. By the third day psychoses resembling schizophrenia with paranoid delusions and vivid hallucinations may occur; sometimes patients die of exhaustion during this psychotic stage, which lasts up to two weeks. Gradually decreasing maintenance doses under medical supervision serves to lessen the trauma of the withdrawal period. Barbiturates tend to enhance the euphoric effects of the AMPHETAMINES while calming the overwrought nervous state they produce. Hence, the two are sometimes combined in capsules, e.g., DEXAMYL, although medical authorities are somewhat skeptical of the value of this combination, especially since it is in fixed amounts, rather than proportions and dosages adjusted by the doctor to the needs of an individual patient.

Many abusers of the barbiturates take them in combination with the amphetamines—often to induce sleep after the amphetamine JAG has become exhausting and unpleasant. Persons taking barbiturates in large amounts to sleep often fall into the habit of taking amphetamines in the morning to wake up and combat the barbiturate hangover. As their barbiturate dosage increases, their amphetamine dosage does also; this results in worse insomnia and necessitates even more barbiturates, and so on in a vicious circle (see MULTI-HABITUATION).

Barbiturates are sometimes used to combat alcoholic hangover and medically to alleviate delirium tremens; similarly, alcohol will alleviate barbiturate withdrawal symptoms, at least for a time; in the long run it will only make matters worse. Some users take barbiturates in connection with alcohol presumably for increased sedation and relaxation. But since alcohol can POTENTIATE the effects of the barbiturates, this practice is extremely hazardous, with results ranging from death by accident to death by respiratory failure.

The barbiturate addict exhibits marked social and emotional deterioration and resembles the chronic alcoholic. He neglects his appearance, loses his job, and is rejected by friends and family.

Addicts undergo wild swings in mood from elation to deep depression or hostility. Some may develop dangerous paranoid delusions; a tendency to suicidal depression will be intensified by chronic intoxication. Chronic barbiturate intoxication shows many of the symptoms of alcoholism, including slurred speech, lack of coordination, sudden blackouts (often resulting in injury), dreamy vagueness, or irrational aggressiveness. The presence of barbiturates in the blood or urine can be determined by laboratory tests. All barbituric acid derivatives not in combination with unrelated drugs are subject to DRUG ABUSE CONTROL AMENDMENT OF 1965. For descriptions of specific commercial preparations see AMYTAL, DEXAMYL, LUMINAL, NEMBUTAL, SECONAL.

CATEGORIES OF BARBITURATES

long-acting	aprobarbital, e.g., Alurate
	barbital, e.g., VERONAL
	diallybarbituric acid, e.g., Dial
	phenobarbital, e.g. LUMINAL
short- to intermediate-acting	amobarbital, e.g., AMYTAL
	butabarbital, e.g., BUTISOL
	cyclobarbital, e.g., Phanodorn
	heptabarbital, e.g., Medomin
	hexethal, e.g., Ortal
	pentobarbital, e.g., NEMBUTAL
	probarbital, e.g., Ipral
	secobarbital, e.g., SECONAL
	talbutal, e.g., Lotusate
	vinbarbital, e.g., Delvinal
very short-acting	thiopental, e.g., PENTHOTHAL

The barbiturate addict presents a shocking spectacle. He can not coordinate, he staggers, falls off bar stools, goes to sleep in the middle of a sentence, drops food out of his mouth. He is confused, quarrelsome and stupid. And he almost always uses other drugs, anything he can lay hands on: alcohol, benzedrine, opiates, marijuana. Barbiturate users are looked down on in addict society: "Goof ball bums. They got no class to them." . . . It seems to me that barbiturates cause the worst possible form of addiction, unsightly, deteriorating, difficult to treat.   —William Burroughs, *Naked Lunch* (1959)

"Do you ever hear voices?" Ziporyn asked.

. . . After a long pause [Richard] Speck said, "Well, sometimes." He paused again and added, "When I take drugs.". . .

"What kind of drugs?"

"Yellow-jackets and red-birds." (Slang names for habituating *barbiturates* [Nembutal and Seconol] capable of causing hallucinations and bizarre actions.)

"And then sometimes I shoot myself with Inhalers. You know, glue and stuff."

"And do you drink?"

"Boy, do I drink."

"What?"

"Anything I can lay my hands on—wine, beer, whiskey, gin, you name it. I drink from the time I get up till I get drunk and fall back into bed. Sometimes it makes me feel real good. But sometimes it puts me in a real bad temper, and then I get into fights." . . .

"Look, I was drinking that day. I told you how I drink. I had six red-birds. To tell you the truth, I don't know nothing about anything from eight o'clock that night till I came to, about eleven o'clock the next day. All I remember is I met three sailors in a tavern on the South Side in the afternoon. We had some drinks, then we went off some place and had a fix—a shot in the arm. I don't know what it was exactly, but it wasn't heroin. It was something in a blue bottle, I think, I don't remember a thing after that. I couldn't tell you or anybody else what any of those nurses looked like." . . .

He talked of his rages. "I got mad at just about everything. When I was a kid, just a teenager, in East Dallas, I was with some guys and we got some red-birds. Whew, they made me wild. We were watching a parade once, and we had some blockbusters (white barbiturate pills with a yellow stripe [Nembutal]). I just passed out, and they took me to a juvenile home. I don't remember exactly what happened after that, but I've been told that when my mother came to get me she says I was talking nice and polite, then suddenly I went wild. Started swinging and kicking at everybody. But I don't remember a thing about it myself." . . .

"I pepped myself up on a few red-birds, six of them, and took a walk by one of the little lakes out there, then went back to the bar for a drink. I had some whiskey and a pint of wine and got talking to these sailors, like I told you before. They took me to their room. It was dark. They had this disposable syringe and took this stuff from a bottle and started 'popping.' I tied a handkerchief around my left arm and stuck it in. All the way. Before I had even got the needle out I could feel, you know, feel—Zzzoommm—a buzzing all over me, and I was feeling real, real good.

"The next thing I know I was back in my own room and it was morning. I had a gun, and I don't know where I got it. I just sat there wondering where the hell I got that gun."

—Jack Altman and Marvin Ziporyn, M.D.,
Born to Raise Hell: The Untold Story of Richard Speck (1967)

B-bombs. [since the 1940s] BENZEDRINE inhalers. Manufacturer (Smith Kline & French Laboratories) removed them from the market in 1949 after widespread abuse. The Benzedrine-impregnated wad inside the inhaler was removed and soaked in liquid to extract the Benzedrine. One inhaler contained the equivalent of twenty-five Benzedrine sulfate tablets.

B.C. birth control pills, as in "half the girls in high school were on *B.C.*"

beast, the [Harlem, since around 1965] LSD-25.

beat. [since around 1850, to rob—*EP*] to rob or cheat someone out of money, usually money owed to the cheated person, as in "to *beat* a prostitute out of her fee."

bee. *1.* [since around 1950] an addict's habit. *Obsolete. 2.* [from *box;* originally an amount of MARIJUANA sufficient to fill a penny matchbox, a measure for purposes of sale] box or BAG of marijuana.

beinsa. [Burma] a plant, *Mitragyna speciosa,* chewed or drunk as an infusion and thought to have narcotic effects, although little is known about it. Compare KRATOM.

belladonna. [from Latin *bella donna,* beautiful lady; the drug causes pupillary dilation, considered a mark of beauty among Romans] a plant, *Atropa belladonna,* belonging to the potato family (Solanaceae) and containing the alkaloids ATROPINE, SCOPOLAMINE, and HYOSCYAMINE. Also known as deadly nightshade, belladonna has been used as a poison and sedative since ancient times and, among certain cults, for the bizarre mental effects produced by toxic doses, e.g., witchcraft and devil-worship rites in the Middle Ages. Tinctures of belladonna root and leaves and the pure atropine are most commonly used today, in combination with other ingredients, as a smooth-muscle relaxant which inhibits gastric secretions controlled by the vagus nerve in treating stomach disorders, peptic ulcers, vomiting, etc. Some closely related plants are mandrake, *Mandragora officinarum;* jimsonweed, or thorn apple, DATURA STRAMONIUM; henbane, *Hyocyamus niger;* and PITURI, *Duboisia hopwoodii.* Compare DATURA.

belly habit. [one WITHDRAWAL SYMPTOM characteristic of OPIUM is a gnawing pain or cramps in the stomach] opium ADDICTION subjectively centered in the area of the stomach. *Obsolete.*

bennies. BENZEDRINE pills.

bent. [from the idea that the mind is warped, altered) HIGH or intoxicated from a HALLUCINOGEN or NARCOTIC.

benz. [since around 1944; perhaps the slang word dates from the widespread issuance of BENZEDRINE to combat troops in World War II] Benzedrine.

Benzedrine. [AMPHETAMINE sulfate, Smith Kline & French Laboratories] a central nervous system stimulant synthesized in 1927, first used in 1932 as an inhaler decongestant and in the treatment of narcolepsy (involuntary sleep). It was also issued in ship's survival kits and to German paratroopers in the Spanish civil war. During World War II, it was issued to troops on both sides to counteract fatigue among frontline units or prior to missions requiring unusual exertion.

Manufacturer recommends dosages from 10 to 100 milligrams daily for (1) depressive states, (2) obesity (to depress appetite as an aid to dieting), (3) alcoholism, (4) narcolepsy, and (5) postencephalitic parkinsonism. Benzedrine is sold in flat pink, three-sided 5- and 10-milligram tablets with a groove down the middle; also in 15-milligram sustained-release capsules. Slang names: benz, bennies.

benzene. a toxic hydrocarbon, either chemically pure or (when derived from the distillation of crude naphtha) containing also xylene and toluene. Benzene is toxic in both forms. Prolonged inhalation or entry into the body by any other route results in acute poisoning, which can cause death by central nervous system depression and respiratory failure, or chronic poisoning, which results mainly from the action of benzene on the bone marrow over a period of months or even years, a serious (often fatal) blood disease being the ultimate result of the chemical's action. Because repeated inhalations of relatively small amounts over long periods of time may result in toxicity, most countries legally regulate the allowable exposure and concentration of the fumes in industrial use of benzene. For an abuse of benzene see SCRUBWOMAN'S KICK. Compare BENZINE.

benzine. a product obtained by the distillation of petroleum and similar to kerosene and GASOLINE. Long used as a cleaning fluid, benzine has been also inhaled for its intoxicative effects.

Benzinomaniac glove-cleaners have also been observed. The statement of a man who used *benzine* in his business apprises us of the sensations experienced after the inhalation of the vapour. He declared that he had previously consumed considerable amounts of liquor, but for six months not a drop had passed his lips. He had inhaled petrol vapour instead, this being abundantly at his disposal in his profession as bandage maker, and these inhalations completely substituted for alcohol. He said that he had experienced a wonderful feeling of peace, and agreeable delicious dreams. . . . But the agreeable effects of benzine diminished after some time. Hallucinations appeared, the patient heard the unpleasant music of barrel-organs and unharmonious singing by voices known to him; red ants crept about on his body, he saw several figures of animals and dwarfs, and once the whole room seemed to be full of colored silk threads which fluttered to and fro. In all probability these symptoms were due to the effects of benzine and cannot be explained by the cessation of the use of alcohol.

—Louis Lewin, *Phantastica: Narcotic and Stimulating Drugs* (1964)

benzodiazepine. the chemical source whose derivatives are used as MINOR TRANQUILIZERS. Among these derivatives are chlordiazepoxide (LIBRIUM) and diazepam (VALIUM), which are used as nonhypnotic sedatives in minor anxiety states and as muscle relaxants.

In potency (as determined by performance-impairment tests) the benzodiazepines are intermediate between MEPROBAMATE (e.g., MILTOWN) and the MAJOR TRANQUILIZERS derived from phenothiazine, e.g., THORAZINE. Since they are classified as minor tranquilizers, they are not used in severe psychotic states. They are reported to produce less euphoria than the BARBITURATES, meprobamate, and NARCOTICS, and so the danger of PSYCHIC DEPENDENCE may be somewhat less, though it is a matter of degree, not kind. They are dangerous when used in conjunction with alcohol, barbiturates, phenothiazines, or MONOAMINE OXIDASE INHIBITORS, all of which POTENTIATE their effects.

PHYSICAL DEPENDENCE can occur after prolonged heavy use (300 to 600 milligrams daily), and identifiable WITHDRAWAL SYMPTOMS will result if use of the drug is abruptly ceased. They include convulsions, depression, abdominal and muscle cramps, vomiting, sweating, agitation, insomnia, loss of appetite, and aggravation of underlying neurotic states.

bernies. COCAINE.

bhang. *1.* leaves, stem, and sometimes fruit of the MARIJUANA plant, CANNABIS SATIVA. *2.* a drink made from an infusion in soft drinks, milk, or water of the plant. It is drunk in India for its mild hallucinogenic effects, as a counteractant to fatigue, and in Hindu religious ceremonies. The leaves are pounded into a fine powder, a little black pepper added and then it is brewed, filtered through a cloth and drunk. When smoked, the leaves, etc., are also known as bhang. Bhang contains only about 5 percent resin; CHARAS and GHANJA are much more potent.

big bags. five- to ten-dollar BAGS of HEROIN.

big bloke. COCAINE. *Obsolete.*

big chief, the. MESCALINE.

big con. LONG CON.

Big D, the. LSD-25.

big man, the. high-level narcotics dealer; generally, the wholesaler who supplies the PUSHER.

big supplier. BIG MAN.

bindle. [from the tramp's *bindle,* his rolled pack; a thinning of a *bundle,* hence, a small packet of some drug; since the 1920s—*EP*] a small folded paper containing HEROIN. *Obsolete?*

bing. [a thinning of *bung,* purse or pocket—*EP*. Since around 1930] solitary confinement, as in "I did thirty days in the *bing.*"

bingle. [around 1950] a narcotics peddler. *Obsolete?*

Biphetamine. [*d*- and *dl*-AMPHETAMINE, Strasenburgh Laboratories] a direct central nervous system stimulant. Sold in 7 1/2-, 12 1/2-, and 20-milligram capsules containing half *d*-amphetamine and half *dl*-amphetamine. The 12 1/2-milligram has a black top and white bottom, the 20-milligram is an all-black capsule, and the 7 1/2 is all white; all are inscribed "RJS RJS." Manufacturer's recommended dose: one capsule daily. Slang name: black beauties.

bit. time served in jail, as in "I did a five-year *bit* on a pot bust."

black beauties. [from the color] BIPHETAMINE capsules.

black gunion. [(?) corruption of GUNGEON] extra potent, thick, dark, gummy MARIJUANA.

black pills. [from the color and shape of OPIUM that is prepared for smoking; since around 1910?] pellets of opium heated over a flame, placed in the pipe, and smoked.

black russian. dark-colored, very potent HASHISH.

black stuff. [from the color] OPIUM.

blank. [perhaps from the expression "I drew a *blank*"] a container filled with a nonnarcotic powder, such as talcum powder, baking soda, or cleanser, and sold to the addict as heroin. Also called lemonade. Compare DUMMY.

blast. [since around 1940?] to smoke (MARIJUANA), as in "I *blasted* marijuana."

blast party. A group gathered to smoke MARIJUANA. *Obsolete.*

blockbusters. white, yellow-striped BARBITURATE pills (possibly 50-milligram NEMBUTAL, which are half yellow, half white).

blow. [to *blow* COCAINE or MORPHINE has meant to inhale it since around 1920—*EP*] *1.* to smoke MARIJUANA as in "*blow* pot." *2.* to miss the vein while injecting HEROIN and "waste" some of the shot.

> "There," Hank said finally, squeezing the eyedropper. "A good hit. Next time be more careful. You keep *blowing* shots like that and all you'll have for an arm is abscesses."
> —James Mills, *The Panic in Needle Park* (1966)

blow snow. [from *blow,* inhale] to inhale COCAINE.

blow your mind. *1.* to drastically alter your consciousness, become HIGH on a hallucinogenic drug. *2.* to achieve a transcendent, ecstatic mental state or any abnormal state.

blow-your-mind roulette. a game played with BARBITURATE or stimulant pills.

> A group of people turn out the lights and throw a large assortment of pills and capsules on the floor. They grope around and swallow the first pill they touch, then everyone waits to see if they got an uppie or downie, an innie or outie, or a carpet tack.
> —Howard Smith, *Village Voice* (1966)

blue acid. [from the pale blue color of the liquid drug in large amounts] LSD-25. Some users also report blue-tinged hallucinations.

bluebirds. [from the color] AMYTAL SODIUM capsules.

blue heavens. [from the color of the capsule] AMYTAL capsules.

blue morning glory seeds. hallucinogenic MORNING GLORY SEEDS of the Heavenly Blue variety.

blue velvets. a combination of elixir terpin hydrate (a turpentine derivative in a high percentage of ALCOHOL), CODEINE and tripelennamine, an ANTIHISTAMINE. The ingredients are combined and taken for the sedative and minor euphoric effects.

body drugs. [probably because they depress the consciousness and induce PHYSICAL DEPENDENCE; invidious term among users of HALLUCINOGENS: "I'll never get hooked on body drugs like a junkie"] drugs of the OPIATE and BARBITURATE type. The antonym is HEAD DRUGS. Compare HARD NARCOTICS, SICKIE.

bogue. *1.* sickness from withdrawal of drugs. *2.* the first stages of WITHDRAWAL SYMPTOMS, as in "I've got the *bogue.*" Compare JONES.

BOL-148. [*d*-2-bromolysergic acid tartrate] a hallucinogenic congener of LSD-25.

bolsa. [from Spanish *bolsa,* pouch, bag] a BAG (DECK) of HEROIN.

bomb. [from the connotation of explosive, perhaps a lethal one, if the dose is of a potency greater than that to which the addict has developed TOLERANCE; since around 1950] *1.* high-potency, relatively undiluted HEROIN. *2.* a fat, prerolled MARIJUANA cigarette resembling a king-size cigarette.

bombed out. HIGH or intoxicated on a drug.

bomber. *1.* [since around 1944] a barbiturate. *Obsolete? 2.* a (fat) MARIJUANA cigarette.

> Besides, I had bought some pot with the five left over and rolled some good-size *bombers* that immediately put me into business. . . . I was selling pot—smoking it, too—regularly. A bomber here, a bomber there; it kept me going inside and out.
> —Piri Thomas, *Down These Mean Streets* (1967)

bombita. [Spanish; little bomb] *1.* ampul of DESOXYN. *2.* by extension, perhaps any AMPHETAMINE in solution. Addicts often inject amphetamines in conjunction with their HEROIN injection to enhance the RUSH (onset) of the drug and to counteract its depressant effect. *3.* COCAINE in liquid form. Compare SPEEDBALL.

boo. [from (?) *boo-gee,* addict's term for the packing between the needle and the medicine dropper used for injections—*EP*] MARIJUANA.

book, the. [by analogy to the Bible] *Physicians' Desk Reference,* an annual compendium of commercial drug preparations manufactured in the United States, with descriptions by their manufacturers intended both as an aid to the physician in looking up drugs he intends to prescribe and as publicity for the manufacturers' products. Published by Medical Economics, Inc., it is given free to physicians, and sells for $10 a copy. Pill users refer to it frequently for identification and descriptions of the pills they are taking.

boost. [from *booster,* a shoplifter; to be a shoplifter, to steal goods from a store—*EP;* since the 1930s] to break, enter, and steal, as in "I *boosted* supermarkets for meat and sold it."

booting. [from (?) *boot,* a strong pleasurable sensation; analogous to *kick—EP*] the technique of injecting *heroin* intravenously a little at a time, letting it back up in the eye dropper, injecting a little more, letting the blood-heroin mixture back up, and so on. The addict believes that this technique prolongs the initial pleasurable sensation of the heroin as it first takes effect—a feeling of warmth in the abdomen, euphoria, and sometimes a sensation similar to an orgasm. Compare DROPPER, GET OFF, GRAVY, and JERK OFF.

boss. [perhaps a deference to the authority and domination of a drug] *1.* high-potency, relatively unadulterated drugs, as in "that was really *boss* HEROIN." *2.* by extension, a dominant feeling of pleasure related to taking drugs, or anything that is the best, the strongest, etc., as in "*boss* clothes," "*boss* feeling," etc. Addicts say "horse (heroin) is boss," meaning both that it runs (bosses) their lives and that it is the superior drug.

> "When you got that *boss* feeling, man, like you're your own boss, there isn't nobody can tell you what to do in this world."
> —addict, quoted in Jeremy Larner and Ralph Tefferteller,
> *The Addict in the Street* (1964)

B.O.T. balance of time. Sentence given to a parole violator; he must serve out his full original sentence, which his parole had, of course, curtailed.

bouncing powder. COCAINE. *Obsolete?*

boxed. HIGH or intoxicated on a drug.

boy. [since around 1920] HEROIN. Also him. Compare GIRL, HER.

brain ticklers. BARBITURATE or AMPHETAMINE pills. Compare CRASH (quotation).

bread. [from *breadbox,* thieves' slang for an easy-to-crack safe, i.e., as easy as opening a breadbox; since around 1925—*EP*] money.

brick. [from the shape] *1.* pressed block of gum OPIUM or MORPHINE for shipment. *2.* pressed block of MARIJUANA, weighing 1 pound or 1 kilogram (2.2 pounds), which is shipped by mail or freight in this form. *3.* intercepted marijuana (often used by narcotics police). Compare BAR.

brick, throw a big. *1.* to commit a crime. *2.* to do something violent.

> "I know I had to go and *throw* just one *big brick*—kill myself, take an overdose; or something."
> —Claude Brown, *Manchild in the Promised Land* (1965)

bring down. [to restore to sanity. "When a customer gets ready to 'cut out' (of the MARIJUANA den) Chappy *'brings* him *down'* with milk . . . to hasten clearing of the brain."—Meyer Berger, *The New Yorker* (1938), quoted in *EP*] *1.* to cause to lose the drug exhilaration; to depress. *2.* to cause or induce a mundane, "square," or depressed state, whether one was using a drug or not. *3.* the complex of social forces antithetical to an ecstatic state of mind, specifically, the narcotics laws which harass the drug user in his search for such ecstacy.

> First Manifesto to End the Bringdown.
> —Title of an *Atlantic Monthly* article by Allen Ginsberg
> in favor of legalizing marijuana (1966)

British system, the. the rubric for the narcotics laws and treatment of addiction in Great Britain. It is not really a system, and when it was adopted, Great Britain had no addiction problem. Up to 1961, the addict population was small (around 300), most of whom were medical addicts. British doctors can legally prescribe HEROIN and

COCAINE to addicts who are registered with the government, in order to prevent WITHDRAWAL SYMPTOMS, and also in decreasing amounts as an adjunct to voluntary withdrawal by an addict. The addict might also be maintained on drugs indefinitely if the doctor believed he would "lead a useful and fairly normal life" when so maintained. (A study found that 50 percent of maintained addicts were unemployed, so that this last criterion was at best a half fiction.)

The system became subject to abuse (overprescriptions, which enabled the addicts to sell their surplus to unregistered users), and the number of narcotics addicts has increased from 300 in 1960 to 2,000 in 1966 (many of these, however, were immigrants from countries with stricter narcotics laws, such as the United States). This rate of increase held steadily upward, the number of new addicts roughly doubling every nineteen months. Addicts were also active in proselytizing among the young, who often bought their drugs illicitly rather than register as addicts (yet organized narcotics traffic, crime, and prostitution to obtain narcotics is otherwise nonexistent). As a result, the ready availability of drugs at low prices or under the National Health Service did not end the practice of PUSHING (selling drugs illicitly at an inflated price). Though the absolute number of addicts is still a tiny percentage of the population—less than in the United States, for example—the increase in addiction led the government in 1967 to tighten the law.

No longer can general practitioners prescribe to addicts; prescriptions are issued only through designated hospitals (teaching hospitals with psychiatric centers). The drugs can be prescribed only through the National Health Service. Although this provision is not expected to end completely the practice of overprescription and illicit sales at inflated prices, it will prevent doctors from prescribing for money with the attendant risk of unscrupulous doctors' prescribing excessive amounts.

brown. HEROIN of a brown color. Mexican heroin is brown; heroin from the Middle East and chemically manufactured in France is white.

brownies. [from the color of the timed-release capsule, which has a brown cap] AMPHETAMINES; perhaps specifically, DEXEDRINE Spansule capsules.

brown stuff. [from the color; as differentiated from *white stuff*, HEROIN; since around 1920] OPIUM.

bufotenine. [2-methylserotonin (5-hydroxydimethyltryptamine)] a substance first isolated from the skin of toads and used medically to raise blood pressure. It has also been isolated in two hallucinogenic plants, *Piptadenia peregrina* (see PIPTADENIA), a member of the mimosa family (Leguminosae), from whose seeds the hallucinogenic snuff COHOBA is extracted, and from the hallucinogenic mushroom FLY AGARIC, *Amanita muscaria*. It is also thought to be present in banana skins (see BANANA SMOKING). While it is not absolutely certain that bufotenine is the active ingredient of these plants, when taken alone, it does have consciousness-altering effects. In an experiment, 16 milligrams of bufotenine injected caused color hallucinations in the form of reddish and red-purple spots and a yellowish haze, an impairment of time and space perception, and mental confusion and cloudiness. The effects disappeared after forty minutes. Bufotenine is close in structure to SEROTONIN, which in turn is similar, structurally, to a part of the molecular structure of LSD.

bum bend. [from *bent, high* or intoxicated from a drug] a psychotic or panic reaction to LSD-25 or STP. Compare BAD TRIP, BUM TRIP.

> This [THORAZINE] is not the way for an STP user to mend a *bum bend.* —*Los Angeles Oracle* (1967)

bum kicks. [from *bum,* bad or malfunctional, and *kicks,* enjoyment, thrills.] troubled, worried, depressed. Compare DOWN TRIP.

> I once gave marijuana to a guest who was mildly anxious about something (*"On bum kicks"* as he put it). After smoking half a cigarette he suddenly leapt to his feet screaming "I got the fear!" and rushed out of the house.
> —William Burroughs, *Naked Lunch* (1959)

bummer. BUM TRIP.

bum trip. [from *bum,* bad or malfunctional, and TRIP, a drug experience.] an adverse reaction to a drug, usually a HALLUCINOGEN, characterized by panic, fear, etc. Compare BAD TRIP.

bundle. a package of twenty-five $5 BAGS of heroin, stacked and held together by a rubber band. The PUSHER buys them from the wholesaler in this form, then resells them individually to the addict in the street at a profit, retaining some bags for use if he is an addict.

bunk habit. [*bunk,* a couch for reclining while smoking OPIUM; since around 1930—*EP*] the practice of lying around in a place where others are smoking opium for the purpose of inhaling the fumes though not smoking oneself. *Obsolete.* Compare CONTACT HIGH.

Bureau of Drug Abuse Control. enforcement agency within the Department of Health, Education, and Welfare charged with controlling the illegal traffic in certain stimulant, depressant, and hallucinogenic drugs. The bureau was created by the DRUG ABUSE CONTROL AMENDMENT OF 1965, which brought these types of drugs under federal regulation, and is under the Commissioner of Food and Drugs of the Food and Drug Administration. The bureau is headed by a director. Its duties are surveillance of drug imports; surveillance of retail druggists to prevent illegal dispensing of drugs without a prescription; auditing the inventory records of drug manufacturers to prevent diversion of drugs into illicit channels; detection of counterfeit drugs put up for sale; investigation of illicit traffic in the proscribed drugs; and educational programs designed to emphasize the social, physiological, and psychological aspects of drugs and warn of their potential dangers. The bureau has agents in the field who have been authorized to carry arms, execute search warrants, and make arrests. Cases are turned over to the Justice Department for prosecution. The bureau's agents are currently active in investigating drug use on campuses, in cooperation with local police.

Bureau of Narcotics, Federal. an agency within the Treasury Department (reporting directly to the Special Assistant to the Secretary for Law Enforcement) responsible for administering and enforcing those sections of the Internal Revenue Code taxing narcotic drugs and marijuana and the Opium Poppy Control Act of 1942 and the Narcotic Drugs Import and Export Act. The bureau is headed by the Commissioner of Narcotics. It investigates, detects, and prevents violations of laws prohibiting unauthorized possession, sale, or transfer of OPIUM, opium derivatives, SYNTHETIC OPIATES, COCAINE, and MARIJUANA (see HARRISON NARCOTICS ACT). The bureau also regulates and sets quotas for the importation of crude narcotic drugs and manufactured narcotics and sets the amount of such drugs that can legally be manufactured in the United States for use in medicine, scientific research, and any other purpose authorized by law. Enforcement activities have been under various agencies of the Treasury Department since 1915, when the Harrison Narcotics Act took effect. The Bureau of Narcotics in its present form was organized in 1931. It has about 300 agents in the field, both in the United States and overseas, and an annual budget of $6 million.

In order to prescribe narcotics a physicians must register with his district Director of Internal Revenue and secure a registry number and tax stamp. Whenever the physician prescribes a drug in this category, he must fill out a form, in ink or typewriter, giving the name and address of the patient and of the physician, including his registry number, which is recorded with the bureau. The physician must also pay a nominal occupation tax and file an inventory of narcotics on hand. Manufacturers, wholesalers, and retailers are also required to register and keep careful and specific records of all their inventory and sales, which are cross-checked periodically by Bureau of Narcotics agents.

burese. COCAINE.

burn. [from *burn,* to cheat, or to be *burned,* to have someone run out on you with your money; since the 1920s; from *burner,* a card or dice cheat, about 1850—*EP*] *1.* to cheat or to be cheated through taking money for drugs, then absconding without delivering them or selling a short weight. A variation of the Murphy game; i.e., telling the victim that you will get him a prostitute if he pays in advance, then absconding. *2.* to inform or be informed upon in connection with drug activity.

burn artist. *1.* anyone, especially a drug peddler, noted for employing the BURN technique in order to cheat others. *2.* a police informer, a stool pigeon.

burned. *1.* to be revealed as a drug peddler by a police informer. *2.* to be revealed to drug users as a police informer or undercover agent. *3.* To have been cheated in a drug sale.

burning. smoking MARIJUANA.

> And *burning* marijuana, that's just like smoking a cigarette, the only thing you inhale it, you don't let it out, you just try to hold it in.
> —addict, quoted in Jeremy Larner and Ralph Tefferteller,
> *The Addict in the Street* (1964)

burn out. to overexploit a source of stolen goods.

> If he [the addict] is a booster [thief] he will recognize the fact that he

can *"burn out"* a certain department store. He will therefore respect the store detectives and move from place to place as the days pass.
—Seymour Fiddle, *Portraits from a Shooting Gallery* (1967)

businessman's lunchtime high (drug). [so called because its effects last only thirty minutes] DMT.

bust. [from Harlem slang for a police raid; a raid on drug addicts' parlors or clubs; since the 1930s—*EP*] *1.* to arrest or to be arrested, as in "the cop *busted* George"; "I was *busted* on a possession rap," "the cops set me up for a BUST." Compare SET UP.

Butisol Sodium. [butabarbital sodium, McNeil Laboratories, Inc.] a short- to intermediate-acting BARBITURATE hypnotic and sedative. The maximum sedative dosage is 120 milligrams a day, taken three times a day. The hypnotic (sleep-producing) dose is 100 milligrams, at bed time. Butisol Sodium comes in flat round green, orange, pink, or lavendar tablets inscribed "McNeil." Subject to the DRUG ABUSE CONTROL AMENDMENT OF 1965.

button, the. [from peyote *buttons,* the surface growth of the peyote cactus] PEYOTE.

buy. a purchase of narcotics from a peddler, as in "I'm going out to make a *buy*." Compare COP, SCORE.

buzz. [onomatopoeic equivalent of subjective feeling] *1.* feeling at the onset of a MARIJUANA HIGH: buzzing in the ears, dizziness, blurring of perceptions and cottony sounds. *2.* by extension, a moderate, pleasant HIGH from any drug, without hallucinations. *3.* a HEROIN HIGH.

buzz, rolling. a moderate HIGH continuing after intake of drugs has ceased.

Gnossos had stopped smoking anything but was still high enough for a *rolling buzz*.
—Richard Fariña, *Been Down So Long It Looks Like Up to Me,*
Random House, New York (1966)

C c

C. COCAINE.

caapi. *1.* a hallucinogenic tea made from the vine BANISTERIOPSIS CAAPI. *2.* the vine itself. Compare AYAHUASCA.

caballo. [Spanish, horse; translation of the American term for heroin] HEROIN.

ca-ca. [Puerto Rican slang for SHIT] shit, counterfeit HEROIN. Compare BLANK, CRAP, FLEA POWDER, GARBAGE, LEMONADE.

> Everybody was buying and nobody was selling except the gyps, and they were mixing milk-sugar with quinine and selling this *ca-ca* for the real thing.   —Piri Thomas, *Down These Mean Streets* (1967)

cactus. [from the peyote *cactus* plant] PEYOTE.

cahoba. see COHOBA.

came down. see COME DOWN.

can. *1.* a car. *2.* [one ounce of MORPHINE, so called because it was sold in tins, around 1930; also, convicts' word for a 1/2 pound of tobacco—*EP*. MARIJUANA was sometimes measured for sale in Prince Albert pipe-tobacco tins or coffee cans] in the western United States, 1 ounce of marijuana, costing $15 to $25. Compare LID.

Canadian black. [from the color] a variety of MARIJUANA grown in Canada.

C and H. COCAINE and HEROIN mixed. *Obsolete.* See SPEEDBALL.

C and M. COCAINE and MORPHINE mixed. *Obsolete.* See SPEEDBALL.

candy man. [from (?) *nose candy*, COCAINE or HEROIN sniffed] a PUSHER, or peddler of drugs.

cannabis. [from Greek *kannabis*] general international term for the flowering or fruiting tops of the hemp plant, the leaves, and sometimes the stems and seeds, which are taken for their hallucinogenic effects by smoking, drinking in an infusion, or eating. American cannabis, i.e., MARIJUANA, differs in pharmacological potency and modes of preparation and ingestion from Indian or North African cannabis, though the species is the same. According to the WHO's definition, cannabis does not encompass the resin alone, which is the most potent product of the plant and is known as HASHISH. Compare BHANG, CANNABIS INDICA, CANNABIS SATIVA, CHARAS, GHANJA, KIF.

Cannabis indica. [correctly CANNABIS SATIVA] the Indian hemp plant. *Obsolete.* The pharmaceutical name for (1) the powder made from the dried, sifted flowering tops of the female *Cannabis sativa,* (2) the tincture made from that powder, or (3) the pure resin, used in the nineteenth century as a remedy for asthma, nasal catarrh, nervous coughs, colds, tuberculosis, facial neuralgia, and insomnia. Also called by its English name, Indian hemp.

It was apparently introduced into European medicine by doctors with Napoleon's forces in Egypt, who were impressed by its sedative and analgesic potentials. Now (except in India, where it is an ingredient in certain patent medicines) cannabis has little medical use, and it is no longer in the United States Pharmacopoeia. Despite its antibiotic properties, few people advocate its use for this purpose. The WHO advises against such use, asserting that it is not so effective as existing antibiotics.

Experiments with cannabis and its semisynthetic derivatives, e.g., SYNHEXYL, were conducted with some success in the 1930s among mental patients suffering from depression; however, it has apparently been dropped in favor of TRANQUILIZERS, perhaps because the latter are more predictable in their effects and do not alter the consciousness. Another disadvantage of cannabis is that in powder form it tends to deteriorate, so that its potency is unstable. The potency also varies with the geographic origin of the plant.

> The fact is undeniable that smoking cigarettes made of the leaves of this plant [cannabis] produces a rapid modification in the state of asthmatic patients. The difficulty of breathing, the stertorous respiration, the tightness of the chest, and the wheezing are promptly relieved; an abundant expectoration most frequently follows almost immediately, the breathing becomes easier, the cough gets moist and a refreshing sleep soon removes all the alarming symptoms. . . . To facilitate the use of Indian Cigarettes and enable the patient to benefit by them under all circumstances, whether travelling or walking, they are sold in elegant little cigar cases which can be carried in a breast-pocket with the least inconvenience. Each can

contains a dozen cigarettes. . . . The smoke must be gently inhaled and allowed to flow through the respiratory passages, so as to be brought in contact with the larynx and the lungs, and then be blown out through the nose. It is essential to do this slowly by short aspirations. . . . It has been observed that the cigarettes act most powerfully when smoked in a close room, the patient sitting quietly in a chair or reclining in a sofa.

—brochure for "Indian Cigarettes," Grimault & Co. Chemists
(ca. 1860)

Cannabis sativa. a hemp plant which exudes a resin containing a HALLUCINOGEN, TETRAHYDROCANNABINOL. The use of the plant for its hallucinogenic effects probably originated in central Asia or China, where it was mentioned in a pharmacy book by Emperor Shun Nung in 3000 B.C., and spread through India and the Near East (in the fourth century B.C. the historian Herodotus described its use among the Scythians) and Africa, and thence to Europe and the Western Hemisphere.

The plant grows wild in most parts of the world, even in countries where attempts to eradicate it have been going on for centuries. *Cannabis sativa* is a tall annual plant which at maturity ranges in height from 3 to 16 feet and grows on the average to 6 to 8 feet. The leaves, usually seven to a stem, are dark green on top, hairy, with sawtooth edges. The stalks are fluted. The male and female plants are similar in appearance until maturity, when their flowers differ. The male plant produces prominent flowers which shed pollen freely. The female flowers grow amidst a profusion of small leaves and stems at the tip of the plant. The male plant yields fibers, or hemp, but is no longer cultivated for this purpose in the United States, imported Manila hemp or synthetics such as nylon being used instead. The female plant yields hard-hulled fruit containing seeds and more copiously than the male produces the resin containing tetrahydrocannabinol, the ACTIVE PRINCIPLE with hallucinogenic properties. The resin is most abundant at maturity.

These flowering tops, twigs, and leaves of the female plant are dried (either naturally in the sun, or artifically by low-temperature baking in a stove) and are smoked like tobacco for their hallucinogenic effects. This dried product is known in North America as MARIJUANA and in India as BHANG. Specially cultivated, unfertilized female hemp plants yield a higher resin content, which coats the fruiting tops of the plant, as a result of being unable to set seeds freely. The pure resin, with its much greater concentration of the active principle, is known as HASHISH, or CHARAS in India. It is related to the soporific yellow powder lupulin, found in the female hop plant, *Humulus lupulus,* used in making beer, which may account for its mild soporific effect. The Indians also use the unfertilized, resin-coated flowering tops, leaves, young twigs, and bark of specially cultivated female plants in making GHANJA, a by-product that is more potent than bhang but less so than charas. Ghanja is smoked or eaten in cakes or candy.

Cannabis sativa varies in resin content, and hence potency, with the area in which it is grown (hence, the loose and obsolete application of such local names as *Cannabis americana* and *Cannabis indica*). Nevertheless, the federal BUREAU OF NARCOTICS holds that there is only one species and that seeds from one part of the world planted in another will, after several generations, assume the characteristics of the local variety of *Cannabis sativa.* (Some other experiments apparently contradict this.) See also CANNABIS.

cap. *1.* gelatin capsule of narcotics, usually HEROIN or MORPHINE. The contents are emptied and dissolved for injection. In the 1940s and 1950s this was the commonest container for heroin, but it is much rarer today, having been replaced by the glassine envelope, or BAG, probably because the latter is easier to fill. *2.* currently, a capsule containing a HALLUCINOGEN, especially LSD-25 in crystal form. See also DECK UP.

Carbona. a brand of CLEANING FLUID, the fumes of which are inhaled for their deliriant effect. Compare CARBON TETRACHLORIDE, GLUE SNIFFING.

carbon tetrachloride. [tetrachloromethane] a heavy, colorless, highly toxic liquid (which alcohol POTENTIATES) with a strong odor used in CLEANING FLUIDS and the source of the deliriant effect sought by drug abusers who sniff them. Toxic reactions to the fumes include headache, mental confusion, depression, fatigue, loss of appetite, nausea, vomiting, coma, and death. Some of these symptoms do not appear until after the passage of several hours. Both the vapor and the liquid irritate the skin and the eyes. It can also cause damage to the liver, kidney, heart, and nervous system if inhaled in large quantities or if swallowed. Compare GLUE SNIFFING, BENZINE.

carry. to have drugs on the person, as in the drug users' admonition "never *carry* when you can stash." Compare ANYWHERE, HOLD.

carrying. possessing narcotics on the person, as in "are you *carrying?*"

cartwheels. [from the scoring, in the form of a plus sign, on the round tablet, which gives it a resemblance to a wheel] AMPHETAMINE tablets. Compare CROSSROADS.

catnip. the strong-smelling herb, *Nepeta cataria,* sometimes sold as MARIJUANA to an unsuspecting buyer and sometimes actually smoked for alleged hallucinogenic effects.

caviar of the hallucinogens. [from *caviar,* a luxury, the finest] STP.

CB. [condensation of CIBA, the manufacturer's name] DORIDEN (GLUTETHIMIDE) pill.

cent. one dollar. (In drug parlance a nickel is $5 and a dime is $10.) Compare NICKEL BAG, DIME.

cephalotropic. modifying the physiological functioning of the brain; opposite of PSYCHOTROPIC.

chalk. [from the white color and chalky consistency] AMPHETAMINE tablets.

changes. *1.* alterations, unexpected events which interrupt the addict's habitual life pattern, or routine, and which he characteristically finds unpleasant. *2.* interruptions in his drug-acquisition pattern, e.g., his PUSHER is not there at the appointed time, causing him to do without his needed drugs. *3.* periods during which no drugs are available. Compare HASSLE, PANIC. *4.* bizarre, surprising reactions to, and personality alteration from, a drug by another as in "he's going through *changes*." *5.* freaking out; unexpected behavior; marked alterations in moods, emotions, volition.

charas. [Hindi word for the unadulterated resin] resin exuded by flowering tops of the female hemp plant, CANNABIS SATIVA. Cultivation in India, Nepal, and Sinkiang, China, has been brought to a fine art. Special techniques include preventing pollination of the female plants so that they produce more resin, trimming off the top leaves and dwarfing the plant, growing the plants in upland areas under hot sun (which seems to increase the pharmacological potency of the resin), and laboriously collecting the resin on cheesecloth by hand and scraping it off so that none is wasted.

Since only the resin is used (in contrast to GHANJA, another form of Indian cannabis, in which the resin-covered flowers, leaves, and twigs are ground up for smoking), charas represents the ACTIVE PRINCIPLE of cannabis in its most concentrated state. It is some eight times as potent as ordinary MARIJUANA from the United States (or what the Indians call BHANG) made from flowers, leaves, and seeds, whether resinous or not.

When freshly exuded the resin is yellowish and smells like mint; it later hardens and turns brown or black. It is customarily smoked in a water pipe (HOOKAH) or eaten in confections. When smoked, the drug's intake can be better regulated than when it is swallowed. By the latter mode, charas can equal, in hallucinogenic effects, a small amount of LSD-25. Charas is commonly known as HASHISH in other parts of the world. Compare CANNABIS SATIVA.

charge. [a dose, especially by injection, of a narcotic drug, around the 1930s; a MARIJUANA cigarette, perhaps a specialization of the first sense, circa 1943—*EP;* derived from (?) electric *charge*] *1.* The sudden, euphoric onset of the effects of an OPIATE drug following injection. *2.* an injection of drugs. *3.* a marijuana cigarette. *4.* (rare) COCAINE. Compare FLASH, RUSH.

charles. [since the 1920s] COCAINE. *Obsolete?*

charlie. a dollar; five *charlies* is $5, etc.

chasing the bag. [BAG, packet of heroin] *1.* hustling for HEROIN. *2.* addicted. Compare GLOBETROTTER.

chasing the dragon. [translation from the Chinese] a favored mode of ingesting HEROIN in Hong Kong among Chinese addicts. The heroin along with BARBITURATE powder is placed on a flat piece of tinfoil over the flame of a match or candle. The fumes that result are inhaled through a paper tube (usually a rolled matchbook cover) or directly. As it melts, the heroin resembles a small black snake and slides about on the tinfoil as if alive; hence, perhaps, the name: the user "chases" the heroin "dragon" in order to inhale the fumes (the dragon's smoke).

chemical. any illicitly used drug.

chevere. [Puerto Rican slang] great, swinging.

chief, the. LSD-25.

chill. [from (?) *freeze,* to ignore, to "cut" someone] *1.* to refuse to sell drugs to an addict who is suspected of being a police informer, as in "I *chilled* Charlie today." *2.* such a refusal as in "the *chill's* on Charlie." *3.* to kill. The murderer of two students in New York is alleged to have said, "I just chilled two dames." The fact that he was a drug addict may or may not indicate a relation between the two usages.

chillum. a clay pipe with a short straight stem issuing from the bottom of the bowl used in India for smoking GHANJA.

Chinese cure. an addict's way of withdrawing himself from HEROIN: opium in daily decreasing amounts is mixed with a tonic, until finally the addict is drinking only the tonic.

chipping. CHIPPYING.

chippying. [from *chippy,* a girl of easy virtue; *chippying,* dallying with such a girl; hence *chippy user,* one who uses narcotics infrequently, sporadically, rather than steadily, for kicks, rather than because of physical dependence—*EP.* Partridge adds regarding the connection between the sexual and narcotic meanings "to numerous men, women are but sexual narcotics"] *1.* infrequent, irregular use of narcotics for pleasure and without physical dependency. *2.* in states where opiate derivatives such as CODEINE or PAREGORIC can be bought without a prescription if the purchaser signs a register at the druggist, the practice of making the rounds of several druggists and buying the legal amount from each.

chloral hydrate. [trichloroacetaldehyde] a nonbarbiturate hypnotic and sedative. Combined with alcohol, liquid chloral hydrate can induce acute intoxication, resembling an overdose of BARBITURATES, and coma. In this illicit use it is known as a MICKEY FINN or KNOCK-OUT DROPS. Excessive, long-term use of chloral hydrate can result in both PSYCHIC DEPENDENCE and PHYSICAL DEPENDENCE, with a characteristic pattern of WITHDRAWAL SYMPTOMS when the drug is abruptly stopped. The toxic oral dose is approximately 10 grams, while the hypnotic (sleep-inducing) dose is 0.5 to 1 gram. Subject to the DRUG ABUSE CONTROL AMENDMENT OF 1965.

chlorpromazine. a MAJOR TRANQUILIZER chemically derived from phenothiazine, chlorpromazine is a dimethylaminopropyl compound. Its derivatives include trifluoperazine and perphenazine. Sold under the name THORAZINE and used in treating severe psychoses, it acts to reduce the patient's fear and hostility, thus preventing acts of violence. It also reduces hallucinations and delusions, or at least the patient's apprehension arising from them. Chlorpromazine is by the same action effective in reversing an LSD-induced panic psychosis by antagonizing the drug's effects, and enabling the subject to return to a normal state of consciousness.

In 1967 the self-administration of chlorpromazine, with which most LSD users are familiar, took an untoward turn. While experimenting with the powerful new hallucinogen STP, which induces a more profound and longer-lasting experience than LSD, several people took chlorpromazine, evidently in an attempt to reverse an unfavorable experience. But instead of reversing STP, it POTENTIATES its effect with possibly fatal results. This is because STP is believed to be similar to ATROPINE, to which chlorpromazine is also similar in chemical structure. Chlorpromazine has a central sedative effect but unlike the BARBITURATES, large doses do not induce coma or anesthesia. PSYCHIC DEPENDENCE and PHYSICAL DEPENDENCE do not seem to occur.

chota. [Puerto Rican addicts' slang] RAT, an informer.

ciba. [from the manufacturer's name, CIBA Pharmaceutical Company, inscribed on the capsule] DORIDEN.

class A narcotics. category established by Federal BUREAU OF NARCOTICS regulations to regulate the prescription and manufacture of addictive narcotics. The class A narcotics are OPIUM and its derivatives and compounds; phenanthrene opium alkaloids (MORPHINE, CODEINE, thebaine), their salts, derivatives, and compounds; COCA leaves, their alkaloids, derivatives, extracts, and compounds (COCAINE, ECOGNINE); MEPERIDINE (pethidine), METHADONE, and thiambutene derivates and other addictive SYNTHETIC OPIATES as defined by the Commissioner of Narcotics.
See also CLASS B NARCOTICS, CLASS M NARCOTICS, and CLASS X NARCOTICS.

class B narcotics. drugs designated by the Commissioner of Narcotics as having relatively little addiction liability, which the physician may prescribe orally without filling out a narcotics order. These include the nonaddictive isoquinoline alkaloids of OPIUM (NOSCAPINE or narcotine, PAPAVERINE, cotarnine, narceine, meconin);

apomorphine; nalorphine (see NALLINE); CODEINE (methylmorphine), if not in excess of 8 grains per fluid ounce or 1 grain (60 milligrams) per dosage unit; HYDROCODONE (dihydrocodeinone) in amounts not greater than 1/6 grain (10 milligrams) per dosage unit or 1 1/3 grains (80 milligrams) per fluid ounce; ethylmorphine (DIONIN) in amounts not greater than 1/6 grain per dosage unit or 1 1/3 grains per fluid ounce.

class M narcotics. "especially exempt" narcotics, considered nonaddictive. Preparations may contain one of the following ingredients in combination with nonnarcotic ingredients, and no narcotics order or prescription is required by law: NOSCAPINE, PAPAVERINE, narceine, cotarnine, or NALORPHINE.

class X narcotics. preparations containing minimal amounts of narcotics combined with nonnarcotic ingredients. They may be prescribed by ordinary prescription form like any other drug. The preparation must not contain (per fluid ounce) more than 2 grains of OPIUM, 1/4 grain of MORPHINE, 1 grain of CODEINE, 1/2 grain of dihydrocodeine, or 1/4 grain of ethylmorphine.

clean. [to rid oneself of stolen property; hence, free from suspicion, carrying no firearms; around the 1920s—*EP*] *1.* not carrying narcotics. *2.* not using narcotics. *3.* MARIJUANA with the twigs and seeds removed. These are considered undesirable by some users, but others brew a tea from this "waste." "A very *clean* NICKEL [i.e., $5] BAG" means, in essence, more for your money, since the marijuana contains a minimum of waste. *4.* the act of removing this waste, often performed by a dealer. The cleaner his lot, the less bulk and the lower his profits.

cleaning fluids. inhaled for the deliriant effects. When sniffed (usually from a rag or a plastic bag), the fumes produce an intoxication, initially accompanied by exhilaration and excitement, uncoordinated actions, slurred speech, double vision, buzzing in the ears, and, rarely, hallucinations. After thirty to thirty-five minutes, drowsiness, stupor, and unconsciousness ensue. The fumes are irritating to the mucous membranes, are extremely toxic, and can cause damage to the kidney, liver, brain, and bone marrow. In their delirium users have been known to fall off rooftops with fatal results. Death can also result (especially among young people, the

chief abusers) from the toxicity of the vapors themselves. Compare
CARBONA, CARBON TETRACHLORIDE, GLUE SNIFFING.

> A boy would pour the *cleaning fluid* into a rag and then hold it to
> his nose, and inhale deeply until he was intoxicated. Each boy would
> do this until they were all high, and then they would stagger around
> the lot playing schoolboy games until they became drowsy and lost
> interest.   —eyewitness account of cleaning-fluid sniffing,
> *World Journal Tribune* (Nov. 6, 1966)

clitch. the decisive factor, the clincher.

> S.F.: I wondered whether you thought that drug addicts are under
> more pressure than people who are not drug addicts.
> M. [an addict]: Yes. Sure! There's more pressure, but there's a
> compen—there's a compensation here that . . . that's when you
> take off. This is the—that's the *clitch*—this is what keeps you in this.
>   —Seymour Fiddle, *Portraits from a Shooting Gallery* (1967)

coast. to be in the somnolent, nodding state of the HEROIN addict,
as in "he'd shot up and started to *coast.*"

coca. a bush, *Erythroxylon coca,* grown on mountain slopes or
terraced ground in the uplands of Bolivia, Peru, and Java. Its
leaves contain the alkaloid COCAINE in amounts ranging from 0.65
to 1.2 percent by weight. Because of its cocaine content, coca has
been consumed for centuries by Indians of the Andean regions of
South America, who seek its stimulant and appetite-depressant effects (which are more manifest in the high altitudes of the region)
while performing heavy labor, making long treks or climbs, and the
like. The Indians traditionally chew the leaves mixed with an alkali
(lime) obtained from bricks of pressed ashes, usually from quinoa,
a local pigweed, *Chinopodium quinoa,* with cornstarch added for
adhesion or wrapped around bird droppings (guano). The alkali
acts with saliva to release the cocaine from the leaves.

Such small amounts of cocaine are actually consumed that the
coca habit is not considered a dangerous drug abuse but rather
analogous to coffee drinking in this country. It has been estimated
that coca is used by 90 percent of the Indians in the Andes. (The
Indian user who chews 2 ounces of the leaf ingests about 0.7 grain of
cocaine per day, while the cocaine addict may consume up to 6 to 8
grains per day.) The Peruvian government, nevertheless, is trying
to discourage the use of coca so that the Indians will replant the

land now used for coca bushes in more profitable, licit crops. Before the arrival of Spanish explorers the Incas chewed coca leaves and considered them divine. In Paris the leaves were infused into wine by Angelo Mariani, who called his mixture *vin coca mariana,* a popular nineteenth-century beverage in Europe. It was also an ingredient of the soft drink Coca-Cola until 1904, when federal authorities proscribed such use.

God is a substance   —Peruvian Indian saying about coca

cocaine. [from COCA and *-ine*] benzoylmethyl ecognine; the alkaloid contained in the leaves of the coca bush, *Erythroxylon coca,* which has a pronounced stimulative effect on the central nervous system. The bush is grown in Bolivia, Peru, and Java, and most of the cocaine in illicit traffic originates in these countries. In its pure form, cocaine is a white crystalline powder. Drug users take it for its almost violently stimulant and euphoric effects, the favored modes of ingestion being sniffing and injection (cocaine loses potency when taken by mouth).

Those who inject cocaine often mix it with HEROIN or inject heroin subsequently in order to dampen the hyperexcitability the cocaine induces. Cocaine acts upon the central nervous system to produce a euphoric excitement and hallucinatory experiences. The euphoria is relatively short-lived, and habitual users of the drug inject it as often as every ten minutes. When injected in small doses at frequent intervals as much as 10 grams has been taken in a day. On the other hand, some authorities consider a single dose of around 1.2 grains (1,200 milligrams) as lethal to most human beings. Lesser doses have been fatal, however; and when an injected toxic dose reaches the heart, death comes too rapidly for any effective therapy.

The body does not develop significant TOLERANCE to cocaine; i.e., the lethal dose remains constant, while the same ingestion will produce a similar effect even after long-term use. PSYCHIC DEPENDENCE on cocaine does occur; the user compulsively seeks the extreme mood elevation, elation, and grandiose feelings of heightened physical and mental prowess induced by the drug. When the drug's effects begin to wane, a corresponding deep depression is felt, which is in such marked contrast to the user's previous state that he is strongly motivated to repeat the dose and restore his euphoria, thus becoming psychically dependent on the drug. Chronic use, however, will engender an increasingly unpleasant hyperstimulation, accompanied by digestive disorders, nausea, loss of appetite, loss of weight, chronic insomnia, occasional convulsions, and paranoid delusions accompanied by auditory and visual hallucinations (often black spots against a light background, mistaken for insects). Such mental aberrations often trigger violent antisocial acts by the user, so that the heavy cocaine user is much more dangerous than the heroin addict, who succumbs to the depressant effects of the drug. Long-term injection of cocaine also produces abscesses on the skin.

Since prolonged use of cocaine depresses the appetite, the user may suffer from malnutrition and anemia. The drug also acts to raise body temperature; this effect is preceded by a dramatic lowering of body temperature and a sensation of cold. In his weakened state, the user may be more susceptible to a lethal overdose of cocaine. Prolonged sniffing of cocaine also results in deterioration of the lining of the nose and, ultimately, of the bone. A common tendency among regular users is to avoid exclusive use of the drug over a period of time because of the unpleasant sensations it produces and to seek sedatives or a morphinelike drug to counter their hyperexcitability. Thus, there is the added hazard of PHYSICAL DEPENDENCE upon one of these drugs, although they temporarily serve to calm the user and prevent him from engaging in violent acts.

Cocaine was formerly used medicinally as a local anesthetic, but this is rare today. A CLASS A NARCOTIC. Compare SPEEDBALL.

> I smelled the sharp sickly-sweet odor of the cocaine. My palms were dripping sweat. He had the "spike" in his right hand. He grabbed my forearm with his left hand. I turned my head and closed my eyes. I bit down on my bottom lip waiting for the stabbing plunge of the needle.
>
> He said, "Damn! You got some beautiful lines [veins]."
>
> I shivered when it daggered in. I opened my eyes and looked. My blood had shot up into the dropper. He was pressing the bulb. I saw the blood-streaked liquid draining into me. It was like a ton of nitro exploded inside me. My ticker went berserk. I could feel it clawing up my throat. It was like I had a million "swipes" in every pore from head to toe. It was like they were all popping off together in a nerve-shredding climax.
>
> I was quivering like a joker in the hot seat at the first jolt. I tried to open my talc-dry mouth. I couldn't. I was paralyzed. I could feel a hot ball of puke racing up from my careening guts. I saw the green, stinking puke rope arch into the black mouth of the waste basket. . . .

> I felt like the top of my skull had been crushed in. It was like I had been blown apart and all that was left were my eyes. Then tiny prickly feet of ecstasy started dancing through me. I heard melodious bells tolling softly inside my skull.
>
> I looked down at my hands and thighs. A thrill shot through me. Surely they were the most beautiful in the Universe. I felt a super-man's surge of power.
>
> —"Iceberg Slim," *Pimp. The Story of My Life* (1967)

cocktail. an ordinary cigarette employed to smoke the butt of a MARIJUANA cigarette, which is placed in one end, after a bit of the tobacco is removed, and then lit. Compare ROACH.

codeine. [from Greek *kodeia,* poppyhead] also called methylmorphine. An alkaloid of OPIUM naturally occurring in the juices of the unripe pod of the white poppy, *Papaver somniferum.* It is usually extracted by methylization of MORPHINE, another natural alkaloid. In its general pharmacodynamic action codeine resembles morphine, but the effects are much milder. Since it has only about one-sixth to one-tenth the analgesic action of an equivalent amount of morphine, it is used only in minor pain. The usual recommended dose is 30 to 60 milligrams; 120 milligrams gives analgesia equal to that of 10 milligrams of morphine, the minimal analgesic dosage.

As an effective antitussive, codeine, like morphine, is a common ingredient in cough medicines. Other side effects of codeine are constipation and sometimes nausea. Large doses have a paradoxical stimulant effect. It is considered only mildly addictive, instances of codeine addiction being rare, though not unknown. When PHYSICAL DEPENDENCE on codeine develops, the WITHDRAWAL SYMPTOMS upon cessation of the drug are much milder than those connected with morphine or HEROIN dependence. PSYCHIC DEPENDENCE, however, is more common, as users seek out the drug's mild euphoric and sedative properties. As with any opiate drug, tolerance to the drug's action develops, necessitating increasing doses to repeat the initially pleasurable effects. Addicts seeking to withdraw themselves from heroin or unable to obtain heroin use codeine to alleviate their withdrawal symptoms. In sufficient quantities this is effective, but when the codeine is stopped, the withdrawal symptoms have the same severity as those by heroin dependence. The nonaddictive drug propoxyphene (Darvon) has analgesic effects of intensity and duration equivalent to those of codeine but with fewer side effects.

Codeinists have the same abnormal desires, sensations, and sufferings as morphinists. Their number is small in comparison with the latter, but nevertheless considerable. One such, an extremely neuropathic young man, on account of his mental erethism, was prescribed *codeine* pills, one of 0.03 gr. to be taken three times a day. He experienced one day a euphoric state after taking a large number of them at once. He continued to augment the dose, increasing it to 50 pills or nearly 2 gr. of codeine per day. Without these pills life seemed impossible to him. The attempt to escape from this necessity produced depression, restlessness and weariness of life. After a year five pills every hour or two did not suffice him. His restlessness increased. On leaving his bed he travelled purposelessly in street cars and by rail. At last he was consuming one hundred pills or nearly 3 gr. of codeine daily. He then procured opium pills and took that fraudulent preparation "Anti-morphine," which contains morphia as well as other narcotics. He lost weight considerably, became extremely pale, and talked slowly and hesitatingly. Withdrawal treatment produced, besides the craving for codeine, restlessness, irritability, depression, life-weariness, and physical disturbances. The wretched man sacrificed his fortune of 10,000 marks to this expensive passion.

—Louis Lewin, *Phantastica: Narcotic and Stimulating Drugs* (1964)

coffee. [because LSD was frequently sold in Cambridge coffee houses, the phrase "let's get some *coffee*" became code for "let's get some LSD"—1964] LSD-25. *Obsolete?*

cohoba. [Arawak Indian name] hallucinogenic snuff prepared from PIPTADENIA by the Indians of Trinidad. The hallucinogenic ACTIVE PRINCIPLE is thought to be BUFOTENINE. Compare YOPO.

coke. [since 1900] COCAINE.

coked, coked up. high on COCAINE.

coke head. [since around 1920; HEAD, one frequently under the influence of a drug, whose mind (*head*) is therefore more or less permanently under its sway] habitual COCAINE user.

cold turkey. [from the gooseflesh that is one of the WITHDRAWAL SYMPTOMS of HEROIN or MORPHINE] abrupt withdrawal from narcotics, when PHYSICAL DEPENDENCE is present, so that the addict goes through the withdrawal symptoms; as opposed to tapering off through gradually decreasing doses of the drug addicted to or a similar drug and other medication. The latter procedure will considerably lessen the withdrawal symptoms; however, it is agreed that cold turkey is not quite the agonizing process it used to be because the highly diluted heroin most addicts purchase gives them only a mild addiction; also, they often employ BARBITURATES or TRANQUILIZERS or DOLOPHINE (METHADONE) pills to allay their symptoms. Nevertheless most addicts undergo cold turkey at one time or another because they have no money for drugs or have lost their CONNECTION. They do not fear the withdrawal symptoms, and their alleged fear is not the prime reason for using drugs. Compare A LA CANONA, KICKING.

collapsed veins. venous thrombosis, swollen and blocked veins; a condition, common among long-term HEROIN addicts, resulting from frequent injections in a vein. When the arm vein has collapsed, the addict starts on a new one in leg, hand, neck, or foot, sometimes continuing until he has none left. Some old addicts then revert to subcutaneous injection (SKIN POPPING).

collar. *1*. an arrest.

> "Who's given you every decent *collar* you've had in the past four weeks?"   —addict-informer in James Mills,
> *The Panic in Needle Park* (1966)

2. to arrest. *3*. a strip of paper or rubber band wrapped around an eyedropper tip to ensure a tight fit where it is joined to the needle. Compare BOO, DROPPER, WORKS.

come down. *1*. to lose the effects of the drug and be restored to a normal state. *2*. invidiously, a depressed, mundane, unpleasant state. *3*. in heroin addicts to develop withdrawal symptoms. Compare BRING DOWN, HIGH.

> He had to go out on the street somewhat "sick" because during the nighttime his habit *"came down,"* that is to say he developed symptoms.   —Seymour Fiddle, *Portraits from a Shooting Gallery* (1967)

coming down. beginning to lose the effects of a drug. Compare BRING DOWN.

> In despair where the lids were swollen
> The heart that was pounding and writhing
> And ears where the sounds were screaming
> And the mind that was ashen and still.
> Cocaine, cocaine
> I'm a *comin' down*
> I'm a comin' down.   —Ed Sanders, *Coming Down* (1966)

Compazine. [prochlorperazine, Smith Kline & French Laboratories] a MAJOR TRANQUILIZER, chemically derived from phenothiazine. Manufacturer recommends in control of nausea, to alleviate anxiety, agitation, and confusion, in chronic alcoholism, and to control unruly behavior in disturbed children. The usual recommended daily dose is 40 milligrams, but in severe psychotic states up to 100 milligrams may be necessary. As a result of overdosage or individual sensitivity to Compazine, unpleasant side effects may occur, including lowered blood pressure (which can lead to fatal cardiac arrest), liver damage, allergic reactions, convulsions, and pseudo parkinsonism (drooling, tremors, shuffling gait).

The drug may act to POTENTIATE the effects of central nervous system depressants, i.e., alcohol, OPIATES, ANTIHISTAMINES, BARBITU-RATES, ANALGESICS, ATROPINE, and should not be used in conjunction with them lest respiratory depression and death result. Sold in 5-, 10-, and 25-milligram tablets, sustained-release capsules, suppositories, syrup, and solutions for injection. Compare CHLORPROMAZINE, THORAZINE.

Conar. [The S. E. Massengill Company] a cough syrup containing, among other ingredients, NOSCAPINE, a nonaddicting alkaloid of OPIUM. Each 5 cubic centimeters contains 10 milligrams of noscapine. Manufacturer recommends for coughs, congestion, and dry, nonproductive coughs. No prescription. A CLASS M NARCOTIC.

connect. *1.* to find a source of drugs. *2.* to buy drugs. Compare COP, SCORE.

connection. [convicts' word for a liaison with the "outside"—*EP;* narcotic connotation since around 1920] *1.* a person from whom one can buy narcotics. *2.* a PUSHER. *3.* a wholesaler, the pusher's source; a high-level dealer. *4.* one's source of supply of narcotics, one's CONTACT.

contact. *1.* a drug supplier, the PUSHER you know. *2.* on college campuses the source of drugs, usually MARIJUANA, LSD, AMPHETA-MINES, and BARBITURATES.

contact habit. vicariously experiencing some of the effects of drug addiction though not oneself addicted; said derisively by addicts of PUSHERS and narcotics agents.

"Selling is more of a habit than using," Lupita [a pusher] says. Nonusing pushers have a *contact habit,* and that's one you can't kick. Agents get it too. Take Bradley the Buyer. . . . Well the Buyer comes to look more and more like a junky. He can't drink. He can't get it up. His teeth fall out. . . . The Buyer takes on an ominous grey-green color. Fact is his body is making its own junk or equivalent. —William Burroughs, *Naked Lunch* (1959)

contact high. [compare BUNK HABIT] *1.* among jazz players, the player who is HIGH on MARIJUANA communicates his mental state through his music to other players who are not high, affecting their playing accordingly. *2.* the mild high obtained by inhaling smoke from another's marijuana cigarette. Among college students it is obtained by having four or five crowd into a closet. One or two actually smoke, and the others inhale the fumes that accumulate in the enclosed area.

cook. to heat the mixture of HEROIN powder and water in the COOKER over a lighted match until the powder has dissolved.

cooker. a small receptacle, e.g., a whiskey-bottle top, bottle cap, or spoon, in which the HEROIN addict heats up a mixture of heroin powder and water in order to dissolve the heroin, draw it up through a cotton filter, and inject it. Often a thin wire is wrapped around the whiskey-bottle cap so that it can be held without burning the fingers. The handle of the spoon may be bent for the same reason. Compare WORKS.

cook up. to COOK.

cop. [to buy; from to take, lay hold of. Since the 1800s—*EP*] to buy narcotics, as in "he went out to *cop*" or "I was *copping* on 125th Street at that time." Compare SCORE.

cop. [from (?) *cop,* to take, and *cop a plea,* to take a plea of guilty to a lesser charge] to admit to something.

cope. to function more or less normally though intoxicated by a drug. But with HEROIN addicts, the ability to cope is a "normal" state, which only an injection of heroin can restore. See HOOKED (quotation).

copilot. one who sits with someone who has taken LSD and cares for him if necessary Compare GUIDE.

copilots. DEXEDRINE tablets.

cop sickness. the anxiety, discomfort, and premature WITHDRAWAL SYMPTOMS experienced by an addict anticipating his next FIX. See HEROIN.

> And when you're hooked, it gets so that every time someone goes out to score [buy drugs] for you even though it's maybe three or four hours until you're due, you get sick. First you get severe cramps in your stomach. It's just like a tiny sick backache, then headache, then sweating, shaking, cigarettes start tasting bad, you can't sit still, you can't sleep, you can't rest, you can't do anything, you're just frantic, and you feel ill, quite ill.
>
> Hellen MacGill Hughes (ed.), *The Fantastic Lodge* (1961)

corrine. COCAINE.

corrine and the girl. COCAINE. *Obsolete.* Compare GIRL.

Coryz. [Marion Laboratories, Inc.] a cough syrup containing NOSCAPINE, a nonaddicting alkaloid of OPIUM. Each 5 cubic centimeters (1 teaspoonful) contains 30 milligrams of noscapine. No prescription. A CLASS M NARCOTIC.

Cosanyl. [Parke, Davis & Company] a cough syrup containing CODEINE. One ounce contains 1 grain (60 milligrams) of codeine. No prescription necessary in most states. A CLASS X NARCOTIC. (Often misspelled as "Cocinol," etc.)

courage pills. BARBITURATES or other sedative pills.

crackers. [when Boston police became aware that LSD was being put on sugar cubes, users switched to putting it on animal crackers —1964] LSD-25. *Obsolete.*

cracking shorts. [from *crack,* to break into, to burglarize, and SHORT, car, since around 1930—*EP*] breaking into cars, a common form of theft among addicts.

crap. [addicts' expression of contempt applied to the highly diluted HEROIN which started appearing on the illicit market in the 1920s: "this is *crap*"—*EP*] *1.* low-quality, diluted heroin. *2.* heroin, however diluted. Compare CA-CA, SHIT.

crash. *1.* finally to fall asleep after being in a high state of stimulation from a drug, especially of the AMPHETAMINE type. *2.* to return abruptly to normal from a state of drug intoxication, either due to a willed effort in order to appear "straight" or because of a shock, such as the appearance of a policeman. *3.* simply to sleep, as in "looking for a place to *crash*." Compare BRING DOWN, COME DOWN.

> Several times when I was looking for somebody I was told, "He's hiding to *crash*." For a while I thought the term had something to do with an overdose of brain-ticklers—the maddened victim having slunk off in the woods like a sick animal, to ride out his delirium without disturbing the others. But crashing means nothing more sinister than going on the nod, either from booze or simple fatigue. When this happens—if the unfortunate has not found a safe hiding place—the others will immediately begin tormenting him. The most common penalty for crashing is the urine shower; those still on their feet gather quietly around the sleeper and soak him from head to foot.
> —Hunter S. Thompson, *Hell's Angels* (1966)

crater. a gaping hole in the flesh at a vein caused by repeated intravenous injections of a drug at the same spot.

> I had cultivated a *crater* and always shot through the same hole. It sure looked awful, though.
> —Piri Thomas, *Down These Mean Streets* (1967)

creep. an addict who, because of fear, incompetence, or isolation, does not engage in risky, criminal activities to raise money for drugs but rather begs them, does errands, or lends out a hypodermic needle in exchange for a TASTE of someone else's drugs. On some days the creep may acquire a large amount of drugs in this manner and on others very little. Hence, if during his successful period he acquires a large habit, he is forced, during lean periods, to support it by (for him) desperate measures such as stealing. Since he is inexperienced and probably unskilled at this, he is more likely to be arrested than the more skilled hustlers. Compare FLUNKY, HUSTLER, HUSTLING.

croaker. [from convicts' term for the prison doctor, from *croak*, to die; the death rattles of a dying man; since 1850—*EP*] any doctor, but especially *1.* a doctor with whom the addict deals, e.g., in narcotics hospital, or *2.* a private practitioner who will illegally prescribe drugs for addicts in exchange for money. Compare MAKING A CROAKER FOR A READER.

crossroads. [from the scoring on the pills] AMPHETAMINE tablets. Compare CARTWHEELS.

cross-tolerance. among certain pharmacologically related drugs, TOLERANCE built up to the effects of one will carry over to the others; thus, if one has acquired a tolerance to LSD and takes MESCALINE, one will experience no effects from the latter; similarly, one who has taken a large dose of METHADONE will perceive no effects from HEROIN. This is the basis of the methadone treatment.

crutch. rolled matchbook cover, hairpin, tweezers, etc., used for holding a MARIJUANA butt (ROACH) that has been smoked down too far to be held between the fingers. Compare ROACH HOLDER.

crystal. [the drug is supplied in white crystals] METHEDRINE or DESOXYN.

cube, the. [from the practice of ingesting tiny quantities of the liquid absorbed by a sugar cube] LSD-25.

cura. [from Spanish, *cura*, cure] a shot of HEROIN.

cut. [from bootlegger's terms for diluting liquor with water or grain alcohol—*EP*] to adulterate HEROIN with MILK SUGAR, mannite, or quinine. Quinine is used because its appearance and bitter taste are identical with those of heroin. The purchaser cannot tell by taste or sight how much pure heroin he is getting, and the PUSHER can take a larger profit. Pure heroin diluted five times by half yields a mixture containing about 3 percent heroin, the usual proportion sold to the addict.

cutting. the process of diluting heroin with MILK SUGAR, mannite, or quinine. Compare DECKING UP, FIVE-DOLLAR BAG, SPOON.

> We would have a mirror, some sugar-milk or quinine, a teaspoon, a woman's stocking and a hanger. You take the quinine, measure out how many spoons you want for each spoon of heroin, then run 'em together through the woman's stocking out onto the mirror. You make a diamond-shape of the wire hanger and you stretch the stocking tight over that. You run a spoon through and it falls right back on the mirror. You rake it back and forth with the spoon, and when it falls on the mirror it's mixed. From there you have a measure: like for a $5.00 bag, an eighth of a spoon.
> —pusher, quoted in Jeremy Larner and Ralph Tefferteller,
> *The Addict in the Street* (1964)

"The different piles there," Santo [a heroin wholesaler] went on, pointing as he spoke, "are heroin, quinine, and milk sugar. We work a four-to-one *cut* here—about four parts of milk sugar or quinine to one part heroin. Actually, of course, the heroin has already been cut way down before we even get it. So the guy on the street gets maybe five percent. The quinine is just to cut the sweet taste of the sugar. Heroin itself has a bitter taste and if a junkie tastes some stuff before he uses it and it's real sweet he figures he's bought a blank and gets upset. So we put in the quinine to make it bitter. The rest is pretty much obvious. You can see how it works just by watching. Any questions just ask. That guy over there is gonna cut Bobby's [a pusher] stuff now."

Bobby had managed to get three pieces out of Santo and one of the men started cutting it. He took a wire coat hanger that had been spread open and covered with nylon from a stocking, and put it in front of him on the glass-topped table. Then he opened one of the ounce envelopes and carefully emptied the contents onto the nylon. He lifted the coat-hanger-and-nylon sieve and shook it gently, sifting the heroin through the nylon onto the table. He shook it slowly, almost tenderly, taking great care not to let the sifted heroin spread too much. When he was through, the heroin sat in a high fluffy mound, almost twice the volume he had started with. He took a razor blade and carefully scraped the heroin that had drifted away from the edge of the mound back toward the center. Next he took a whisky shot glass, filled it once with heroin, and emptied it onto the coat-hanger-nylon sifter. He added two shots each of milk sugar and quinine. He mixed the chemicals together on the nylon, then sifted the whole mess again.

Now everyone pitched in. The three men at the table and Santo and Bobby each took baby measuring spoons and dipped them into the mound of cut heroin. When each had a spoonful, he leveled it off with a razor blade and dumped it in a neat pile on the glass. After they had about ten piles, one of the men started shoveling each pile into one of the stamp-sized bags. Everyone else measured, and the one man bagged. When everything was in bags, Bobby and Santo started folding them over and sealing them shut with Scotch tape. The others went to work on Bobby's second and third ounces. Finally everything was cut and all the bags were rubber-banded together in bundles of twenty-five bags each. Hundreds of bundles were stacked up on the table. Each bundle would sell for $75—and sell as easily as water in hell.   —James Mills, *The Panic in Needle Park* (1966)

cyc. CYCLAZOCINE.

cyclazocine. a long-acting narcotic antagonist, which, administered either normally or by injection in given amounts, will reduce the psychological and physiological effects of a corresponding amount of any morphinelike drug. Cyclazocine, like other narcotic antagonists, will precipitate WITHDRAWAL SYMPTOMS when administered to someone physically dependent upon narcotics. Doses of 0.25 to 2 milligrams have the analgesic effects of 10 milligrams of MORPHINE.

Experiments conducted with cyclazocine in curing narcotics addiction, although limited, have been encouraging. The addict is first withdrawn from HEROIN. Then he is given regular maintenance shots of cyclazocine, which acts to build up a large degree of tolerance to heroin in his system. As long as he continues taking the cyclazocine, a heroin injection will have no or little effect on him, except in large amounts. Thus, under medical supervision, on an outpatient basis, the patient can be effectively weaned from his dependence upon heroin, making it easier for him to break out of the addict's heroin-centered life pattern.

Most patients find the drug subjectively pleasant—more like MARIJUANA or BARBITURATES than heroin—and are motivated to continue the treatment. PHYSICAL DEPENDENCE on cyclazocine develops, but the withdrawal symptoms are much milder than those of heroin, and the patient has no craving for cyclazocine during or after the withdrawal. Compare METHADONE.

D d

D. DORIDEN (GLUTETHIMIDE).

dabbling. [since the 1950s] using narcotics moderately, irregularly. Compare CHIPPYING.

dagga. [from the Hottentot *dachab,* to smoke gladly, to tread down gladly and frequently] CANNABIS in South Africa, where employers give it to laborers to stimulate their production and increase their endurance (a similar practice is followed in Jamaica). It is also used as medicine for headache and snakebite, as an anesthetic in childbirth, and to wean children.

datura. [from Hindi for jimsonweed, DATURA STRAMONIUM] in India, thieves surreptitiously mixed datura with HASHISH and offered it to their victims. The interaction of the two drugs causes mental derangement followed by coma. In addition to *Datura stramonium,* several other species are found in the southwestern United States and Mexico, the main ones being *D. meteloides,* known as *tolgucha* in Mexico and used as a narcotic since ancient times, and *D. inoxia.* The species found in the Andes include *D. candida, D. sanguinea, D. aurea, D. dolichocarpa,* and *D. vulcanicola.*

The Indians of these regions often pulverize the seeds and mix them with locally brewed beers. The intoxication produced begins with the characteristic excitation, sometimes so extreme that the drinker becomes violent and has to be forcibly restrained. This is followed by a deep sleep, marred by dreams and hallucinations, which the witch doctor often interprets as an aid to diagnosing diseases, discovering culprits, or predicting the future.

Datura stramonium. a plant of the potato family (Solanaceae) containing poisonous alkaloids with narcotic and hallucinogenic properties. In the United States, it is known variously as jimsonweed, stinkweed, thorn apple, and devil's-apple. It contains the alkaloids STRAMONIUM, HYOSCYAMINE, and ATROPINE.

> This [jimsonweed] being an early Plant, was gather'd very young for a boil'd salad, but some of the Soldiers sent thither, to pacifie the troubles of Bacon; and some of them ate plentifully of it, the effect of which was a very pleasant Comedy; for they turned natural Fools upon it for several Days. One would blow a Feather in the Air; another would dart straws at it with much Fury; and another stark naked was sitting up in a Corner, like a Monkey grinning and making Mows at them; a Fourth would fondly kiss and paw his Companions, and snear in their Faces, with a Countenance more antik than any in a Dutch Droll. In this frantik Condition they were confined, lest they in their Folly should destroy themselves; though it was observed that all their Actions were full of Innocence and Good Nature. Indeed, they were not very cleanly; for they would have wallow'd in their own Excrements, if they had not been prevented. A Thousand such simple Tricks they play'd and after Eleven Days, return'd themselves again, not remembering anything that had pass'd.
>
> —Robert Beverley, *History and Present State of Virginia* (1705)

Magic ointments or witches' philtres procured for some reason and applied with or without intention produced effects which the subjects themselves believed in, even stating that they had intercourse with evil spirits, had been on the Brocken and danced at the Sabbat with their lovers, or caused damage to others by witchcraft. The mental disorder caused by substances of this kind, for instance *Datura,* has even instigated some persons to accuse themselves before a tribunal. The peculiar hallucinations evoked by the drug had been so powerfully transmitted from the unconscious mind to the consciousness that mentally uncultivated persons nourished in the absurd superstitions of the Church, believed them to be reality. . . .

Besides other disagreeable symptoms these *solanaceae* and their active elements, especially atropine and scopolamine, give rise to hallucinations of sight, hearing and taste, which differ, however, from those produced by the other Phantastica. They are not of an agreeable but on the contrary of a terrifying and distrustful kind.
—Louis Lewin, *Phantastica: Narcotic and Stimulating Drugs* (1964)

dawamesk. a small green aromatic cake composed of CANNABIS plant tops, sugar, orange juice, cinnamon, cloves, cardamon, NUTMEG, musk, pistachios, and pine kernels. Eaten in North Africa for the hallucinogenic effects of the CANNABIS. Cannabis was introduced to Europe from North Africa in this form through Le club des HASCHISCHINS, a group of Paris intellectuals, in the 1840s. Compare MAJOON.

day-glo paint. paint with an iridescent sheen suggesting the intensification of colors during an LSD experience. LSD users sometimes paint their bodies with it and also wear clothing in such colors, which sometimes can trigger, in the frequent user, a brief state of altered consciousness as if he had taken LSD.

The next day [after taking LSD] we felt cold and remote, but got through a lot of work. Driving the children to school, I nearly crashed when a coloured girl came out of a grey house wearing *day-glo* orange trousers: they went off on my retina like a bomb in a free-church assembly.   —Peter Laurie, *Drugs* (1967)

deadly nightshade. BELLADONNA.

deal. [from DEALER, a trafficker in narcotics; since around 1925—*EP*] to peddle narcotics.

dealer. trafficker in narcotics, PUSHER.

dealer's band. a rubber band securing packets of HEROIN to the wrist in such a manner that if flipped it will send the packets flying. Used by peddlers so that they can rid their person of narcotics quickly the moment they spot a police officer.

dealing. peddling narcotics.

deck. [from its resemblance to a deck of cards; a small packet, a thin paper fold of some drug; since 1890. Since the 1940s it generally has implied HEROIN—*EP*] a folded paper or glassine envelope containing heroin. Compare BAG, PAPER.

deck up. to fill the DECK with diluted HEROIN. Compare CUTTING.

> We just take it [heroin] and put it in the bag. It's a special bag that they use mostly for stamp collecting. We could *deck up* 2–300 in an evening's time. It all depends on how much you got and how fast you deck up.
> —pusher, quoted in Jeremy Larner and Ralph Tefferteller, *The Addict in the Street* (1964)

deeda. [from D, diminution of LSD; Harlem since around 1964] LSD-25.

Demerol. [MEPERIDINE HYDROCHLORIDE, Winthrop Laboratories] a SYNTHETIC OPIATE used as an analgesic and sedative, Demerol is one of the most widely used of the synthetic opiates, especially as an analgesic in childbirth. It is also, perhaps because of this accessibility in hospitals and the mistaken view that it is not addictive, the most frequent choice of medical personnel who became addicts and who prefer it to MORPHINE.

The usual clinical dosage is 50 to 100 milligrams repeated at three- to four-hour intervals. Demerol does not produce so much sedation as morphine, nor is it so effective in severe pain, but it causes less nausea, constipation, or vomiting. Danger of respiratory depression is relatively small except when administered intravenously. A CLASS A NARCOTIC.

dependence, drug. the World Health Organization's Expert Committee on Addiction-producing Drugs recommended in its Thirteenth Report (1964) that the terms *drug addiction* or *drug habituation* be dropped because they were too general and imprecise. WHO recommended that the term *drug dependence* be substituted, defining it as follows:

> *Drug dependence* is a state of psychic or physical dependence, or

both, on a drug, arising in a person following administration of that drug on a periodic or continuing basis. The characteristics of such state will vary with the agent involved, and these characteristics must always be made clear by designating the particular type of drug dependence in each specific case; for example, drug dependence of morphine type, of amphetamine type, etc.

See PHYSICAL DEPENDENCE and PSYCHIC DEPENDENCE.

Desbutal. [methamphetamine hydrochloride and pentobarbital sodium, Abbott Laboratories] an AMPHETAMINE and BARBITURATE in combination, recommended as a mood elevator and an aid in dieting. The amphetamine stimulates the central nervous system and acts to depress the appetite; the barbiturate provides sedation and enhances the mood elevation of the amphetamine while minimizing some of its undesirable effects, e.g., hyperexcitement, insomnia, and nervousness. TOLERANCE may develop both to the amphetamine and the barbiturate, so that increasing dosages are a temptation. PSYCHIC DEPENDENCE accompanied by frequent and prolonged usage may also develop. If taken in large amounts over prolonged periods, PHYSICAL DEPENDENCE will occur, accompanied by chronic barbiturate and amphetamine intoxication and resulting in severe WITHDRAWAL SYMPTOMS if the drug is suddenly stopped.

Desbutal is sold as green capsules containing 5 milligrams of methamphetamine hydrochloride (DESOXYN) and 30 milligrams of pentobarbital sodium (NEMBUTAL) and in Desbutal Gradumet delayed-release 10- and 15-milligram tablets. Desbutal 10 Gradumet (pink top half, pale blue bottom half) contains 10 milligrams of methamphetamine hydrochloride and 60 milligrams of pentobarbital sodium; the Desbutal 15 Gradumet (yellow top half, pale blue bottom) contains 15 milligrams of methamphetamine hydrochloride and 90 milligrams of pentobarbital sodium. Manufacturer's recommended dosages are one capsule two to three times daily or one Desbutal 10 or 15 Gradumet once daily, in the morning. Subject to the DRUG ABUSE CONTROL AMENDMENT OF 1965. Compare DEXAMYL.

Desoxyn. [methamphetamine hydrochloride, Abbott Laboratories] a direct central nervous system stimulant of the AMPHETAMINE type. Recommended by manufacturer for depressing appetite during dieting, mood elevation, counteracting drowsiness, narcolepsy (involuntary sleep), chronic alcoholism, parkinsonism, and depression.

Dose is 2.5 to 5 milligrams, up to three times daily. (Manufacturer warns against exceeding 15 milligrams in a single dose.) Sold in ampuls and tablets, upon which is inscribed the Abbott symbol *a*. Subject to the DRUG ABUSE CONTROL AMENDMENT OF 1965. Compare METHEDRINE.

> Tolerance to the drug may develop during prolonged administration. In such cases careful supervision is essential to avoid excessive dosage or abuse which can lead to chronic intoxication and addiction. If this should occur, psychotic manifestations of chronic amphetamine intoxication may require temporary sedation. The drug should be withdrawn without delay. Lethargy, which may persist for some weeks, has been seen following withdrawal. Methamphetamine should not be used to combat fatigue or to replace rest in normal persons. The occurrence of paradoxically increased depression or agitation in mentally depressed patients is an indication for withdrawing the drug.
> —Abbott Laboratories (1967)

Dexamyl. [*d*-amphetamine sulfate and amobarbital, Smith Kline & French Laboratories] a central nervous system stimulant of the AMPHETAMINE type combined with a central nervous system depressant. The BARBITURATE ingredient acts to dampen down any overstimulation produced by the amphetamine ingredient without counteracting its appetite-depressant and euphoric properties. Manufacturer recommends as an aid in dieting, in mild depressive states, and as a mood elevator. Recommended maximum daily dose 15 milligrams of *d*-amphetamine sulfate and 97 milligrams of amobarbital. It is sold as elixir, sustained-release capsules (Spansules), or tablets, with contents as follows:

form	d-amphetamine sulfate, mg	amobarbital, mg
Spansule:		
No. 1	10	65
No. 2	15	97
tablet	5	32
elixir, 1 tsp	5	32

The Spansules have a green cap and a clear body showing green and white pellets. The tablets are flat, three-sided, green, and scored down the middle. Long-term use may result in PSYCHIC DEPENDENCE and PHYSICIAL DEPENDENCE (on the amobarbital) and increasing TOLERANCE to both ingredients. Psychic dependence on the amphetamine ingredient may also occur. Overdose may result in excessive stimulation or excessive depression, which may reach the point of shock in severe cases. In Great Britain this combination is sold as DRINAMYL ("purple hearts" or "French blues"), a purple tablet. Subject to the DRUG ABUSE CONTROL AMENDMENT OF 1965.

Dexedrine. [d-amphetamine sulfate, Smith Kline & French Laboratories] a central nervous system stimulant of the AMPHETAMINE type considered twice as potent as other amphetamines. Manufacturer recommends as an appetite depressant in dieting, as a mood elevator in minor depression, and for alcoholism and narcolepsy (involuntary sleep). Recommended dosages range from 30 to 50 milligrams total a day. As with all amphetamines, TOLERANCE and PSYCHIC DEPENDENCE may develop.

Sold as elixir, timed-release capsules, or tablets. The timed-release capsules (Spansules) come in three sizes, 5, 10, and 15 milligrams. They have a brown lid and a clear bottom showing orange and white pellets and are inscribed "SKF." Two dots by the "SKF" mean 15 milligrams; one dot, 10 milligrams; and no dots, 5 milligrams. The tablets contain 5 milligrams of d-amphetamine sulfate. They are pale orange in color, three-sided, flat, and scored down the middle. Subject to the DRUG ABUSE CONTROL AMENDMENT OF 1965. Slang names: dexies, BROWNIES.

dexies. DEXEDRINE tablets.

dextromoramide. a SYNTHETIC OPIATE analgesic, dextromoramide has a somewhat higher pain-relieving potency than MORPHINE: 5 to 7.5 milligrams injected equal the analgesic effects of 10 milligrams of morphine, with the effects lasting four to five hours. PHYSICAL DEPENDENCE occurs after prolonged use, but WITHDRAWAL SYMPTOMS are similar to those of METHADONE dependency and less severe than those of morphine or HEROIN. Dextromoramide is sold under the trade name PALFIUM. A CLASS A NARCOTIC.

dihydrocodeine. a semisynthetic derivative of MORPHINE, about twice as potent as CODEINE. A dosage of 60 milligrams produces the analgesia of 10 milligrams of morphine, lasting four to five hours. Dihydrocodeine is generally prescribed for minor pain and as an ingredient in cough medicines. Prolonged use will result in PHYSICAL DEPENDENCE, with WITHDRAWAL SYMPTOMS somewhere between those of codeine and morphine in severity. A CLASS B NARCOTIC. Compare DROCOGESIC NO. 3, SYNALGOS-DC, TUSSANIL.

dihydrocodeinone. HYDROCODONE.

dihydromorphinone. HYDROMORPHONE.

Dilaudid. [HYDROMORPHONE (dihydromorphinone), Knoll Pharmaceutical Company] a semisynthetic derivative of MORPHINE. Although derived from morphine, Dilaudid is a much more potent pain reliever. Injections of 2 milligrams provide the analgesia of 10 to 15 milligrams of morphine or 100 milligrams of MEPERIDINE, with effects lasting four to five hours. There is less nausea, vomiting, and sedation than with morphine. PHYSICAL DEPENDENCE develops after prolonged use, and the WITHDRAWAL SYMPTOMS are similar to those of morphine in severity.

Dilaudid is sold in small white saccharinelike tablets (1, 2, 3, or 4 milligrams), as rectal suppositories (yellow, shaped like the upper half of a bowling ball), and ampuls for injection. Dilaudid Cough Syrup contains 1 milligram of Dilaudid hydrochloride and 100 milligrams of glyceryl guaiacolate per teaspoonful, in a reddish-orange peach-flavored syrup. Recommended adult dosage is 1 teaspoonful repeated in three to four hours. Both Dilaudid and Dilaudid Cough Syrup are CLASS A NARCOTICS.

> And any doctor who wasn't suspicious [of the forged prescription for *Dilaudid*] would write out a script for twenty or thirty Dilaudids. Possibly one, definitely two would get me straight. But that's no good either. I mean a Dilaudid habit is no good. First of all, your habit on Dilaudid you get it much faster than you do on stuff [heroin]. Your body tolerances build up fast and before you know it you're taking fifteen or twenty Dilaudids at once, where maybe three days before, one or two would help. It goes up fantastically high. Second, there isn't a doctor in New York that isn't hip to junkies. But I'll tell you that if a doctor can be conned by anyone, I can do it. I can con anyone.
> —addict in James Mills, *The Panic in Needle Park* (1966)

Dilocol. [(HYDROMORPHONE) hydrochloride and other ingredients, Table Rock Laboratories, Inc.] cough syrup containing a semisynthetic derivative of MORPHINE. Each 30 cubic centimeters (6 teaspoonsful) contains 6 milligrams of dihydromorphinone hydrochloride, upon which PHYSICAL DEPENDENCE can develop after prolonged use. Recommended for coughs, reducing mucous irritation, and liquefying phlegm. Recommended dose is 1 teaspoonful every three or four hours. A CLASS A NARCOTIC.

dime. [codeword formerly used in discussing prices during narcotics transactions] ten dollars, as in "sell me a *dime* bag." Compare CENT, NICKEL.

Dionin. [Merck Sharp & Dohme] ethylmorphine hydrochloride.

Diosan. [commercial name in Spain] ethylmorphine hydrochloride.

dipipanone. a SYNTHETIC OPIATE analgesic somewhat less potent than MORPHINE. A 20-milligram injection gives the analgesic effects of 10 milligrams of morphine, lasting four to five hours. PHYSICAL DEPENDENCE develops after prolonged use, with WITHDRAWAL SYMPTOMS similar to those of METHADONE dependence and considerably less severe than those of morphine or HEROIN. A CLASS A NARCOTIC.

dirty. [antonym of CLEAN] *1.* carrying narcotics on the person. *2.* applied to marijuana from which the stems, twigs, and seeds have not been removed.

discon. disorderly conduct charge or conviction.

> "What happened to you?" I asked.
> "*Discon.* Helen said she told you. The judge threw it out. He said the cop never should have busted me while I was in the phone booth. Like how could I be disorderly if I was just standing in the booth talking to someone on the phone? Which is right. The cop was a real jerk."
> —addict in James Mills, *The Panic in Needle Park* (1966)

Ditran. [piperidyl benzilate, Lakeside Laboratories, Inc.] a HALLUCINOGEN and PSYCHOTOMIMETIC drug. Experiments with Ditran induced clear psychotic symptoms, toxic organic symptoms, hallucinations (mainly auditory), delusions, and a catatonic state.

The drug produced the following sequence of reactions in one experiment: (*1*) upon injection: odd sensations, heaviness of limbs; (*2*) after fifteen to twenty minutes: slurred speech, inertia, sensory cloudiness; and (*3*) one hour after injection: unresponsiveness both to questions by the examiner and to environmental occurrences. Subjects would have brief lucid intervals of ten to thirty seconds approximately every three minutes, when they responded to questions with fair coherence; then they would sink back into a with-drawn state. Other mental disorganization occurred, especially dis-orientation as to time and place. Changes in perception altered the form, distance, movement, and color of objects. Subjects sank into a state of immobility, occasionally making slow, aimless movements of the hands and mouth. The drug's effects are markedly different from those of LSD: there are no visual hallucinations, and the loss of contact with the surrounding environment is more nearly total.

djamba. [Brazil] CANNABIS. See DJOMA.

djoma. [central Africa; the similarity of this word to the Brazilian word for cannabis lends credence to the theory that the use of cannabis was introduced to the Western Hemisphere by African slaves] CANNABIS. Also called diamba, liamba, lianda, and maconha.

DMT. [*N,N*-dimethyltryptamine] a semisynthetic, fast-acting hal-lucinogenic chemical very similar in structure to psilocin, the hallu-cinogenic substance to which PSILOCYBIN, the active ingredient in the hallucinogenic mushrooms, is converted in the body. DMT is also thought to be the active ingredient of the hallucinogenic plants PIPTADENIA and BANISTERIOPSIS CAAPI. It is easily synthesized with rudimentary equipment and common ingredients, and there is evi-dence that illicit use is on the increase. Several close chemical vari-ants, including DPT and DET, are also hallucinogenic. The onset of the drug occurs within two minutes, and its effects last upward of thirty minutes. The usual mode of ingestion is to soak parsley in the drug, let it dry, then smoke it in a pipe or cigarette. PHYSICAL DEPENDENCE does not develop, but TOLERANCE probably does, as is the case with psilocybin.

> My desperate attempts to climb toward sunlight and release from horror occupied the reminder of the experience—barely thirty min-utes by clock time, but an infinite eternity subjectively during which I experienced total evolution, from the primary amoeboid stage, crawling and grasping for something to hold onto even though I was on the floor, slowly and then ever more rapidly growing and hurtling through both time and space.
> —anonymous DMT user, quoted in Dr. Donald Louria,
> *Nightmare Drugs* (1966)

dogie. HEROIN. Also doojee, duji.

Yet there is something about *dogie*—heroin—it's a superduper tran-

quilizer. All your troubles become a bunch of bleary blurred memories when you're in a nod of your own special dimension.
—Piri Thomas, *Down These Mean Streets* (1967)

dollies. DOLOPHINE pills. Often secured by addicts to alleviate WITHDRAWAL SYMPTOMS when there is a shortage of HEROIN, when they wish to withdraw from heroin, or when they are about to be imprisoned.

dolls. [coined by Jacqueline Susann, author of *Valley of the Dolls;* not true slang] BARBITURATE or AMPHETAMINE pills.

Dolophine. [METHADONE hydrochloride, Eli Lilly and Company] a SYNTHETIC OPIATE analgesic slightly more potent than MORPHINE. An injection of 10 milligrams gives analgesic action equivalent to that of 15 milligrams of morphine. Dolophine produces considerably less euphoria than morphine. It may also cause dizziness, dryness of the mouth, and vomiting. Even when the first doses are well tolerated, nausea may appear after several doses. Overdosage can cause drowsiness, sweating, mental depression, delirium, hallucinations, circulatory collapse, and coma. PHYSICAL DEPENDENCE occurs after prolonged use, but WITHDRAWAL SYMPTOMS are considerably less severe than those of morphine dependency. Sold in ampuls, in syrup containing 33.33 milligrams of Dolophine per 100 cubic centimeters, and tablets of 5, 7.5, or 10 milligrams. A CLASS A NARCOTIC.

DOM. see STP.

doojee. HEROIN. Also dogie, duji.

dope. any narcotic. The word is coming to be applied to MARIJUANA and other HALLUCINOGENS, and perhaps AMPHETAMINES and BARBITURATES.

dope fiend. a term applied with defiant irony by addicts or other drug users to themselves (less frequently, by society to addicts).

Doriden. [GLUTETHIMIDE, CIBA Pharmaceutical Company] a non-barbiturate hypnotic and sedative, comparable to short-acting BARBITURATES in onset and duration of sedative action. Manufacturer recommends for simple insomnia, calming ambulatory patients suffering from insomnia, in preoperative sedation, and as a daytime sedative (TRANQUILIZER).
Recommended doses range from 0.125 gram (for sedation) up

to 0.5 gram for sleep. Doses of thirty times the hypnotic dose (15 grams) have been taken in suicide attempts, resulting in prolonged coma, absence of reflexes, high fever, and occasionally death. Taken in combination with alcohol or other sedatives (which POTENTIATE its action), Doriden has caused fatal respiratory and circulatory failure.

TOLERANCE to the drug's effects develops; PHYSICAL DEPEND-ENCE also develops after prolonged heavy usage (above 1.0 gram per day). WITHDRAWAL SYMPTOMS are comparable to those of barbiturate dependence in severity, if the drug is abruptly ceased. Symptoms range from anxiety to grand mal (major epilepticlike) seizures. Chronic Doriden intoxication, which can appear when amounts of 1.5 grams and more are taken daily for several months, resembles chronic barbiturate intoxication and manifests itself in unsteadiness, tremors, slurred speech, loss of memory, irritability, delirium, etc. Doriden is supplied in tablets of 0.125, 0.25 and 0.5 gram (white, round, flat with "CIBA" inscribed) and in capsules of 0.5 gram (white bottom, blue cap bearing inscription "CIBA"). Subject to the DRUG ABUSE CONTROL AMENDMENT OF 1965.

do rights. first-time patients at LEXINGTON who are considered good prospects for a cure.

do up. [analogous to *fix;* from *tie up,* to tie a cord around an arm to distend the vein, thus making injection easier] to inject HEROIN.

down. DOWNIE.

downer. DOWNIE.

downie. [from *down,* antonym of HIGH] a BARBITURATE or TRAN-QUILIZER pill, often taken by AMPHETAMINE users to reverse the stim-ulant action of the drug when it becomes uncomfortable. Compare COMING DOWN, UP, UPPER.

down trip. [from *down,* antonym of HIGH, and TRIP, hallucinogenic drug experience] boring; depressing. Compare BRING DOWN, BUM KICKS.

dragged. frightened, hysterical after smoking MARIJUANA.

dreamer. MORPHINE.

dried out. detoxified, withdrawn from a drug, usually in a hospital, as in "I went into Manhattan General and got *dried out*." A process of at least 10 days.

Drinamyl. [British drug] see DEXAMYL.

Drocogesic No. 3. [DIHYDROCODEINE bitartrate with other ingredients, Carrtone Laboratories, Inc.] an analgesic preparation containing dihydrocodeine, an addictive MORPHINE derivative. A dose of 60 milligrams of dihydrocodeine gives analgesia equivalent to 10 milligrams of morphine; PHYSICAL DEPENDENCE can occur after prolonged use, with WITHDRAWAL SYMPTOMS less severe than those of morphine.

Each Drocogesic tablet contains 30 milligrams of dihydrocodeine. Manufacturer recommends it for headaches, neuralgia, and pain connected with upper respiratory infection. Recommended dosage is one to two tablets every three to four hours. A CLASS B NARCOTIC. Compare CODEINE.

drop. to swallow (a pill), as in "they were sitting around *dropping* ACID."

dropper. medicine dropper used as a hypodermic syringe for injection of HEROIN. The needle is fastened to the tip of the dropper, with the glass part acting as the barrel of a hypodermic and the rubber bulb as the plunger. Most addicts find an eyedropper less clumsy than a regular hypodermic. Held upright, the bulb between thumb and forefinger, the dropper is easily manipulated, and the addict can inject the drugs in graduated amounts—injecting a little, withdrawing a little mixed with blood, and so on—thus prolonging and graduating the pleasure of the heroin's initial onset. Compare BOOTING, COLLAR, FIX.

Drug Abuse Control Amendment of 1965. (also called Harris-Dodd Act). an amendment to this country's food, drug and cosmetic legislation which brings dangerous stimulant, depressant, and hallucinogenic drugs under federal law. The act defines "depressant or stimulant drugs" as (1) drugs containing barbituric acid or barbituric acid derivatives which have been found upon investigation to be habit-forming; (2) drugs containing AMPHETAMINE or any of its optical isomers, salts of amphetamine or of any optical isomer, or any other substance found by investigation to be habit-forming because of its stimulant properties; and (3) any drug found by investigation to have "a potential for abuse because of its depressant or stimulant effect on the central nervous system or its hallucinogenic effect" excluding narcotic drugs and MARIJUANA, now regulated by the HARRISON NARCOTICS ACT.

Under the act, no person may possess any of the proscribed drugs except for his personal use or for the use of members of his family or for administration to an animal owned by him or his household; persons who manufacture, process, sell, deliver, or otherwise dispose of these drugs must keep records of all drugs so handled; prescriptions for these drugs are limited to five refills, and none may be refilled after six months; only authorized manufacturers, suppliers, wholesalers, pharmacies, hospitals, clinics, public health agencies, physicians, researchers, and government employees acting in the course of their official duties can sell, deliver, or otherwise dispose of the proscribed drugs. Penalties for violations are provided by the federal Food, Drug, and Cosmetic Act, except that the amendment provides that a person over eighteen who illegally transfers a drug to a person under twenty is liable to not more than two years in prison and a fine of $2,000 for a first offense and for subsequent violations a maximum of six years in prison and a fine of $15,000.

The act is intended to crack down on the trade in AMPHETAMINE and BARBITURATE drugs (and several TRANQUILIZERS and non-barbiturate hypnotics and sedatives), whether these drugs have been legitimately manufactured but diverted into the illicit traffic or illegitimately manufactured. It is also aimed at stopping the underground traffic in HALLUCINOGENS, which are mostly manufactured in clandestine laboratories or smuggled in from abroad.

Drugs regulated by the amendment may be subsumed under the following general categories:

1. Drugs containing any quantity of barbituric acid or its salts, or derivatives of barbituric acid, which have been designated by the Bureau of Drug Abuse Control as "habit-forming." See BARBITURATES; Appendix III.
2. Drugs containing any quantity of amphetamine or any of its optical isomers (containing the same number of elements and atoms but arranged in a different structure, e.g., dextro-amphetamine but not methamphetamine); any salt of amphetamine or its isomers; or any other substance which the BDAC designates as "habit forming" because of "its stimulant effect on the central nervous system." See AMPHETAMINES; Appendix III.
3. Combinations. This category flows out of the previous two and includes

drugs containing barbiturate and amphetamine in combination (see DEXAMYL, DESBUTAL), or one or both of these in combination with another drug which is not regulated by the statute but which combination the BDAC designates as "habit forming."

4. Drugs containing any quantity of a substance which the BDAC, after investigation (including hearings with the parties involved), has found to have a "potential for abuse" because of "its depressant or stimulant effect on the central nervous system, or its hallucinogenic effect" (excluding marijuana or any other drug regulated by Federal narcotics law). See Appendix IV.

drug automatism. ingestion of drugs without conscious awareness of the amount being taken or previously taken. This state occurs with heavy BARBITURATE users. Taken in large amounts, the drug clouds the mind and paralyzes the judgment. When sleep fails to come, because of TOLERANCE to the drug's effects, the users take more of the pills. This practice often results in a fatal overdose.

druggies. college students who experiment widely and frequently with a variety of drugs. Compare HEADS, SICKIES.

> On campus they cluster into three distinct groups. The *"druggies"* try anything, mix pills, and are high much of the time. They are steady LSD users. The casual potheads dabble in pills and "hash" and try acid once or twice. The fringe majority, friends, roommates of "heads," puff pot a couple of times and use amphetamines before exams. —*Look* (Aug. 8, 1967)

drug traffic. TRAFFIC, DRUG.

duby. MARIJUANA.

duji. HEROIN. Also spelled dogie, doojie.

dummies. DUMMY.

dummy. [from *dummy,* a phony, not the real thing] counterfeit HEROIN; white powder such as kitchen cleanser, talcum, or quinine placed in a BAG and sold to the addict as heroin. The addict rarely can tell whether he has bought heroin until he injects the purchase. Compare BLANK, GARBAGE, LEMONADE.

> "I saw a guy get caught dealing *dummies* [fake heroin] in a vestibule. This other cat took a taste from the bag, and he began yelling. 'You sold me a dummy!' He took out a gun, the rest of us hit the wall like postage stamps, and he blew the dealer away."
> —addict, quoted in Tom Alexander, in *The Drug Takers* (1965)

dusting. [from *dust,* tobacco; and *dust,* narcotics, as in *happy dust,* COCAINE—*EP*] mixing HEROIN in a MARIJUANA cigarette. Compare A-BOMB.

dynamite. *1.* COCAINE and HEROIN taken in combination (see SPEED-BALL). *2.* relatively undiluted, high-potency heroin. Compare BOM-BITA, DYNO.

dyno. relatively undiluted, high-potency HEROIN, often stronger than the addict is tolerant to. Inadequate TOLERANCE can result in a fatal overdose of dyno.

E e

ecognine. the principal part of the COCAINE molecule. Obtained by hydrolysis of cocaine and other COCA alkaloids. Cocaine can also be synthesized from ecognine. A CLASS A NARCOTIC.

eighth, an. *1.* one-eighth ounce of diluted HEROIN. *2.* a rough measure for the purpose of sale. Compare CUTTING, SIXTEENTH, SPOON.

electric. influenced by or containing a PSYCHEDELIC drug, as in ELECTRIC KOOL-ADE.

electric Kool-Ade. a punch containing LSD-25, frequently served at ACID TESTS.

elemicin. [3,4,5-trimethoxyallylbenzene] a compound present in oil of NUTMEG and thought to be the ACTIVE PRINCIPLE causing its hallucinogenic effects. It is very similar in structure to TMA, another HALLUCINOGEN.

embalao. [Puerto Rican addicts' slang] strongly addicted, with accompanying physical debilitation; STRUNG OUT.

enchaioui. [Arabic] a man who has centered his life around KIF (CANNABIS).

epena. a hallucinogenic snuff used by the Waika Indians of northern Brazil and made from the bark of the *epena* and *amasita* trees, which is ground up to produce a fine powder. One end of a long hollow tube containing the snuff is held to the nose, and another person blows through the other end, driving the snuff up the nasal passages. At onset, the effects are nausea and vomiting. Then the user straightens up and struts about, emitting an occasional laugh or yell. He experiences hallucinations in which everything is seen in giant size and he becomes a giant towering into the clouds, where he converses with the Indian deities.

Equanil. [MEPROBAMATE, Wyeth Laboratories] a nonhypnotic muscle relaxant and MINOR TRANQUILIZER. Manufacturer recommends in conditions involving muscle spasm, neuromuscular disorders, anxiety and tension, as adjunctive therapy in rehabilitation of alcoholics, in minor epilepsy (petit mal), and as an aid to sleep. Recommended dosages are 400 milligrams three or four times a day. Sold as white scored 200- and 400-milligram tablets, yellow-coated 400-milligram tablets, in a liquid base (200 milligrams per teaspoonful), and continuous-release 200-milligram capsules.

A danger of Equanil, as with many tranquilizers, is that PSYCHIC DEPENDENCE will occur, the drug being a "crutch" for the user seeking to alleviate deep-set anxieties. PHYSICAL DEPENDENCE possibly develops after prolonged, excessive use. After excessive use, if the user's crutch is abruptly withdrawn, his underlying symptoms (anxiety, insomnia, poor appetite) will characteristically return with greatly increased severity. In some cases of excessive use WITHDRAWAL SYMPTOMS have included vomiting, loss of bodily equilibrium, muscle twitching, and epilepticlike seizures. Equanil has been used in a number of suicide attempts, with amounts up to 20 to 40 grams (20,000 to 40,000 milligrams) being taken (the manufacturer's maximum recommended total daily dose is 2,400 milligrams). Fatalities in such attempts have been rare, but such dosages produce coma, shock, and respiratory collapse. Alcohol POTENTIATES the drug's effects. Subject to the DRUG ABUSE CONTROL AMENDMENT OF 1965. See also MILTOWN.

esrar. [Turkish, meaning secret preparation, evidently from the practice of mixing cannabis with tobacco to avoid detection; cannabis smoking was outlawed in Turkey in the nineteenth century] CANNABIS.

ethanol. ETHYL ALCOHOL.

ethchlorvynol. a nonbarbiturate hypnotic and sedative compounded of a carboamic acid ester of alicylic alcohol. Its onset and effects are similar to those of secobarbital, a short-acting BARBITURATE. Like the other nonbarbiturate sedatives, ethchlorvynol has not proved to be the "safe alternative" to barbiturates. Prolonged excessive use can result in PSYCHIC DEPENDENCE, accompanied by increasing doses, PHYSICAL DEPENDENCE, and WITHDRAWAL SYMPTOMS when the drug is abruptly stopped. The latter may include convulsions and epileptic-like seizures similar to those accompanying barbiturate dependence. However, ethchlorvynol is useful as a sedative for patients who are allergic to the barbiturates.

Since it is a less potent central nervous system depressant than the barbiturates, larger amounts (500 milligrams) are needed to produce sleep, and only extremely large doses produce fatal respiratory failure. Dosages ranging from twenty to fifty times the hypnotic dose of 500 milligrams have produced comas lasting a week and sometimes death. Alcohol taken in conjunction with ethchlorvynol POTENTIATES its effects and hence its dangers. Subject to the DRUG ABUSE CONTROL AMENDMENT OF 1965. See also ETHINAMATE, PLACIDYL, TRANQUILIZERS.

ethinamate. a nonbarbiturate hypnotic and sedative, compounded of a carboamic acid ester of alicylic alcohol. Its onset and effects are similar to those of secobarbital, a short-acting BARBITURATE, though of shorter duration. Prolonged, excessive use can result in PSYCHIC DEPENDENCE requiring increased dosages, PHYSICAL DEPENDENCE and WITHDRAWAL SYMPTOMS similar to those of barbiturate dependency when the drug is abruptly halted.

Overdosage can be fatal, but the lethal dose of ethinamate is unknown, a dose of 15 grams proving fatal while a dose of 28 grams was not. The usual sedative dose is 0.5 to 1 gram (500 to 1,000 milligrams), and one experiment showed that 0.5 gram was equal in sedative effect to 100 milligrams of secobarbital with some persons, while with others it performed scarcely better than a placebo used as a control. Subject to the DRUG ABUSE CONTROL AMENDMENT OF 1965.

ethyl alcohol. also called ethanol. A primary and continuous depressant of the central nervous system. The effect is analogous to a general anesthetic, though usually less profound and longer lasting since the alcohol is slowly metabolized, at the average rate of 10 milliliters per hour (the equivalent of 0.6 ounce of 100-proof whiskey). The amount necessary to produce anesthesia is dangerously close to the lethal dose. The body can metabolize at the very maximum 400 to 500 milliliters in a day, the equivalent of about a fifth of 100-proof whiskey. It takes the average adult five or six hours to metabolize the alcohol in 4 ounces of whiskey or 1.25 quarts of beer, however, which means that roughly a pint of 100-proof whiskey or 5 quarts of beer would be metabolized in a day.

Alcohol acts on the primitive part of the brain, the reticular activating system, releasing it from the integrative control of the cortex, with the result that thoughts occur in a disorganized, jumbled fashion and bodily coordination is disrupted. Though basically a depressant, alcohol can foster a pseudo-stimulant effect which results from the hyperactivity of various primitive parts of the brain suddenly freed from the inhibitory control of the cortex. This activity is short-lived and gives way to the depressant effects, with resultant coma if consumption is continued.

The degree of alcoholic intoxication is fairly accurately reflected by the percentage of alcohol in the bloodstream. Various "drunkometer" tests to establish this percentage have been devised and are employed by legal authorities to determine whether a person was criminally under the influence of alcohol when he committed a crime, i.e., certain crimes such as negligent homicide with a motor vehicle in which the key element is whether the driver was drunk or not. The following percentage concentrations of milligrams of alcohol in proportion to milliliters of the blood are commonly accepted as causing corresponding states of alcoholic intoxication:

0.05%	no intoxication (but the American Medical Association says that this concentration can impair driving ability in some individuals)
0.05–0.15%	some intoxication, but not in itself legal proof of intoxication
0.15%	legal presumption of intoxication according to the criterion established by the National Safety Council (which later recommended it be lowered to 0.10%)
0.25%	mild to moderate intoxication
0.3%	severe intoxication
0.4%	extremely severe intoxication, at the threshold of coma and even death
0.5–0.8%	fatal concentration of alcohol in the blood

It is estimated that the ingestion of 4 ounces of whiskey or 5.5 ounces of martini on an empty stomach results in a blood concentration of 0.06 to 0.09 percent or 0.03 to 0.05 percent on a full stomach. The same amount of alcohol taken as beer (1.25 quart) results in a maximum blood concentration of 0.041 to 0.049 percent on an empty stomach and 0.023 to 0.029 percent on a full one. Thus four average-sized highballs or martinis will produce a concentration in the blood of 0.134 to 0.184 percent, the legally defined state of intoxication.

PSYCHIC DEPENDENCE upon alcohol, where the user drinks in ways and amounts that are abnormal for his culture, may be mild, i.e., he misses the presence of alcohol at social functions; moderate, i.e., he feels compelled to drink in order to work or function socially and makes determined action to see that alcohol is available for those purposes; or strong, i.e., he uses amounts far in excess of the norm, drinks more or less steadily and on occasions not customary in his culture, and is so obsessed with obtaining alcohol that he will go to any lengths to do so and will drink whatever is available, even poisonous mixtures. Motivations for psychic dependence range from (1) socially acceptable half rationalizations (he "needs" it to relax, to stimulate appetite, relieve boredom, or to sleep) to (2) subconscious compulsions (anxiety, latent aggression that he can express only when inhibitory controls are removed, or inhibited masculinity or femininity) to (3) a desire to withdraw from a world perceived as threatening.

TOLERANCE to the action of alcohol develops, but imperfectly; during sustained drinking the amount of alcohol necessary to maintain an intoxicatory percentage in the blood must be increased, and an alcoholic's performance while intoxicated may be slightly less impaired than that of a nonalcoholic. But this tolerance is nothing like that seen with MORPHINE. The symptoms of chronic alcoholic intoxication, too well known to be described here, resemble chronic BARBITURATE intoxication. PHYSICAL DEPENDENCE on alcohol definitely occurs (an estimated 10 percent of the 60 million users of alcohol in the United States are alcoholics), with WITHDRAWAL SYMPTOMS ranging in severity from the morning-after hangover to convulsions and delirium, including confusion, disorientation, delusions, and vivid visual hallucinations. Delirium tremens, when severe, has an 8 percent fatality rate. There is a degree of CROSS-TOLERANCE between the barbiturates and alcohol; hence, barbiturates will relieve the alcoholic withdrawal syndrome, as will certain nonbarbiturate hypnotics, especially the frequently used PARALDE-HYDE. TRANQUILIZERS are also effective in alleviating the rigors of the withdrawal state.

Prolonged use of alcohol, especially in conjunction with the inadequate diet often associated with it, also has a debilitating effect on the body (cirrhosis of the liver, lowered resistance to disease, stomach trouble, heart disease); the barbiturates do not have these effects. Because of its action in releasing aggressive drives from inhibitory controls, alcohol is a significant factor in over half the crimes of violence in this country and over half the automobile fatalities.

Because of its ability to POTENTIATE many drugs, alcohol is often an important factor in drug fatalities, especially when large doses are not involved.

Eucodal. [OXYCODONE hydrochloride] A semisynthetic derivative of MORPHINE.

explorers' club. a circle of illicit LSD users.

F f

factory. a clandestine location where illicit drugs are processed in preparation for sale; e.g., pure HEROIN is diluted with quinine and packaged; marijuana is CLEANED and packaged. The word is used mainly by police and newspaper reporters.

falling out. dozing off, while under the influence of a drug, going into a half sleep.

fatty. a thickly rolled MARIJUANA cigarette. Compare BOMBER.

Federal Bureau of Narcotics. BUREAU OF NARCOTICS, FEDERAL.

feds. [traditionally applied, mainly by criminals, to members of any federal law-enforcement agency] Federal BUREAU OF NARCOTICS agents.

firing the ack-ack gun. [translation of the Chinese] a mode of taking HEROIN prevalent in Hong Kong. Heroin is applied to the tip of a cigarette which is then smoked.

five-cent paper. [from the folded PAPER in which HEROIN is sometimes packaged] a quantity of heroin in a folded piece of paper sold for $5. Compare FIVE-DOLLAR BAG.

five-dollar bag. a package of HEROIN sold for $5 and containing perhaps 5 grains (0.011 ounce) of heroin diluted with MILK SUGAR or quinine; about 1/8 teaspoon. The proportion of heroin varies from 0 to 80 percent; however, it is usually around 1 to 5 percent, or 3 to 15 milligrams. This is equal in potency to 9 to 45 milligrams of MORPHINE, the amount given medically for very severe pain.

fives. tablets containing 5 milligrams of the active ingredient; usually refers to BENZEDRINE or other AMPHETAMINE tablets.

fix. [from *fix-up*, a shot of narcotics; since the 1920s. A ration of drugs since the 1930s. Just enough to *fix up* or satisfy the addict— *EP*] *1.* to inject oneself with narcotics, as in "I *fixed*." *2.* an injection, a dose of narcotics, as in, "I gave myself a *fix*" or "I need a *fix*." *3.* the amount of drugs in the bag or packet which make up the fix, as in, "I couldn't find anybody to sell me a *fix*."

> After an intravenous injection of morphine, former narcotic addicts report that they feel *"fixed."* This term seems to denote a state of gratification in which hunger, pain and sexual urges are greatly reduced or abolished. In addition, intravenous injection of morphine results in a highly pleasurable "thrill" which is described as similar to orgasm except that the sensation seems to be centered in the abdomen. —Abraham Wikler, *Opiate Addiction. Psychological and Neurophysical Aspects in Relation to Clinical Practice* (1953)

> It's not only a question of kicks. The ritual itself, the powder in the spoon, the little ball of cotton, the matches applied, the bubbling liquid drawn up through the cotton filter into the eye-dropper, the tie round the arm to make a vein stand out, the *fix* often slow because a man will stand there with the needle in the vein and allow the level of the eye-dropper to waver up and down, up and down, until there is more blood than heroin in the dropper—all this is not

for nothing; it is born of a respect for the whole chemistry of alienation. When a man fixes he is turned on almost instantaneously . . . you can speak of a flash, a tinily murmured orgasm in the bloodstream, in the central nervous system. At once, and regardless of preconditions a man enters "Castle Keep." In "Castle Keep" and even in the face of the enemy, a man can accept.

—Alexander Trocchi, *Cain's Book* (1960)

flake. COCAINE.

flaky. [addicted to COCAINE, since around 1925; from the flaky appearance of the cocaine crystals—*EP*] general slang for being a bit crazy, just as cocaine makes the user a bit crazy.

flash. [from the sense of sudden light, combined with the idea of a deliberately quick showing of something, e.g., the pea in the shell game] *1.* the sudden onrush of pleasurable effects, euphoria following injection of heroin. *2.* the pleasurable effects of any drug at the moment they are first perceived. Compare FIX (quotation), RUSH.

flashing. [used mainly in California; from (?) FLASH] GLUE SNIFFING.

flea powder. inferior, highly diluted HEROIN. Compare DUMMY, GARBAGE, LEMONADE.

flip out. *1.* a temporary or chronic psychotic reaction to a drug, characterized by panic and loss of control over one's actions. *2.* divine madness or ecstasy, a mystical experience, in which one completely transcends one's normal state through the use of drugs, meditation, or religious techniques such as yoga.

floating. HIGH or intoxicated on a drug.

flower children. FLOWER PEOPLE.

flower people. [coined by a California disk jockey promoting a rock and roll group called The Seeds] also called flower children. Predominately youths in their teens and early twenties (but also older persons) who use HALLUCINOGENS, consider themselves to have dropped out of conventional materialistic society, and practice—or try to practice—communal living, free love, free drugs, free food, and so on. A kind of utopianism of the 1960s, with an emphasis on altering consciousness through drugs and finding God, pacifism, and noncompetitiveness, without the asceticism of American utopian movements during the nineteenth century.

flower power. the power of love, rather than force (or any other conventional mode of social action such as politics, strikes, etc.) to change society and men's hearts. In the language of LSD users, one scorns playing the conventional power games and seeks to convert or change what one does not like through the power of innocence and beauty, as symbolized by the flower. Compare FLOWER PEOPLE.

flunky. also called fool. An addict who takes large risks in acquiring money for drugs, often in ways that will bring him only small amounts, either because he is a novice and lacks criminal know-how or because he is a convicted burglar known to the police. The only way he can obtain drugs is to carry drugs for PUSHERS, buy drugs for other addicts, or otherwise expose himself to risks that addicts and pushers prefer to avoid when they can afford to.

flush. [from FLASH, sudden drug euphoria; or perhaps *flush,* blushing, hot skin, etc., analogous to sudden physiological changes induced when the drug takes effect] *1.* the sudden onrush of euphoria. *2.* relief from withdrawal sickness after HEROIN is injected.

fly agaric. [the poison in the mushroom was used on flypaper] a hallucinogenic, poisonous mushroom *Amanita muscaria* which grows in North America, Siberia, and Europe. The North American variety has a whitish, yellowish, or orange-red cap from 3 to 8 inches wide mottled with whitish, yellowish, or reddish warts; in Europe the cap is bright red or purple. The mushroom contains an alkaloid, MUSCARINE, which in sufficient quantities will stop the heart. Death usually follows the ingestion of one to three of the mushrooms unless the antidote ATROPINE is administered in time.

Death follows delirium, convulsions, and deep coma, and the action of the poison is rapid. In smaller toxic amounts the fly agaric induces vomiting, diarrhea, and rapid breathing. It also causes hallucinations, intoxication, gaiety, a form of perception distortion in which small objects such as pebbles seem large and the victim ludicrously tries to step over them, and sometimes paranoia and aggressive behavior. The intoxication always ends with a deep sleep. (Such doses, survivable by adults, are usually fatal to children.)

The action of the kidneys, as the drug passes through, seems not to affect it and even to enhance its potency. Consequently, the urine of persons who have eaten the mushroom contains powerful amounts of the ACTIVE PRINCIPLE. The indians of northern Siberia, who call the mushroom *muchamor,* collect the urine and drink it for continued intoxication. It is believed that the mushroom's active principle is BUFOTENINE, which is chemically similar to the HALLUCINOGENS PSILOCYBIN and DMT. A close relative of fly agaric is the death cup, *Amanita phalloides,* which is much deadlier, 60 to 100 percent fatal upon ingestion. It, too, has hallucinogenic properties and is found in North America.

> The poorer sort, who love mushroom broth to distraction as well as the rich, but cannot afford it at first hand, post themselves on these occasions around the huts of the rich and watch the opportunity of the ladies and gentlemen as they come down to pass their liquor, and holding a wooden bowl catch the delicious fluid, very little altered by filtration, being still strongly tinctured with the intoxicating quality. Of this they drink with the utmost satisfaction and thus they get as drunk and as jovial as their betters.   —Oliver Goldsmith (1762)

flying. in a state of drug intoxication, as in *"flying* on LSD." Compare COMING DOWN, HIGH, WINGS.

Flying Saucers. [trade name] a variety of morning glory, the seeds of which have hallucinogenic properties. See MORNING GLORY SEEDS.

fool. FLUNKY.

footballs. [from the shape?] Diphetamine pills; also, pill containing DILAUDID, a synthetic opiate.

forwards. AMPHETAMINE pills.

freak. [from the sense of grotesque, bizarre, distorted in appearance; not necessarily ugly, except to the "square" who come to gape, and certainly not to the freaks themselves] *1.* to hallucinate, implying a grotesque, grandiose, perhaps bizarrely beautiful or abnormally horrifying distortion of consciousness. *2.* a bad reaction to a hallucinogenic drug, as in "it's not so much the LSD trip that *freaks* me, it's getting back." (See FREAK OUT.) *3.* one who prefers a certain kind of drug, as in ACID FREAK or METH FREAK. *4.* by extension, one who is obsessed with a certain way of thinking as in "political *freak*" or "flying-saucer *freak.*" When the drug user refers to himself as a freak, he is either saying "well, if that is what society calls me, that is what I'll be; if *we're* freaks, then freaks are better than ordinary people" or expressing criticism of grotesque, compulsive drug use. When he refers to nonusers of drugs as freaks, he means that their mental set, prejudices, view of life are altered by whatever it is they are seemingly (to him) obsessed with in the same way a drug user's consciousness is altered under the influence of his drug, and the term becomes one of opprobrium.

freaking freely. spontaneous, random, LSD-induced behavior.

freak out. *1.* a panic reaction to LSD-25, causing the user to lose control of himself and his mind. *2.* [perhaps because the object of the LSD experience is to "lose one's mind," i.e., escape one's normal mental state] to take LSD, as in "to *freak out* on LSD." *3.* an LSD (or other hallucinogenic drug) experience, as in "I tried the LSD *freak out.*" Compare FLIP OUT.

> It is kicks man. It is The Kick. You *freak out* and there is nothing but greatness and madness. . . . It's Zen and Jesus Christ and all the mad magicians rolled into one big freak.
> —anonymous college student, quoted in W. R. Young and J. R. Hixon (eds.), *LSD on Campus* (1966)

freak rock. ACID ROCK.

freak up. *1.* deliberately to act in a bizarre, grotesque way, as in "the rock and roll group was *freaking* it *up* on stage." *2.* a kind of hoax as in "the performance was a *freak up* from first to last."

freaky. *1.* freakish. *2.* bizarre, abnormal behavior induced by drugs.

Frisco speedball. mixture of HEROIN, COCAINE, and LSD-25.

front. *1.* [from the sense of "putting up a *front*," i.e., a false display of respectability] a conventional set of clothing, as opposed to bohemian or HIPPIE attire.

> Have three sets of clothes, including one *"front"* with which you can go back into the square world for a job—or an appearance in court if need be. —Doc Stanley, "How to Survive on the Streets," *Los Angeles Free Press* (1967)

2. [from the idea of "put your money *in front,* and the delivery will follow] also front money. Payment in advance for drugs.

fruit salad. among teen-agers, a game in which each participant takes one pill from every bottle found in the family medicine cabinet.

full moon. *1.* a large PEYOTE chunk about 4 inches in diameter. *2.* the entire top of the peyote cactus (as opposed to the BUTTONS or slices).

fumo d'Angola. [Brazilian Portuguese, Angolan smoke] CANNABIS. This reference to the Portuguese colony of Angola in Africa lends further credence to the theory that cannabis smoking was introduced to the Western Hemisphere by African slaves. Compare DJOMA.

fuzz. *1.* policeman or detective. *2.* [shortening of NARCO FUZZ] narcotics officer.

gage. GAUGE.

gammon. one microgram (one-millionth of a gram), as in "500 *gammons* of LSD."

ganga. GUNGEON.

gangster. MARIJUANA.

gangster pills. BARBITURATES or other sedative pills.

gaping. [from the excessive yawning that is an early WITHDRAWAL SYMPTOM] experiencing OPIATE (HEROIN) withdrawal symptoms.

garbage. weak, heavily diluted HEROIN. Compare BLANK, FLEA POWDER, LEMONADE.

gasoline. the fumes, when inhaled, have a deliriant effect similar to GLUE SNIFFING or CLEANING FLUID and are highly toxic. Compare BENZINE.

gauge. [from *gauge butt,* a marijuana cigarette; since the 1930s. Tenuous is "marijuana sends people insane; gauge or measure of insanity"—*EP*. Perhaps a corruption of GHANJA or GUNGEON] MARI-JUANA.

gay. [a person who takes drugs for the exhilarating effect they produce is either "gay" or "high" or "sent"—*EP;* since around 1945] in a state of drug intoxication. *Obsolete.* The meaning homosexual seems dominant nowadays. But also note that prostitutes in nineteenth-century England were called "gay girls." "She is gay" meant she is a prostitute. So gay "homosexual" may have originated from the gay "prostitute" sense (prostitutes "cruise around" looking for clients, and homosxuals cruise around looking for someone of kindred sexual predilection).

G.B. [from GOOFBALL] a BARBITURATE pill.

gear. [in England, drugs in general, especially MARIJUANA since around 1945—*EP*. Perhaps this drug usage surfaced and was broadened to its present meaning. Compare BOSS] among English teen-agers the word means *1.* stylish, "in," up-to-the-minute or *2.* clothes.

gee head. [from thinning of P.G.?] a PAREGORIC addict.

get in the groove. [to become familiar with the drug traffic or proficient in drug taking—*EP;* from the jazz sense of playing *in the groove,* with the right swinging beat] *obsolete,* but see GROOVING.

get off. [probably from get off, have an orgasm, and the sexual thrill HEROIN users feel when they inject into the vein] to inject heroin, as in "he *got off* right there in the hallway." Compare FIX, JERK OFF.

get on. to take drugs for the first time. Compare TURN ON.

getting on. smoking MARIJUANA. Compare TURN ON.

ghanja. [Compare the Jamaican words GUNGEON, ganga] the flowering tops, twigs, leaves, and stems of the female hemp plant, CANNABIS SATIVA, covered with a sticky resinous exudate that contains the hallucinogenic ACTIVE PRINCIPLE of the plant in highly concentrated form. Special techniques of cultivation are used in India to increase this resinous exudate. In India ghanja is usually smoked or mixed into cakes and sweetmeats. This form of CANNABIS is more potent than BHANG (the Indian form of MARIJUANA, consisting of the leaves, stems, and twigs) and somewhat less potent than CHARAS (HASHISH). Compare CANNABIS INDICA.

ghost, the. LSD-25.

giggle weed. MARIJUANA.

gimmicks. [from a secret knack; any trick aiding the operations of a device or a game or a sales trick; pitchmen and criminals' slang— *EP*] equipment for injecting drugs. *Obsolete?* Compare WORKS.

girl. [antonym of BOY, HEROIN, both in the slang usage and as a rough metaphor for their effects, since cocaine is a stimulant and heroin a depressant; probably rose out of the practice of taking the two drugs together, and perhaps from the quasi-sexual thrills obtained] COCAINE. Compare GET OFF, HIM, HER, SPEEDBALL.

globetrotter. an addict who circulates around a drug-selling area, making inquiries of PUSHERS, in order to select the best HEROIN.

glow. *1.* HIGH. *2.* drugged euphoria.

> You had to be a lot harder to be a pusher; you couldn't have a soft heart, like "no dough, no *glow*."
> —Piri Thomas, *Down These Mean Streets* (1967)

glue sniffing. sometimes called flashing. Inhaling the fumes of model-airplane glue (containing toluol) for their deliriant effect. Generally the user squeezes some of the glue into a paper bag, holds the bag tight over his nose, and inhales the fumes. These induce, in the first stage, a feeling of hazy euphoria something like that from alcohol. Soon follows a disordering of perception: double vision, ringing in the ears, and even hallucinations. The user's speech becomes slurred, and he staggers around with poor coordination, as if he were drunk. After thirty-five to forty minutes he falls into a state of drowsiness or stupor lasting an hour, during which he is unable to recall what he was doing.

Occasionally sniffers erupt into violence or have delusions of grandeur, during which they think they can fly, or lie on railroad tracks; such impairment of judgment has resulted in serious or fatal accidents. Overinhalation can result in kidney damage or even death, though such occurrences are rare.

PHYSICAL DEPENDENCE does not develop in glue sniffing (though a case has been reported of a glue sniffer who experienced cramps and abdominal pains when withdrawn from the practice). A form of PSYCHIC DEPENDENCE can develop, and some users increase the amount sniffed each time in order to intensify their experience.

Eventually, however, the user gives up the practice. Glue sniffing is regarded as "kid stuff" by many older adolescents (although cases have been reported of addicts unable to obtain their HEROIN supply who resorted to glue sniffing). Since most cases are in the twelve to fourteen age group, it appears that either the glue sniffer will outgrow his habit or will go on to more "adult" drugs, such as AMPHETAMINES, BARBITURATES, and even heroin.

Glue sniffing was first reported in the United States in 1955; the 1960s brought a sharp upsurge. In New York City there were 2,003 cases reported, as compared with 779 in 1962. Although manufacturers no longer sell tubes of airplane glue separately from model kits, it is doubtful that this measure has reduced the practice in the slightest. Compare CARBONA, CARBON TETRACHLORIDE, CLEANING FLUID.

glutethimide. a nonbarbiturate hypnotic and sedative used to induce sleep and as a preoperative and daytime sedative (TRANQUILIZER). Glutethimide closely resembles phenobarbital in molecular structure; its effects resemble those of secobarbital, a short-acting BARBITURATE. Although glutethimide was once touted as being safer than barbiturates, the Council on Drugs of the American Medical Association says, "Glutethimide is now regarded as a typical general depressant having no special advantage over barbiturates, but constituting a satisfactory alternative to the latter if one is needed."

If taken in excessive amounts (above 1 gram, or 1,000 milligrams, per day) for a prolonged period of time, the drug produces PHYSICAL DEPENDENCE. Abrupt withdrawal of the drug from one who has become physically dependent will cause WITHDRAWAL SYMPTOMS, ranging from anxiety to epileptic (grand mal) seizures, accompanied by abdominal cramping, chills, numbness of extremities, and difficulty in swallowing. Newborn infants of mothers dependent upon glutethimide may also suffer withdrawal symptoms. The drug often produces euphoria, as well as generalized sedation, which makes it similar to the barbiturates in its liability to induce PSYCHIC DEPENDENCE in the patient, especially habitual users of other drugs and alcohol, accompanied by a tendency to increase the frequency and amount of the dose.

The drug has been used in suicide attempts, in amounts averaging 15 grams, or thirty capsules. Acute intoxication will result from doses of 3 grams (six times the usual therapeutic dose) or above; doses of 10 grams or more will induce respiratory depression, coma, and perhaps death. Fatalities in such attempts have occurred, especially when the drug is taken with alcohol, barbiturates, or other depressants which POTENTIATE its depressant effects. Subject to the DRUG ABUSE CONTROL AMENDMENT OF 1965. Compare DORIDEN.

goblet of jam. [translation of Arabic *m'jun-i akbar*] MAJOON, a confection containing CANNABIS, eaten in North Africa for the hallucinogenic effects. See also DAWAMESK.

going down. *1.* going well. *2.* happening.

going high. a pleasurable, continuing state of drug intoxication, not necessitating ingestion of any further drugs for the time being.

> *How can I make out of this?* I was thinking. "Nay, dad, I've been blasting *yerba;* I have a *going high,* and I don't want to mess it up."
> —Piri Thomas, *Down These Mean Streets* (1967)

going up. see GO UP.

gold. ACAPULCO GOLD.

gold dust. [since the 1930s] COCAINE. *Obsolete.*

gold duster. [since the 1930s] COCAINE user. *Obsolete.*

golden leaf. ACAPULCO GOLD.

goods. *1.* narcotics. *2.* any drugs.

good sick. the nausea and vomiting that HEROIN sometimes induces soon after injection. Addicts do not consider it unpleasant, associated as it is with the drug's euphoria.

> "Just a minute," I said. I climbed off the bed, walked round him and across the kitchen to the bucket he used for a w.c. I vomited. It wasn't painful. It's not like getting sick on alcohol. The little food I had eaten during the day was soon regurgitated. Geo was standing beside me with a saucepan full of water.
> "Here."
> I drank and regurgitated, drank and regurgitated, the spasms lessening as whatever nervousness caused the nausea was neutralized first by the thought of my transcendent immunity, and then by the extreme but indefinable ecstasy at my senses. There was a wet, prickly sweat at my belly and thighs and temples.
> —Alexander Trocchi, *Cain's Book* (1960)

good stuff. [from STUFF, heroin] HEROIN of superior quality.

goofball. [from *goofy, goof,* a stupid, silly, or crazy person; hence a pill that makes one behave in this manner; since around 1940] *1.* BARBITURATE pill. *2.* (rare and erroneous) an AMPHETAMINE pill.

goofing. *1.* under the influence of BARBITURATES and hence acting in a random, uncoordinated, drunken manner. *2.* conversely, sitting staring dreamily into space. Compare NOD, NODDING.

gorilla pills. BARBITURATES or other sedative pills.

go up. *1.* to experience the onset of drug intoxication. *2.* to be in a state of drug intoxication, as in "he'd *gone up* on marijuana." Compare COME DOWN, HIGH.

gow. [from a Chinese character for opium; since the 1920s—*EP*] *1.* OPIUM. *Obsolete?* *2.* DRUG. *Obsolete?*

grass. [from the greenish appearance of the leaves, twigs, and fruit of CANNABIS SATIVA prepared for smoking] MARIJUANA.

> Keep off the Grass
> —underground button slogan meaning "legalize marijuana"

gravy. mixture of blood from the addict's vein and HEROIN which is reheated in the COOKER because it has coagulated and cannot be injected. Compare SHOOTING GRAVY.

greasy junky. a passive, indolent addict whose drug-hustling activities are at a minimum and who will make no great effort to get money to buy narcotics, relying on begging and personal services instead.

green. [from the color; generalized term for any MARIJUANA of that color, whatever the origin] a "grade" of marijuana sometimes of relatively low potency because it is low in resin content. Usually MEXICAN GREEN, because of its origin. This is the cheapest grade.

green pepper. JACKSON ILLUSION PEPPER.

grefa. [from the Spanish] MARIJUANA.

greta. [probably a variation of *grefa*] MARIJUANA.

grifa. [Mexican] MARIJUANA.

griffo. MARIJUANA.

groovers. teen-agers (thirteen- to seventeen-year-olds) who use drugs largely for thrills, especially sexual thrills and bizarre mental effects.

grooving. [from *in the groove,* musician's term for playing well, with a good beat, etc.] becoming intoxicated on a drug, as in "he was *grooving* (on) pot."

groovy. the euphoric, HIGH experience under a drug or like that under a drug, as in "feeling *groovy.*"

ground control. a person who attends an LSD user undergoing the drug's effects in case he has a panic reaction.

ground man. GROUND CONTROL.

group grope. [from *grope,* to caress, pet] indiscriminate, multiple petting; the lights are turned out, and the participants stimulate each other sexually.

guide. an experienced LSD user who supervises a novice's first experience with the drug; literally, one who teaches another how to use LSD, controls and directs the TRIP, and administers tranquilizers when necessary. Compare GURU.

gun. [from *shoot,* to inject] a hypodermic needle, used to inject narcotics. Compare BANG, POP.

gunga. [England; from "Gunga Din," meaning Indian hemp, i.e., marijuana.—*EP;* since around 1945; but perhaps from the Indian word *ghanja,* or the Jamaican word *ganga.* As in the United States, the practice of marijuana smoking began in England among colored minority groups] MARIJUANA.

gungeon. [an American spelling; it may be a variant of the Jamaican *ganga;* Jamaica was a source for American MARIJUANA in the 1940s] *1.* especially potent marijuana from Jamaica or Africa. *2.* a cigarette containing gungeon.

gunja. [American, probably a variation of *ganga* or *gungeon.*] MARIJUANA. *Obsolete.*

guru. [Hindi, a religious teacher, a spiritual master] an experienced LSD user who guides, directs, and sits with a novice on his first LSD experience. Compare GUIDE.

H h

H. HEROIN.

habit. [a fierce craving for drugs; since around 1910—*EP*] the state of being physically dependent upon a drug as in "he had a $50-a-day *habit*," or "he knew he had a *habit* when he started getting cramps and chills." (Since the addict cannot know the strength of the diluted heroin he buys, he cannot speak of a "2-grain-a-day habit" but must measure it by the amount he spends; this amount varies with the potency of the drug he purchases, i.e., how much it is diluted, which in turn determines how much is needed to forestall WITHDRAWAL SYMPTOMS.)

habit-forming. used by drug manufacturers, the familiar "Warning —May Be Habit-Forming" means that prolonged use will result in PHYSICAL DEPENDENCE and specifically that the medicine contains an OPIATE, opiate derivative, SYNTHETIC OPIATE, or BARBITURATE. See also ADDICTION, HABITUATION.

habituation (habit), drug. a term formerly used by the WHO Expert Committee on Addiction-producing Drugs to describe compulsive drug abuse of a lesser degree than ADDICTION. The committee later decided that the distinction was unclear and the definition unscientific and has adopted the phrase "drug dependence of the [name of drug] type." The discarded definition read:

> Drug habituation (habit) is a condition resulting from the repeated consumption of a drug. Its characteristics include (1) a desire (but not a compulsion) to continue taking the drug for the sense of improved well-being which it engenders; (2) little or no tendency to increase the dose; (3) some degree of psychic dependence on the effect of the drug, but absence of physical dependence and hence, of an abstinence syndrome; (4) detrimental effects, if any, primarily on the individual [as distinguished from harmful effects upon society].

hacks. [from prisoners' term for prison guards; since the 1920s— *EP*] attendants at the U.S. Public Health Service (Narcotics) Hospital, Lexington, Kentucky.

Haight, the. HAIGHT-ASHBURY.

Haight-Ashbury, the. [from intersecting streets in the center of the area] a section in San Francisco to which bohemians (generally young) have gravitated since 1966 and set up communal quarters in the large old houses of a decaying residential area. The common motivation seems to center around HALLUCINOGENS and "dropping out" of conventional society. While the drug user cannot escape the legal prohibitions against drugs, he can use them more or less freely among others of like inclination and escape social disapproval.

The area has thus become—temporarily, perhaps— a mecca for those of this inclination, who are vaguely lumped together under the term HIPPIES. Because of the bizarre dress of the inhabitants and its reputation as a West Coast bohemia, the area has also become a tourist stop for visitors to the city. Stores selling clothing, posters, MARIJUANA pipes, bells, and other accoutrements of the PSYCHEDELIC life have sprung up. Various loosely organized communal efforts among the hippies themselves have also been formed to deal with the problems faced by the immigrants, many of whom come without money, e.g., employment centers, community kitchens dispensing free food, centers giving information about free lodgings, and even free medical care to deal with health problems peculiar to the area, including venereal disease, serum hepatitis (from using unsterile needles to inject drugs, mostly LSD or AMPHETAMINES), and panic psychoses resulting from the use of LSD or other hallucinogens. Like many urban dwellers, a number of the hippies have a desire to move to the country, where they set up communal farms and raise all their own food.

haircut. *1.* [local; *obsolete?*] MARIJUANA. Compare SCISSORS.

> [At Shimer College, Mt. Carroll, Illinois.] "I need a *haircut*" means "I want to buy any pot you can sell me."
> —Richard Goldstein, *One in Seven: Drugs on Campus* (1966)

2. [from the erroneous belief that the lesion has been caused by a cut from the wiry pubic hair of the female] the primary lesion of syphilis.

half load. fifteen packages, or BAGS, of HEROIN wrapped together with a rubber band and purchased in this form by the PUSHER from the wholesaler for resale to addicts. Compare BUNDLES, LOAD.

hallucinogen. [from Latin, *hallucinari,* to wander mentally, and

-*gen* (from Greek -*genes,* be born), one that generates] a hallucina-tion-producing drug, a category of drugs producing this effect. The hallucinations are dislocations of consciousness similar in some as-pects to those suffered by psychotic patients; however, the user of a hallucinogenic drug is almost invariably aware that what he is seeing are hallucinations, or else they are recognized distortions of known objects in the physical environment, while the psychotic cannot dis-tinguish the "real" from the "unreal," and his delusional world tends to be persistent, obsessive, and integral to the structure of his psychosis.

With the more powerful hallucinogenic drugs, such as LSD-25, the hallucinations can become startlingly real to the subject, and he may indeed be caught up fully in them for temporary periods. How-ever, in the majority of users these powerful hallucinations pass and are recalled as such in the return to a normal state. In a small num-ber of cases, the hallucinations persist or recur, to a troubling degree, for weeks or months after the drug has been taken; in which case, the user may enter a true psychotic state. As a descriptive term for the drugs or the experience they produce, HALLUCINOGEN is rejected by partisans of the drugs, who prefer PSYCHEDELIC (mind-manifest-ing). The term PSYCHOTOMIMETIC (psychosis-miming) is also em-ployed, mainly by the psychiatric profession, but has fallen into disfavor; PSYCHOTOGENIC is more frequent. Hallucinogen has been adopted by journalists (with psychedelic a close second), doctors, and federal authorities. It acquired the government's imprimatur in the DRUG ABUSE CONTROL AMENDMENT OF 1965, which out-lawed possession of hallucinogenic drugs. The Food and Drug Administration's Drug Abuse Control Bureau has named the fol-lowing as hallucinogenic drugs under the terms of the statute:

DMT
LSD-25
mescaline and its salts
peyote
psilocybin
psilocin

Unlike the other categories of drugs, i.e., BARBITURATES and AMPHETAMINES, which were found by FDA to be habit-forming, hallucinogens were brought under federal regulation because they have a "potential for abuse."

hand to hand, go. to transfer narcotics at the point of sale, as opposed to "drop," where the buyer picks them up after paying his money.

hang tough. ["to tell him to hang on would be too square."—Seymour Fiddle] phrase used (e.g., at SYNANON) to encourage addict undergoing WITHDRAWAL SYMPTOMS COLD TURKEY to stick it out, hang on.

hara, la. [Puerto Rican addicts' slang] a policeman; the cop.

hard drugs. HARD NARCOTICS.

hard narcotics. [*hard,* in the sense of potentially painful, onerous; the term is becoming invidious] addictive drugs, the OPIUM and MORPHINE derivatives and their synthetics; COCAINE; usually opposed to soft drugs. Usually the narcotics falling under federal narcotics laws, although in common parlance MARIJUANA is considered a soft drug even though it is a narcotic by federal Bureau of Narcotics definition. Compare BODY DRUGS, HEAD DRUGS.

hard stuff. HARD NARCOTICS.

harmine. also called banisterine, telepathine, yageine, and yagenine. an alkaloid found in the South American vine BANISTERIOPSIS CAAPI and thought to be hallucinogenic. Harmine is an indole derivative originally identified in the seeds and roots of harmal, *Peganum harmala.* Recent investigations have uncovered two other active alkaloids in *Banisteriopsis caapi,* harmaline and *d*-tetrahydroharmine, which are thought to be more hallucinogenically active than harmine.

Harris-Dodd Act. DRUG ABUSE CONTROL AMENDMENT OF 1965.

Harrison Narcotics Act. the nation's basic law regulating narcotics. When passed in 1914, it was basically a revenue measure designed to make narcotics transferrals a matter of record. A nominal tax of 1 cent per ounce was imposed on the narcotics; forms were required to be kept recording all transfers of the drug between manufacturer, wholesaler, retailer, and doctor. Persons authorized to handle or manufacture drugs were required to register, pay a fee, and keep records of narcotics in their possession.

This system still obtains today. Under several Supreme Court decisions interpreting the basic law, however, it was expanded to prohibit possession of smuggled drugs by an addict, i.e., anyone, rather than, as some interpreted the law, merely establishing a presumption that any unregistered person who possessed drugs was guilty of illegal possession only if he was among those persons specifically required to register under the law. Further decisions of the court made it illegal for a doctor to prescribe narcotics to an addict to relieve WITHDRAWAL SYMPTOMS and keep him comfortable over a period of time (maintenance doses). These decisions were embodied in Treasury Department regulations, which are still in force, even though the Supreme Court later modified its stand (1925) and implied that the physician should be the judge of what drugs, in what quantities, and in how many dosages be prescribed for the patient, if he does so in good faith, and he may do so to relieve an addict's withdrawal symptoms. The federal Bureau of Narcotics has ignored this decision, and physicians have been prosecuted for giving addicts drugs, even though in good faith. In sum, the act says that only persons who have paid the tax on narcotics may possess, transfer, prescribe, or manufacture them, and only persons who are authorized to possess, transfer, prescribe, or manufacture them may pay the tax. The addict caught with such untaxed drugs in his possession is automatically a criminal and can receive medical treatment only as an adjunct to his incarceration. Two subsequent pieces of narcotics legislation, the Boggs Amendment of 1951 and the Narcotic Drug Control Act of 1956, supplemented the Harrison Act by making convictions under it easier and stiffening penalties. Current penalties are as follows, according to Alfred Lindesmith in *The Addict and the Law:*

first possession offense	2–10 years; probation and parole permitted
second possession or first selling offense	mandatory 5–20 years with no probation or parole permitted
third possession or second selling and subsequent offenses	mandatory 10–40 years; no probation or parole permitted
sale of heroin to person under 18 by one over 18	10 years to life; no probation or parole; or death if jury recommends

Such mandatory sentences and prohibition of parole or probation limit the judge's flexibility in sentencing, say critics of the law, and give the prosecution (which is the U.S. Department of Justice) all the discretion because it can manipulate charges and recommend

sentences to the court. See also CLASS A NARCOTICS, CLASS B NAR-
COTICS, CLASS M NARCOTICS and CLASS X NARCOTICS.

harry. Heroin.

haschischins, Le club des. a group of French literary men who
met periodically to eat HASHISH. The club was founded in 1844
by the novelist Théophile Gautier, author of the scandalous *Made-
moiselle de Maupin*, a hedonist who extolled pleasure as the supreme
virtue. Gautier had been introduced to the drug by Dr. Jacques
Joseph Moreau, a specialist in mental illness, who noted similarities
between the mental disorientation produced by hashish and that
produced by mental illness and sought to test the drug's effects on
Gautier and his friends. These "experients" were conducted in
settings of exotic splendor, and the subjects' motives were, apparently, mainly sybaritic. The club's membership included Victor
Hugo, Honoré de Balzac, Gerard de Nerval, Charles Baudelaire,
and a number of other Paris intellectuals.

> The meal drew to an end; already some of the more fervent mem-
> bers felt the effects of the green jam [MAJOON]: for my part, I had
> experienced a complete transformation in taste. The water I drank
> seemed the most exquisite wine, the meat, once in my mouth, became
> strawberries, the strawberries, meat. I could not have distinguished
> a fish from a cutlet. My neighbors began to appear somewhat strange.
> Their pupils became big as a screech owl's; their noses stretched
> into elongated proboscises; their mouths expanded like bell bottoms.
> Faces were shaded in supernatural light. One among them, a pale
> countenance in a black beard, laughed aloud at an invisible spectacle;
> another made incredible efforts to raise his glass to his lips and the
> resulting contortions aroused deafening hoots from his companions;
> a man, shaken with nervous convulsions, turned his thumbs with
> remarkable agility; another, fallen against the back of his chair, his
> eyes unseeing and his arms inert, let himself drift voluptuously in
> the bottomless sea of nothingness.
>   My elbows on the table, I considered all this with clarity and a
> vestige of reason which came and went by intervals, like the light of
> a lantern about to flicker and die. A deadening warmth pervaded
> my limbs, and dementia, like a wave which breaks foaming onto a
> rock, then withdraws to break again, invaded and left my brain,
> finally enveloping it altogether. That strange visitor, hallucination,
> had come to dwell within me.
>   "To the salon, to the salon!" cried one of the guests; "can't you

hear those heavenly choirs? The musicians have been gathered for a long time." —Théophile Gautier, *Revue des Deux Mondes* (1846) (Translation by Polly Kraft, *The Drug Experience*, 1961)

hash. *hashish.*

Hashbury, the. [contraction of Haight and Ashbury, with the *hash* predominating, perhaps because of the connotations of HASH] the HAIGHT-ASHBURY section of San Francisco.

hashish. [Hasan-ibn-al-Sabbah, the first "Old Man of the Mountain," Persian founder of the Assassins in the eleventh century; both the word HASHISH and the term for his thugs, assassins, come from his name] the pure resinous exudate of the female hemp plant, CANNABIS SATIVA. In medical use hashish was sifted and powdered, sometimes prepared in a tincture with alcohol, and known as CANNABIS INDICA, or Indian hemp. Among drug users, it is usually seen as a hard, brown lump, the resin having hardened after being harvested from the plant at maturity. The darkness determines the strength: light ochre brown is least and deep cocoa brown or black most potent. It has a sweetish, minty smell and taste. Since the resin contains the ACTIVE PRINCIPLE, TETRAHYDROCANNABINOL, in highest concentration, hashish is the most powerful form of CANNABIS consumed. (The MARIJUANA used in the United States, for example, is considered about one-eighth as potent.)

In India, hashish is known as CHARAS and is generally consumed by smoking, while in North Africa, it is smoked or eaten in a confection called MAJOON or DAWAMESK. When smoked, a water pipe (HOOKAH) is frequently used, for filtering through water regulates the intake and cools the smoke. Hashish intoxication has much in common with that produced by MESCALINE and, in sufficient quantities taken orally, that of LSD. These effects include distorted perceptions of various parts of the body, depersonalization or "double consciousness," the feeling of being here and there simultaneously, spatial and time distortions, intensification of scents, tastes, colors and sounds, visual hallucinations, seeing faces as grotesque, synesthesia, i.e., the merging of the senses so that sounds are seen as colors, heightened suggestibility, grandiose delusions of being godlike, and anxiety, dread, and paranoia.

The effects of hashish are more violent when it is swallowed, for the smoker can regulate the degree of intoxication by spacing out his intake and, in effect, making it more gradual. The final stage of hashish intoxication is deep sleep. As with other hallucinogenic drugs, hashish can trigger acute or chronic psychosis in a small percentage of users.

The question of whether there is a "cannabis psychosis," i.e., that excessive use of hashish causes a psychosis characteristic of the drug, has been debated. Studies in Morocco and India, where hashish is used more widely than it is in the United States, have resulted in the identification of such a psychosis occurring among approximately five out of every thousand users. One Moroccan investigator has broken the psychosis down into three types: acute or subacute (the majority), resulting from a toxic overdose, sometimes erupting in violence, usually lasting for a few days; residual, resulting in schizophrenia, mental confusion, and mild recurring hallucinations, usually disappearing after a few months; and psychical deterioration resulting from prolonged, excessive use and producing premature senility, vagabondage, and other behavior reminiscent of the skid-row alcoholic in this country. Most American investigators doubt that marijuana produces psychoses of itself, believing instead that the psychosis was already latent, waiting to be born, and the drug acted the part of midwife. Conversely, the heavy user of cannabis (hashish or marijuana) may actually be masking a psychosis through the drug and preventing it from asserting its hold upon his mind.

TOLERANCE to hashish develops only to a slight degree, which may be partially a result of the user's learning to control its effects subjectively as he becomes more familiar with them. As a general rule, however, the same dose of cannabis, no matter how frequently taken, will have the same effects. PHYSICAL DEPENDENCE upon hashish does not develop; there are no characteristic WITHDRAWAL SYMPTOMS, although long-term, heavy hashish users do suffer some discomfort if they abruptly stop using the drug. These symptoms are of much less severity than those associated with physical dependence upon the OPIATE and BARBITURATE drugs.

Aside from the occasional transient or even chronic psychoses triggered by its use, the chief hazard of the drug is the debilitation of the will and mental deterioration resulting from PSYCHIC DEPENDENCE with prolonged, heavy usage. This deterioration from long-term involvement with the drug, often seen in North Africa and India and described above, appears to be almost nonexistent in the United States because heavy users of cannabis predominantly choose marijuana, a much milder form. Also, in the United States, at least at the present time, hashish is rarer and consequently more expensive than marijuana ($40 to $100 an ounce, roughly the same as the cost of a pound of marijuana; 1 ounce of hashish, it is said, lasts the heavy smoker about as long as 1 pound of marijuana, though this could vary widely, depending on the habits of the smoker). Finally, there is no tradition of hashish smoking in the United States, to the extent there is in India and North Africa. On the other hand, hashish is increasingly appearing on the illicit market, most of it smuggled in by tourists from North Africa or Nepal.

> The earliest encroachments of the drug, like symptoms of a storm that hovers before it strikes, appear and multiply in the very bosom of . . . incredulity. The first of them is a sort of irrelevant and irresistible hilarity. Attacks of causeless mirth, of which you are almost ashamed, repeat themselves at frequent intervals, cutting across periods of stupor during which you try in vain to pull yourself together. . . . This mirth, with its alternating spells of languor and convulsion, this distress in the midst of delight, generally lasts only for a fairly short time. Soon the coherence of your ideas becomes so vague, the conducting filament between your fancies becomes so thin, that only your accomplice can understand you. . . . One of the most noticeable sensations resulting from the use of hashish is that of benevolence; a flaccid, idle, dumb benevolence resulting from a softening of the nerves. . . . At this [next] phase of intoxication . . . a new subtlety or acuity manifests itself in all the senses. . . . The eyes behold the Infinite. The ear registers almost imperceptible sounds, even in the midst of the greatest din. This is when hallucinations set in. External objects acquire gradually, and one after another, strange new appearances; they become distorted or transformed. Next occur mistakes in the identities of objects, and transposals of ideas. Sounds clothe themselves in colors, and colors contain music. . . . It sometimes happens that your personality disappears, and you develop objectivity—that preserve of the pantheistic poets—to such an abnormal degree that the contemplation of outward objects makes you forget your own existence, and you soon melt into them. . . . A new stream of ideas carries you away: it will hurl you along in its living vortex for a further minute; and this minute, too, will be an eternity, for the normal relation between time and the individual has been completely upset by the multitude and intensity of sensations and ideas. You seem to live several men's lives in the space of an hour. You resemble, do you not?, a fantastic novel that is being lived

instead of being written. There is no longer any fixed connection between your organs and their powers; and this fact above all, is what makes this dangerous exercise, in which you lose your freedom, so very blameworthy.

—Charles Baudelaire, *Les Paradis Artificiels* (1860)

hassle. *1.* annoyances, bother, exertion in obtaining drugs. *2.* to obtain drugs in a difficult, etc., manner as in "*hassle* marijuana." *3.* to bargain over price.

Customers are funny. Some *hassle* for an hour before they buy and some don't even open the envelope.

—"Ric," "Confessions of a Campus Pot Dealer," *Esquire* (September, 1967)

"You get hung up with all the *hassle,*" said one [marijuana dealer], "and it becomes a full-time profession." . . .

Yet the typical dealer, although cautious, is nonchalant, and well aware that the first arrest is not likely to lead to prison. "It reaches the point where it's [avoiding arrest] not worth the *hassle* [elaborate precautions]," said a 19-year-old marijuana merchant. "If I get busted, I get busted."

—Don McNeill, *Village Voice* (Dec. 1, 1966)

hassling. *1.* buying drugs; used especially of a small-time dealer who must locate a wholesaler, meet him clandestinely to avoid being followed, argue the price with him, test the quality of what is offered him, and arrange the transferral. *2.* the process of doing this, as in "I got tired of the *hassling* all the time, so I'd buy MARIJUANA in large amounts so there'd be less of a hassle."

hawk, the. [the hawk, among Chicago Negroes, is the powerful wind that blows off Lake Michigan; hence, implying the drug's powerful, stormy effect on the mind] LSD-25.

hay. [from the appearance of marijuana prepared for sale] MARIJUANA. Compare BALE, GRASS, TEA.

H-caps. HEROIN in gelatine capsules, each of which contains, roughly, 1 grain of CUT (diluted) heroin. From 1/4 ounce of pure heroin the wholesaler can fill up to 100 capsules for resale to the addict. In the 1940s and 1950s this was the favored container for selling heroin, but it is less common today.

head. [a drug addict; since the 1900s; especially HOPHEAD (OPIUM addict); also VERONAL head (BARBITURATE addict); perhaps suggested by *deadhead,* a useless person—*EP*. The latter origin seems unlikely. Perhaps from the idea that the drug fills or alters one's consciousness, i.e., brain or head, and dominates it] A frequent, fairly heavy user of drugs, though not an addict; often qualified by the specific kind of drugs the head prefers, as in ACID HEAD, AMPHETAMINE head, POT head, etc. The word has the slight connotation that the head prefers his mental state while under the drug to his normal one.

head drugs. [used, often invidiously, in opposition to BODY DRUGS] *1.* drugs which produce higher, finer states of consciousness in the mind of the user and do not produce PHYSICAL DEPENDENCE. *2.* drugs that stimulate the brain. *3.* nondepressant drugs. In practice, HALLUCINOGENS and possibly AMPHETAMINES but not OPIATES, ALCOHOL, or BARBITURATES.

hearts. AMPHETAMINES.

heat, the. [to *have a heat* is to be taking drugs; *with a heat on,* exhilarated by drugs, since the 1930s, and in trouble with or being sought by the police, since the 1920s—*EP*] the police or narcotics detectives.

heaven dust. COCAINE.

Heavenly Blue. [trade name] a variety of morning glory the seeds of which produce hallucinogenic effects. See MORNING GLORY SEEDS.

heavy drugs. HARD NARCOTICS, i.e., addictive OPIATES and COCAINE, which come under the federal narcotics laws; MARIJUANA is usually not included, though it also comes under these laws.

heavy stuff. [from *heavy,* onerous, weighty; the effects of these drugs, compared to LIGHT STUFF] HEROIN, COCAINE, other OPIATE drugs. Compare BODY DRUGS, HARD NARCOTICS, LOAD.

heeled. [from *heeled,* armed, weaponed; since the 1900s; the origin of that sense is the practice of arming a fighting cock with spurs on its feet—*EP*] possessing drugs. Compare CLEAN, DIRTY.

hemp. [from Middle English *hemp,* CANNABIS SATIVA, the Indian hemp plant] MARIJUANA.

henry. HEROIN.

her. COCAINE. Compare GIRL, HIM, BOY.

herb. MARIJUANA.

heroin. [from German, *heroisch,* large, powerful] (diacetylmorphine hydrochloride) a semisynthetic derivative of MORPHINE obtained by the action of acetic anhydride or acetylchloride on morphine. The result is a white, odorless, crystalline powder with a bitter taste, which is soluble in water. (Mexican heroin, however, is brown.) Heroin was developed in 1898 by the Bayer Co., in Germany, as an analgesic more potent than morphine and a highly effective cough suppressant. When it was discovered that heroin relieved morphine WITHDRAWAL SYMPTOMS (then a perplexing medical problem because morphine and OPIUM were widely prescribed for a number of diseases and many people had become physically dependent), it was touted as a cure for morphine addiction. Heroin itself was considered to be nonaddictive. Twelve years passed before medical authorities discovered that, on the contrary, heroin was as addictive as morphine. By this time, opium addicts (centered mainly among the criminal elite and Chinese) and novices alike had discovered heroin's efficacy; and the word "junk," meaning heroin, had entered the underworld language by the early 1900s.

By 1924 Congress had prohibited the manufacture of heroin in the United States and by 1956, all existing stocks on hand at pharmacies and manufacturers were required to be surrendered. The League of Nations took similar action to discourage the export of heroin, and by 1963 it was imported and used medically in only five countries and manufactured in three. The use of heroin in medicine today is practically nonexistent. But at the same time heroin was steadily replacing opium and morphine as the drug of choice in the underworld of addicts. To understand this fact, it helps only a little to understand the pharmacological action of the drug. Heroin is two to three times as potent, analgesically, as morphine (a widely accepted ratio is 4 milligrams of heroin equals 10 milligrams of morphine). In equipotent doses, however, the effects are very similar: analgesia, drowsiness, euphoria, constipation, vomiting, sedation, and respiratory depression in large doses and relief of anxiety and tension.

Experiments in which addicts were given "blind" intramuscular injections of morphine and heroin in equipotent doses revealed that the addicts were not able to tell the difference between the two and showed no preference for one drug over the other. However, when the drugs were injected intravenously, most former addicts could identify the heroin. And once PHYSICAL DEPENDENCE had set in, five-eighths of the former addicts said they preferred heroin for continuing administration. What caused them to prefer heroin is another matter, since they described the effects of both drugs as being identical. Furthermore, though the WITHDRAWAL SYMPTOMS of heroin dependence are somewhat briefer in duration than those of morphine, they are qualitatively so similar in severity that there seems to be no real difference between them. Goodman and Gilman's standard text on pharmacology says that heroin produces more euphoria and stimulation and that physical dependence develops more quickly than with morphine. (On the other hand, heroin produces less euphoria when injected intravenously than when injected into the muscle!)

Addicts' preference aside, a more significant factor in the predominance of heroin may lie in the logistics of the illicit traffic. As a natural alkaloid of opium, morphine, before being refined to a soluble salt so that it can be injected, is in the form of a solid block, which is too bulky for efficient smuggling. Reduction to heroin provides the most potency with the least bulk (half the bulk of morphine, even when the latter is in soluble powder form) and the greatest profits. Because it was more profitable, heroin usurped the market, at least in the United States, where injection is the leading mode of consumption, and addicts acquired a "taste" for it, even though its effects were roughly the same as those of morphine. Thus, the preference for intravenous heroin was in part, at least, a matter of habit, in more ways than one. Heroin has become the classic drug of ADDICTION in the United States. (During World War II, when heroin shipments to the United States were cut off, addicts returned to morphine.)

This addiction consists of craving for the drug, use in quantities and settings considered abnormal by the culture, TOLERANCE to the effects of the drug so that increasing amounts are needed, a compulsion to continue acquiring the drug, a preoccupation to the point where obtaining a supply dominates the user's entire life, and a high tendency to relapse after the drug is withdrawn and seek it again. Addiction is invariably accompanied by physical dependence, which sustains and intensifies it, for the avoidance of withdrawal symptoms and related anxiety is a powerful motive—perhaps the most powerful—to continue taking the drug. Indeed, physical dependence may be the sole factor in addiction; the medical addict, i.e., one who has received prolonged treatment with morphine to relieve pain, becomes physically dependent after his pain has gone and has no other psychic motivation than the avoidance of withdrawal symptoms. In true addiction there must also be a craving for the drug's psychic effects, specifically, the sum of the conditioned interaction between the addict personality and the pharmacology of the drug.

To understand this, we should consider heroin (or rather morphine since the latter is used medically and the effects are approximately the same) in a purely medical setting. Primarily, morphine is given for its analgesic actions; the side effects, ranging from drowsiness to constipation, are incidental. Morphine accomplishes three things: (1) it raises the threshhold of pain; i.e., the patient is unable to perceive the pain he has; (2) it decreases the patient's anxiety about pain, so that although he knows the pain is there, he feels detached from it; and (3) morphine appears to quiet the self-preservation drive, which takes up arms against the interloping pain regarded as an ego threat. Pain being regarded with drowsy equanimity, the ego is lulled into a sense of security that would be false except that the disease which is the cause of the pain, the real threat it signals, is being treated or, when terminal, is beyond treatment anyway. In the normal pain-free individual a therapeutic dose of morphine (or heroin) usually produces a predominately unpleasant reaction. Further, pain acts as an antidote to the drug, so that the greater the pain, the more tolerance there is to the action of the drug and the larger the necessary dose.

Remove physical pain from the situation, and the patient may suffer toxic effects from a dose level he previously tolerated. How then can we explain the action of the drug which the addict finds so necessary that he must repeat it again and again? In alleviating pain, morphine often produces a state of euphoria, a subjective state of well-being produced by the patient's dramatic release from his pain and the anxieties and tensions accompanying it. Since he has this state of well-being even though his body is threatened by disease, in a sense his euphoria goes counter to his true situation: his body is frantically signalling that something is wrong, but the patient, lying in a narcotized half sleep, is at peace with the world.

A similar cause-and-effect series must be at work in the addict; he too seeks that state of euphoria, of "escape" from the world and from himself. The reasons for seeking this escape are probably as numerous as the individuals who use heroin. One might be a prosperous doctor who takes regular shots of morphine in order to cope with the strain and stress of a busy practice. Another might be a fifteen-year-old boy from the slums whose anxieties stem from both the conditions of his existence and an underlying neurosis. At this point, we should note that both of these chose heroin, rather than some other drug; further, many others of the same background and with similar personalities did not choose heroin. There was, in short, a factor of availability: the doctor with ready access to narcotics (actually morphine) and practically no chance of being caught at it, the slum kid who lives in Harlem, where pushers flourish and where his peers are also experimenting with drugs. So there must be availability of the drug as a necessary prerequisite for heroin addiction, and further—and less precisely—there must be an inner need which heroin satisfies and a tendency, partially determined by availability, to seek out escape in drugs. The heroin addict differs from other abusers of drugs because of the drug he has chosen—or that has chosen him. ALCOHOL or BARBITURATES act to release inhibitions. They encourage aggressive behavior, pseudo masculinity. Probably the alcoholic is acting out some underlying sexual and aggressive drives that he cannot express in a sober state because of his inhibitions and because they are so conflicting and contradictory. Heroin acts to depress sex, aggression, even hunger; in his torpor, the heroin user is free from strivings, relaxed and detached. And the heroin addict suffering from some psychic pain due to inner anxiety arising from unrelievable subconscious drives and feelings of inadequacy or weak identity palliates this pain by suppressing these drives at their source. Immediately the source of pain is deadened, he experiences euphoria, well-being, detachment from the world, and an almost complete absence of normal human hungers. He does not even desire to defecate.

With many users heroin injection has more positive aspects, a kind of sexual pleasure akin to an orgasm and centering in their stomach. In others the initial shock, when the drug is taken intravenously, is so powerful that it is akin to death, followed moments later by an immense relief at being alive. (Injection of a foreign substance—water alone would have a kindred effect—into the bloodstream destroys some blood cells, lowers the blood pressure suddenly, and induces a near state of shock.) In any case, the user is HIGH—high above it all, above all cares and hurts, above hungers that are doomed not to be satisfied subconsciously felt to be wrong and tainted, above the fears that are nameless; in short, he is in a state of euphoria, unrelated and unrelatable to his objective condition.

Different methods of taking the drug play their part in what the user's future relationship with the drug will be. The classic progression among slum youths is from SNIFFING to subcutaneous injections (SKIN POPPING) to intravenous injections (MAINLINING). It is essentially a path from less intense experience to a more sudden and intense one. Heroin is the only opiate which can be experienced (like COCAINE) through its action on the mucous membranes of the nasal passages. Sniffing produces the euphoria all right, but the heroin has a bitter flavor, and many find it unpleasant. Skin popping will also do the job and is certainly more efficient. Consequently, many users stay at this level for several years or permanently, taking the drug occasionally on weekends for kicks (see JOYPOP). Others, usually because of an upsurge of unbearable anxiety and tensions which sets off a craving, find the drug necessary to their well-being and begin to take it regularly. It is a short step from injecting into the skin to injecting into the vein—especially when one has the WORKS—the needle and so on—with all the necessity for secrecy and satisfying ritual these entail. This necessity further alienates the user from normal society; indeed by some inborn self-fulfilling prophecy, this alienation is exactly what he is seeking—what he obtains when he is high on the drug—increasingly the sole motive of his life. Mainlining is, as the name implies, the most direct route of this state, for by prosaic medical fact, intravenous injection is thriftier; it takes less of the drug to produce an effect (about two-thirds as much), and the initial thrill (RUSH) is more immediate, while the dividends are inordinate in relation to the investment—at least at first, for now the user is developing TOLERANCE to the heroin and is well on his way to getting HOOKED.

In a hospital, a patient can develop a mild physical dependence after about three weeks of daily injections of morphine, and the narcotic antagonist Nalorphine (see NALLINE) will precipitate withdrawal symptoms after only *three days* of regular injections. In the STREET the user shooting a grain (60 milligrams) a day (roughly three or four BAGS) will acquire a fairly substantial habit within two weeks. All this time, he has been undergoing a learning and conditioning process. First, he had to learn how to inject the drug and was probably taught this by the friends who "turned him on."

Most addicts are introduced to the drug by friends, not PUSHERS. But the friend usually is acting as an agent for his pusher; he turns the neophyte on in exchange for money, which he uses to support his own habit. He does not reveal his pusher to the neophyte and uses part of the latter's money to buy drugs for himself. Thus he is assured of income to support his own habit, while the neophyte does not get his money's worth. But he must also learn to experience the effects of the drug; he must learn to experience it as the answer to his underlying needs—the inner psychopathology that triggers the intense pleasure he—as distinct from the normal person—experiences with heroin from the beginning, and this satisfaction must continue, reinforcing his motivation to repeat. Thus, each time the drug relieves his anxieties, fears and depression, his desire to use it again is strengthened. Also bound up in this motivation is a profound self-hatred and self-destructive drive. The addict is consciously committing suicide slowly! As one addict put it, heroin "has all the advantages of death without its permanence." Addiction, then, is a kind of suicide-in-life. The addict learns that nothing else can quite do for him what the heroin does. This conditioning is so powerful that a former addict visiting a place where he suffered withdrawal symptoms years before starts yawning, his nose runs, and so on, even though he has not taken drugs in the interim, and such a visit to his old haunts can set off an intense craving for the drug. A single shot after years of abstinence will set off withdrawal symptoms.

Some addicts even become conditioned to the smell of the match they habitually use to COOK UP their heroin; and just the smell of a burning match will set off preliminary withdrawal symptoms. The addict has been conditioned to associate the smell of the match with both his symptoms that accompany his need and with the fiercely demanded relief his body knows will automatically come when the cooking up is finished and the drug injected. The bodily craving has become a demanding, autonomous entity, operating irrespective of the addict's conscious will or reason.

While this cycle is continuing, his body is making a thousand minute cellular adjustments to the drug that is being introduced into it. Now, he finds he must take more to relieve his pain (pain is an antidote). He finds, too, that he cannot reexperience quite the same intensity of that first intravenous shot and that, as one addict said bitterly, "horse [heroin] is a cheat": its effects are not quite what they first were. Perhaps then, in order to intensify the drug's initial rush he will take to injecting SPEEDBALLS (heroin and cocaine) or BOMBITAS (heroin and AMPHETAMINES). Nevertheless he is hooked now: *he must continue to take the drug,* both physically and mentally. Frequently, a craving for the drug, akin to an intense hunger for food, but many times stronger, will accompany this compulsion. But physical dependence throws up new anxieties. Each time the effect of the drug starts to wear off, the addict can feel cramps and the other vague miseries. Now, the anxieties of his psyche are overborne by the anxieties of anticipatory withdrawal. The habit is feeding upon itself. Euphoria, pleasure, whatever, are secondary, as avoidance of withdrawal becomes an end in itself. (Yet the amount the addict takes is greatly in excess of the amount necessary to prevent withdrawal symptoms.) In this state, *he does continue to take the drug,* for he has become conditioned in the classic Pavlovian manner to the drug as an alleviator of withdrawal anxiety. His pleasure is lessened, but his desperation is increased. Now he does not shoot for pleasure but to avoid pain, or, at best, to achieve what many addicts call a "normal state" or a satisfactory NOD. If he is a younger addict from the slums, without a solid career, he is probably involved in HUSTLING for drugs, that is, devoting full time to stealing or perhaps small time pushing in order to obtain money for drugs. (In New York City an addict needs $10,000 a year to support his habit, meaning he must steal and resell, at one-fifth their value, $50,000 worth of goods. Drug users account for about one-fourth of the crimes against property, 1.2 percent of crimes against persons and a majority of the female prostitution in New York City.) He is a part of an addict's world, a subculture with a language and way of life all its own, all revolving about obtaining drugs.

Perhaps, though, he is a middle-class addict, who holds down a job or is even a professional man. This type is rarer but not uncommon. They are able to function with more or less success in their daily routine, while administering a daily, controlled ration of drugs. Some of this type may be medical addicts, who took drugs to relieve pain, and who have never obtained any pleasure from them, but take them simply to maintain a physiological state of equilibrium. Those who cannot obtain drugs from doctors must found a secret life, with its necessary pipeline to the underworld source of drugs. The possibility of blackmail, of being informed upon to the police, of one's family finding out, the onerous expense of the habit, all are everpresent threats to his public life.

The life of the lower-class addict is also plagued with stress and anxiety which are compensated for to some extent by paradoxical satisfactions that come from being able successfully to hustle one's daily supply—the pride in one's ability to outwit the "square society." But the police are not his only threat. There is the danger of INFECTION from unsterile needles, resulting in serum hepatitis, abscesses, or tetanus. Gradually the addict's veins become scarred (COLLAPSED VEINS) and he uses those on his wrist, feet, and neck; older addicts who have run out of veins revert to SKIN POPPING, and their bodies become covered with sores.

There is the constant fluctuation in supplies. Narcotics agents might intercept a large shipment of heroin, the heat may be on one's pusher. A drug PANIC is the result; the addict finds his sources of supply suddenly dried up, and he must frantically search out another or else suffer withdrawal. Then there is the danger of OVER-DOSE; perhaps a pusher who fears arrest dumps on the market a load of especially strong, undiluted heroin. The addict's tolerance has been built up to the weak, diluted kind, containing perhaps 3.5 percent pure heroin in each bag. Given a shot of above 20 percent heroin, the odds are good that he will O.D.—with perhaps fatal results. Finally, as his tolerance increases, the addict finds his habit becoming too expensive, beyond his capacity to supply. At this juncture withdrawal is in order. To accomplish this the addict might self-medicate with codeine or DOLOPHINE (METHADONE) pills to ease the pains of withdrawal although this is rare; or, more likely, he will undergo withdrawal COLD TURKEY or, if space is available, commit himself to the hospital for a three-week detoxification. Once detoxified, he can, and most probably will, start anew, shooting up a smaller dosage. This most imperative motive is, then, to achieve a high, not to avoid withdrawal pains. This cycle will probably continue for years, unless he dies (and probably half will) or does time in prison. The death rate for addicts is over twice that for the normal population. At the age of forty, he may begin gradually to slip out of the addicts' life; only about 10 percent of the addicts in the United States are over forty. Some addicts, however, continue for years with their addiction.

Heroin in itself is not physiologically harmful; it may even have an added virtue of preventing a latent schizophrenia from asserting itself. Nevertheless, it is the addict's *way of life* that is hazardous; if an overdose or unsterile needle does not get him, the addict's characteristic neglect of his health will. Malnutrition is a common debilitation among addicts, a by-product of the drug's suppression of hunger. Chronic bronchitis may also ensue because it deadens the cough reflex. On the other hand, eventually a small percentage of addicts will seek a cure or else will be forced to confront the possibility of one by a judge who sentences them to one of the Federal narcotics hospital-prisons in Lexington, Kentucky, or Fort Worth, Texas. The addict may enroll in group therapy courses such as SYNANON, addicts anonymous, or Daytop; he may commit himself voluntarily to the federal narcotics hospital or, in New York or California, to one of the state narcotics centers. Drug therapy such as the METHADONE, CYCLAZOCINE or apomorphine treatments is a possibility. Or, if he is rich enough, psychiatric care or a private sanitorium may be arranged. The prognosis for cure at the present time is not good; the percentage of successful cures (lasting seven years) runs about 10 to 15 percent, but even withdrawing an addict temporarily from drugs for several months or years is a cure of sorts—certainly a start—and not to be deprecated. Society's efforts to stamp out the illicit heroin trade have aimed a two-pronged legal effort at the traffickers and the addict in the streets—with mixed success. The federal BUREAU OF NARCOTICS, which is under the Treasury Department and administers and enforces the nation's narcotics laws (which are ostensibly revenue measures taxing narcotics), estimates the number of known addicts in the country at about 60,000—and has for several years. Even if this figure is accurate (and most authorities think it is too low at least by half), it means that 1 in 3,000 are addicts in the United States, as opposed to around 1 in 400 at the turn of the century, when heroin and other opiates were legal, despite narcotics laws that are some of the harshest on the books.

It is doubtful that more than 10 percent of the heroin smuggled into this country is intercepted. An estimated 1,500 kilograms of heroin enters the United States annually, or 1/2 of 1 percent of the world's total *legal* production. The federal Bureau of Narcotics and U.S. Customs seized 277.8 kilograms of heroin or the equivalent in fiscal 1966. The main heroin smuggling route begins in the hills of Turkey where the opium poppy (*Papaver somniferum*) is legally grown; other United States sources include Mexico and, to a small extent, Thailand via Hong Kong. The grower sells the raw opium for about $35 a kilogram (2.2 pounds). It is processed in Turkey or Syria and turned into blocks of crude morphine weighing one-tenth of a kilo for easier shipment. Then it is smuggled—often by merchant seamen—to Marseilles. In secret laboratories in France it is then converted into heroin, a fairly sophisticated process chemically. Thence the 1/10 kilogram of 85 percent pure heroin goes to Milan for shipment to the United States for distribution under the aegis of the Mafia, which controls 80 percent of the United States narcotics market (recent indications are that the Mafia is leaving the drug traffic—due to the long prison sentences if caught and a preference for making money in less hazardous ways—and Latin American dealers are moving into the vacuum). By the time it is sold to the addict on the street, perhaps cut ten times (see CUTTING), the original kilogram of opium sold for $35 has grown to a worth of $41,000 in the retail market. The shot for which the addict in the street pays $5 would be worth a few pennies if he had bought it in a drug store. Only when the law-enforcement agencies can make a serious dent in the traffic and social agencies can effect a higher percentage of cures among the addicts in the street will heroin addiction be brought under control. It will probably never be eliminated, however, for the history of mankind shows that there will always be those who cannot live without a chemical crutch. See BRITISH SYSTEM.

The mind under *heroin* evades perception as it does ordinarily; one is aware only of contents. But that whole way of posing the question, of dividing the mind from what it's aware of, is fruitless. Nor is it that the objects of perception are intrusive in an electric way as they are under mescalin or lysergic acid, nor that things strike one with more intensity or in a more enchanted or detailed way as I have sometimes experienced under marijuana; it is that the perceiving turns inward, the eyelids droop, the blood is aware of itself, a slow phosphorescence in all fabric of flesh and nerve and bone; it is that the organism has a sense of being intact and unbrittle, and, above all, *inviolable*. For the attitude born of this sense of inviolability some Americans have used the word "cool."

At certain moments I find myself looking on my whole life as leading up to the present moment, the present being all I have to affirm. It's somehow undignified to speak of the past or to think about the future. I don't seriously occupy myself with the question in the "here-and-now," lying on my bunk, and, under the influence of heroin, inviolable. That is one of the virtues of the drug, that it empties such questions of all anguish, transports them to another region, a painless theoretical region, a play region, surprising, fertile, and unmoral. One is no longer grotesquely involved in the becoming. One simply is.   —Alexander Trocchi, *Cain's Book* (1960)

high. [drug-exhilarated (from *high* spirits) since around 1920; from the sense of being at the top of one's form—*EP*. With LSD users a literal sensation of being on an aerial voyage; also, perhaps, a sense of being "above it all"] in a state of drug euphoria. Compare TAKE OFF, COME DOWN, FLYING, UP.

him. HEROIN. Compare BOY, HER, GIRL.

hippie. [from *hep*, wise, informed, which is in turn from *hep! hep!*, encouragement of a team of horses, who "get hep"—*EP*. Also, *hep-cat*, a connoisseur of swing music and jazz; *hip*, related to *hep*, but in a wider sense of *hip* to life, as well as to music, sophisticated; *hipster*, one who is *hip*, "cool," alienated, who lives in the present, a pure hedonist, who acts out psychopathically his drives of sex and aggression. *Hippie* is sort of the diminutive of hipster, i.e., the hipster's little brother, and descendant. But compare Laurie: *hip*, "addicts' jargon meaning to be an initiate, to have sores on the hips from lying on boards to smoke opium"; hence, a drug addict] a self-styled dropout from (usually middle-class) society, one whose life centers around hallucinogenic drugs, poverty, and hedonism, who seeks none of society's accepted means and ends, and who seeks to live a withdrawn life on as little money as possible, devoting himself to drug experiences, introspection, private ecstasy, religious quest, and love, sexual and fraternal.

The hippie subculture centers around the HAIGHT-ASHBURY section in San Francisco (where there were about 11,000 in 1967, at the movement's peak), the lower East Side in New York City (5,000), and various smaller pockets, rural and urban, scattered about the country. Most but not all hippies are young, dress shabbily, have long hair, and wear beads (and other artifacts associated with Eastern religions) and colors inspired by the hallucinogenic experience.

Many support themselves by DEALING in drugs. The hippie is oriented toward Eastern mysticism, a religion of quietism and withdrawal; it avoids aggression and power seeking and stresses meditation and pansexualism, in which the body is an instrument for making contact with others. Drugs are not considered the only means of achieving mystical enlightenment, the Zen Buddhist's *satori*, but they are considered valid shortcuts to the meditation and spiritual discipline of the mystics, and in practice the hippie's life centers about drug taking.

How many hippies achieve a profound and lasting religious experience is, of course, another question; jejune hedonism, escape, and KICKS may be a dominant motive for many, who come from well-to-do middle-class homes and see drugs as a way of rebelling against their parents, to whom HALLUCINOGENS and MARIJUANA are unfamilar and repugnant. The publicity surrounding the hippies is wide; their romantic image attractive abroad. Some observers see the movement as a children's crusade for mass schizophrenia; certainly the mass movement of hippies into urban ghettos, where the rents are cheap, has created new tensions and health problems.

hit. [*hit oneself,* take drugs, Australian addicts since 1944. *Hit, make, make the man,* purchase drugs, since around 1910; *hit it,* use a drug—*EP*. More probably from the sense of *hitting* a target] a successful injection of HEROIN into the vein.

> You put the spike in slow, and the only way you know you got a *hit* is by watching the blood come up; then you take off the strap and squeeze it in.
> —addict, quoted in Jeremy Larner and Ralph Tefferteller,
> *The Addict in the Street* (1964)

> At the third attempt she found a vein and the blood rose up through the needle into the eye-dropper and appeared as a dark red tongue in the colourless solution. *"Hit,"* she said softly, with a slow smile.
> —Alexander Trocchi, *Cain's Book* (1960)

hold. [to have drugs for sale; since around 1910; compare *holding heavy,* having plenty of money—*EP*] *1.* to have drugs in one's possession (and thus be more liable to arrest) or in one's dwelling place for one's own use. *2.* to have drugs for sale. See STASH.

> Never *hold* when you can stash.   —drug user's saying (1966)

holding. possessing drugs, as in "are you holding?" Compare ANYWHERE.

homatropine. a semisynthetic derivative of ATROPINE considered to have fewer undesirable side effects and to be about one-fiftieth as toxic.

hookah. also hubbly bubbly. A pipe for smoking CANNABIS which bubbles the smoke through water, thus cooling it and softening the characteristic harshness of cannabis smoke. Compare NARGHILE.

hooked. [gripped by the drug habit; since 1925—*EP*] physically dependent upon a drug, usually an OPIATE drug. Compare ADDICTION, CRAMP UP, PHYSICAL DEPENDENCE.

> When you're *hooked* it's different. The cool feeling you had when you're not hooked gradually diminishes, the amount that you have to take always getting larger, and with it less and less effect as you go on. . . . Then, as you go along that's when you begin to find out that horse [heroin] is a cheat, a real cheap cheat. Before this, you can have a whole evening or a whole day of wonderful I'm-great-and-the-world-is-all-cool feeling. But after you get hooked you have to take 8 or 10 caps to get that feeling and even after you take your 10 caps it is just sort of a recreation of that old relief. It isn't really there because for one thing just after you've taken off, you're already back in the position within an hour, maybe, you're going to look at things in the cold gray light of dawn already. And so, desperately hoping to hang on to this much nicer, much finer world, and in order to keep re-creating this capable-of-coping-with-things feeling you must keep opening a cap every few hours. . . . And the, finally, the third stage is when all you're trying to do is keep from getting ill, really.
> —Helen MacGill Hughes (ed.), *The Fantastic Lodge* (1961)

hooking. [from a resident of "the Hook," Caesar's Hook section, in New York, where there were a number of brothels, hence the sailors called the prostitutes from that area *hookers*—*EP*] working as a prostitute to earn money for narcotics.

hop. [opium, narcotics; since around 1900; probably a corruption of some Chinese ideograph, but perhaps because it exhilarates—makes the addict *hop* (?)—*EP*] OPIUM.

hop dog. [also, *hop hog*—*EP;* compare *hog*. "Anyone who uses more junk than you do. To use over five grains (300 milligrams) per day puts a user in the hog class."—William Burroughs, *Junkie* (1953)] an OPIUM addict.

hophead. [drug addict; since around 1900; compare HEAD—*EP*] HEROIN or OPIUM addict.

horror drug. any drug containing BELLADONNA alkaloids (mainly ATROPINE) or SCOPOLAMINE, a related alkaloid.

horse. [heroin; since around 1940; one "rides high"—*EP*. But also perhaps from the initial *h* sound, like HIM, HARRY, and the idea of a powerful steed carrying the rider where it will] HEROIN. Compare CABALLO.

> *Horse* is boss.   —addicts' saying

hot shot. *1.* an injection of what the addict believes to be HEROIN but which is actually poison. *2.* a dose containing an unusually high percentage of heroin, higher than the addict is tolerant to. The intention is to kill an addict who is believed to be informing to the police. Often the poison used is strychnine, which looks and tastes like heroin.

> "Ever see a *hot shot* hit, kid? I saw the Gimp catch one in Philly. We rigged his room with a one-way whorehouse mirror and charged a sawski to watch it. He never got the needle out of his arm. They don't if the shot is right. That's the way they find them, dropper full of clotted blood hanging out of a blue arm. The look in his eyes when it hit—Kid, it was tasty."
> —William Burroughs, *Naked Lunch* (1959)

House of D. Women's House of Detention, Greenwich Ave., New York City.

> "but she's been booked now, she's in the *House of D* right now, so what can he do? It's got to go to court now."
> —addict in James Mills, *The Panic in Needle Park* (1966)

hubbly bubbly. HOOKAH.

hump. see OVER THE HUMP.

hungry croaker. [from *hungry,* i.e., in need of money, or eager to take money, and CROAKER, convicts' term for prison doctor] a doctor who will prescribe narcotics for addicts in exchange for money.

hustler, good, ace boss, five-star—general term of admiration, variously employing all the listed adjectives, for an addict who aggressively and successively engages in a variety of activities, mostly criminal, to obtain money for drugs. According to the mores of the addict subculture the good, etc., hustler is a go-getter, a sharp entrepreneur, admired for his success at supporting his habit and his skill in outwitting the law and the square world. Compare HUSTLING, GREASY JUNKY.

hustling. *1.* obtaining money for drugs by theft, prostitution, pimping, small-time narcotics peddling, con games, etc., in order to buy drugs. *2.* prostitution. *3.* the addict's characteristic behavior pattern revolving around illicitly obtaining money and drugs, a way of life inextricable from the narcotics habit for many. Compare STREET, ON THE.

Hycodan. [DIHYDROCODEINONE bitartrate, Endo Laboratories Inc.] a cough syrup containing HYDROCODONE, a semisynthetic derivative of OPIUM, in amounts of 5 milligrams per teaspoonful or tablet, and 1.5 milligrams of HOMATROPINE methylbromide. Prolonged use will result in PHYSICAL DEPENDENCE. Manufacturer's recommended dosage is 1 teaspoonful four times a day. A CLASS B NARCOTIC.

Hycomine. [DIHYDROCODEINONE bitartrate and other ingredients, Endo Laboratories Inc.] a cough syrup containing HYDROCODONE. Compare HYCODAN.

hydrocodone. also called dihydrocodeinone; a semisynthetic derivative of MORPHINE. Taken orally, 5 to 10 milligrams of hydrocodone gives analgesia equal to that produced by 10 milligrams of morphine, lasting from four to six hours. Prolonged administration will result in PHYSICAL DEPENDENCE. The WITHDRAWAL SYMPTOMS are milder than those associated with morphine dependence but more severe than those of CODEINE dependence. Hydrocodone is primarily used as an antitussive (cough-reflex suppressant). A CLASS A NARCOTIC. Compare HYCODAN, HYCOMINE.

hydromorphone. also called dihydromorphinone. A semisynthetic derivative of MORPHINE, hydromophone is a more potent analgesic than morphine: an injection of 2 milligrams will give the analgesic effect of 10 milligrams of morphine. The analgesia lasts three to four hours. Not widely used among addicts, hydromorphone will produce PHYSICAL DEPENDENCE after prolonged administration, with WITHDRAWAL SYMPTOMS close to those of morphine dependence in severity. A CLASS A NARCOTIC. Compare OPIUM, DILAUDID, DILOCOL.

hyoscine. SCOPOLAMINE.

hyoscyamine. active alkaloid found in jimsonweed, DATURA STROMONIUM, henbane, *Hyoscyamus niger,* and BELLADONNA, *Atropa* *belladonna,* among others. The action of hyoscyamine is similar to that of ATROPINE, although its effects on the peripheral nervous system are approximately twice as great. Difficult to obtain in its pure form, it is rarely used in medicine.

hype. [from *to hypo,* to inject with a needle, to prick; hence, to sting, and hence its meaning of shortchanging or swindling someone. Also, from *hypodermic,* a hypodermic user and hence a morphine or heroin addict; since the 1920s—*EP*] *1.* a phony story; a hoax, a put-on. *2.* to deceive someone with a phony story, hoax, put-on. *3.* a narcotics addict.

hyperventilated. see STEAMBOAT.

I i

iboga. the leaves of the plant *Tabernanthe iboga,* chewed in the Gabon Republic as a stimulant and antifatiguant. Poisonous alkaloids, IBOGAINE and iboganine, have been isolated from the leaves. No direct accounts of the drug have been published.

ibogaine. an alkaloid found in the IBOGA plant. Physiological effects include increase in blood pressure, increase in body temperature, excitation of secretory glands, and probably stimulation of the central nervous system. Ingestion of large amounts of ibogaine can be fatal.

ice cream habit. infrequent, moderate use of drugs.

idiot pills. barbiturate or other sedative pills.

IFIF. an organization (International Foundation for Internal Freedom) founded by former Harvard psychologists Timothy Leary and Richard Alpert in the fall of 1962. They had been conducting experiments with PSILOCYBIN, a hallucinogenic substance, and IFIF was formed after the university expressed displeasure with their researches. After the two were fired by Harvard for administering hallucinogenic drugs to students, IFIF moved to Mexico, where further experiments were conducted, until the Mexican government expelled the group. IFIF is apparently no longer in existence, and Leary heads a new, quasi-religious organization known as LSD (League for Spiritual Discovery).

Indian hay. MARIJUANA.

Indian hemp. CANNABIS SATIVA.

infection. one of the major hazards of drug addiction is the risk of infection from unsterile needles or needle sores. Two diseases, frequently fatal, are common among addicts, tetanus and serum (or virus) hepatitis. Tetanus infections are almost always associated with the practice of SKIN POPPING, or subcutaneous injection. The tetanus bacillus enters the body through the open sores that cover the addict's body as a result of his frequent injections. Older addicts, whose veins have collapsed, are particularly prone to this practice and to the resultant disease. Tetanus infections are relatively infrequent but the majority of all cases occur in addicts; of these over 50 percent are fatal.

Virus hepatitis, a contagious form of jaundice, is always associated with the practice of MAINLINING, or intravenous injections. Since addicts do not always own needles, and since they naturally associate with other addicts, they tend to borrow from their fellows or to rent out their needles as a source of money, thus exposing themselves to infection. The virus inhabits the bloodstream and is thus easily transmitted from one addict to another in a single injection. Virus hepatitis follows the needle, of course, rather than the drug. It has broken out among California HIPPIES and others who inject AMPHETAMINES or LSD-25.

Other infections associated wth drug injection are phlebitis (infection of the vein), endocarditis (infection of the inside lining of the heart), abscesses, syphilis, and superficial venous thrombosis (collapsing)—swelling and blocking of veins—and (now rarely) malaria.

infinity machine. a sort of elaborate kaleidoscope, invented by Richard Aldcroft in 1966, which projects an infinite series of changing colors and patterns on a movie screen with the idea of emulating the hallucinations produced by LSD-25.

inhalers. psychotoxic, deliriant substances such as airplane glue (see GLUE SNIFFING) or CLEANING FLUID, which are inhaled for their intoxicant effects.

into. *1.* possessed of a special, secret relationship with, or strategic position vis-à-vis, a situation, person, or organization which provides a steady source of income, the obvious examples being blackmail, extortion, or stealing goods as a result of one's trusted position in a firm. *2.* to be using a kind of drug, as in "a lot of kids were *into* pot."

in transit. on an LSD TRIP.

intsaga. [Africa] CANNABIS.

intsangu. [Africa] CANNABIS.

IT-290. an indole analog of AMPHETAMINES which produces hallucinogenic effects.

jab. to ambush someone.

Jackson illusion pepper. [From the surname of the discoverer] a rotten green pepper with holes in either end through which a king-size cigarette is smoked (the smoke traveling through the pepper and inhaled from the opposite hole, sometimes through a straw); claimed to produce a feeling of HIGH accompanied by hallucinations of color and elaborate designs. Possibly the pepper is analogous to BANANA SMOKING: a hoax, a case of suggestibility among young, inexperienced drug users, or actually the action of some alkaloid in the plant (such as BUFOTENINE, as in the case of bananas) which is formed by the heat of the cigarette smoke. First described in the HIPPIE newspaper, *The East Village Other,* the pepper smoke caused a flurry of reaction among the younger drug users, who thought a cheap, legal hallucinogenic drug had been discovered.

jag. [intoxication, whether from liquor or from a drug; slang since the 1930s—*EP*] a state of prolonged, agitated, intense stimulation caused by a drug, especially MARIJUANA, AMPHETAMINES, or BARBITURATES.

jammed up. [since the 1950s] taken an overdose of drugs.

jasper. a lesbian.

jay smoke. a MARIJUANA cigarette.

jduq jmel. [Arabic] small black DATURA seeds, sold in magic shops in Marrakesh, which have a hallucinogenic effect and probably contain SCOPOLAMINE.

jefferson airplane. [after (?) a rock and roll group of that name; local at University of Missouri] a paper match split into a Y shape and used to hold the butt, or ROACH, of a MARIJUANA cigarette.

jerk off. [from *jerked off,* masturbated; compare GET OFF] to inject a little HEROIN at a time, letting it flow back into the needle mixed with blood, reinjecting it, and so on. Supposed to prolong the initial RUSH; also, the first drawing of blood indicates that one has a HIT. Compare BOOTING.

> and after tying Gene's tie around her lower arm, [she] pricked a vein and *jerked off*—that is, pushed the stuff in and then brought it up with blood.
> —Rabbi Joseph R. Rosenbloom, in *The Reporter* (June 25, 1959)

> Over and over again one hears addicts describe the effects of their injection in sexual terms. One addict said that after a fix he felt as if he were coming from every pore. Another said that he used to inject the solution in a rhythmic fashion until it was all used up, and said that this was akin to masturbation albeit much better.
> —M. Hoffman, *Comprehensive Psychology* (1964)

joint. [the narcotics user's (especially the opium smoker's) tools and equipment; since around 1920. A MARIJUANA cigarette since around 1945—*EP*. Perhaps from the sense of *joint,* implying section; i.e., in rolling a cigarette one rolls a section, portion, of one's supply. Or perhaps *joint,* the penis. This latter theory is confirmed by Charles Winick in "Marijuana Use by Young People," included in *Drug*

Addiction in Youth, edited by Ernest Harms (1965). He says that marijuana's "traditional association with sex" may be the reason a marijuana cigarette is referred to as a "joint" and a "root."] a marijuana cigarette, usually the roll-your-own kind. Compare STICK. *2.* [with *the*] prison.

jones. [since the 1950s; perhaps related to *the jakes,* a form of peripheral neuritis prevalent in the South in the 1920s, caused by bad homemade whiskey] DRUG DEPENDENCE, a HABIT; the WITHDRAWAL SYMPTOMS arising out of this habit.

> "He just beat me out of $5 and my *jones* is on me."
> —Claude Brown, *Manchild in the Promised Land* (1965)

joy juice. CHLORAL HYDRATE, appetizers, tonics.

joypop. [a bout of OPIUM smoking; from *pop,* a shot, a hypodermic injection; since the 1930s—*EP* and *joy,* i.e., just for pleasure] to inject HEROIN occasionally for pleasure, not motivated by the need to prevent WITHDRAWAL SYMPTOMS. Some heroin users continue to joypop on weekends for years without ever taking it frequently enough to become physically dependent. Many addicts, however, follow the classical route to addiction: SNIFFING to SKIN POPPING to MAINLINING. Usually, the joypopper injects the drug subcutaneously.

juanita. [Mexico] MARIJUANA.

juice. liquor.

> "*Juice* is a down trip. Grass brings you up—up and away."
> —"The Hippies," *Time* (July 7, 1967)

juice head. one who drinks liquor.

jungle drug, the. AYAHUSCA.

junk. [*junker,* drug user; since the 1920s; from *junker,* a pusher or peddler—*EP.* Since heroin was synthesized in 1898 and addicts were calling it *junk* in the early 1900s, either the name was taken from a word for opium or it was coined for heroin. If the latter, it apparently lacks the invidious connotation of such synonyms as CRAP, SHIT, and POISON, which *EP* says originated in the 1920s in addicts' expressions of contempt for diluted heroin. Another possibility is that, being readily available and a kind of patent medicine, heroin was considered inferior to opium and in this sense *junk*] *1.* HEROIN. *2.* any drugs. *3.* inferior, diluted heroin.

junkie. [from JUNK; also, perhaps, the idea developed of the addict as "human junk." Veteran addicts sometimes apply it as a term of contempt to new addicts or those unable to support their habits] a HEROIN addict.

K k

kat. KHAT.

kava. a mild, soporific beverage made from the roots of the plant *Piper methysticum,* a member of the pepper family. It is drunk by South Sea Islanders of New Guinea (where it is called *kavakava*) and Hawaii (where it is called *ava*). The beverage is served hot; it is aromatic, rather soapy in taste, and astringent. Kava is not addictive, and its action is sedative; if enough is drunk, the user will fall asleep. In Tonga the drink is prepared by young men or girls who chew the roots thoroughly, then expectorate the pulp into a bowl, where it is mixed with water and served.

key. also spelled ki. A kilogram (2.2 pounds) of a drug, especially a pressed block of MARIJUANA of this weight.

khat. also nat, q'at. The buds or fresh leaves of *Catha edulis* which are chewed or drunk as tea in Yemen, East Africa, and the Arabian peninsula. It is a central nervous system stimulant very similar in chemical structure and effects to AMPHETAMINES. In Yemen it is used to banish sleepiness and hunger on long treks and also for its exhilarating effects. The drug's adverse effects include restlessness, insomnia, overstimulation of the heart, and loss of sexual desire. The usual mode of ingestion is to chew the leaves when they are fresh; chewing limits the amount ingested and prevents tolerance from building up. However, PSYCHIC DEPENDENCE, without PHYSICAL DEPENDENCE, does occur: habitual khat users feel strongly impelled to use it once a day or more and will do so in preference to eating.

ki. KEY.

kick. to break the (drug) habit, as in "I'm going into the hospital and *kick*."

kickback. [a return to taking narcotics after kicking a habit; a relapse; since around 1930; from *kick back,* to return stolen property to the victim—*EP*. But also may be a pun on KICK THE HABIT] a relapse, a return to taking drugs after one has been withdrawn from them.

kick cold turkey. [from COLD TURKEY] *1.* to abruptly withdraw from drugs. *2.* to undergo full WITHDRAWAL SYMPTOMS unalleviated by any medicine. Compare A LA CANONA.

kicking. ridding oneself of addiction to narcotics.

kicks. [*kick,* a drug taking, since around 1945—*EP*. Probably from the jolt, the RUSH of the drug's initial onset; analogous to the *kick* in strong liquor. From that, any strong pleasure, as in "I get a *kick* out of you"] sheer pleasure, sheer hedonism, without any other redeeming qualities. To "take a drug for kicks" thus has a sharply ambivalent meaning in our society. Those who disapprove of drug taking cite the fact that users do so "just for kicks" as morally wrong; while the hedonists say that taking something for pleasure is a worthy motive in itself.

kick sticks. MARIJUANA cigarettes. Compare JOINT.

> Joints are pulled out of the brims of hats and soon there's no noise except the music and the steady hiss of cats blasting away on *kick-sticks.*   —Piri Thomas, *Down These Mean Streets* (1967)

kick the habit. [from *kick it out,* to suffer physically or mentally (withdrawal symptoms); since the 1920s—*EP*. Probably *kick it out* has its origin in the muscle spasms the addict endures during withdrawal, and so was extended from meaning withdrawal symptoms to ridding oneself of addiction by undergoing withdrawal. "I soon learned where the expression 'kick the habit' came from. When my drug quota was progressively cut down I got spasms in the muscles of my arms and my legs actually kicked."—Barney Ross and Martin Abramson, *No Man Stands Alone,* J. B. Lippincott, Philadelphia, © 1957 by Barney Ross and Martin Abramson] to break the drug habit, including undergoing WITHDRAWAL SYMPTOMS. Thus, to kick the habit is not the same as to KICK COLD TURKEY. Kick the habit also has a connotation of finality, i.e., one permanently stops using drugs.

kick the habit on the elevator. to undergo mild WITHDRAWAL SYMPTOMS. The modern addict's HEROIN is often so heavily diluted that he develops only a mild addiction, and when he goes into the hospital for detoxification, his withdrawal symptoms are comparable to a case of flu.

> I've seen guys go into jail and, like the expression goes, they *kicked their habit on the elevator.* In two or three days they're eating, sleeping, doing pushups.
> —anonymous addict, James Mills, in *The Drug Takers* (1965)

kief. KIF.

kif. [Arabic, tranquillity, peace] name used in Northwest Africa, especially Morocco, for CANNABIS.

> *Kif* is like fire; a little warms, a lot burns.   —Moroccan folk saying

kilo. a kilogram (2.2 pounds). Bulk sales of HEROIN and MARIJUANA are often made in kilo lots and the drugs shipped in kilo packages.

kilter. MARIJUANA.

king-kong pills. BARBITURATES or other sedative pills. Compare GORILLA PILLS.

KISS BIG. in 1962, the telephone number of the IFIF spelled with the letters on the dial KISS BIG. It became a sort of game among LSD users in Cambridge, Massachusetts, to dial the number and say "kiss big," to which the voice on the other end would reply, "if, if." Among initiates it was a way of saying, "I am using LSD."

kit. equipment for injecting drugs; usually a hypodermic needle, eyedropper, cotton, bottle cap or spoon, water, and a strap to use as a tourniquet to distend the vein. Compare GIMMICKS, WORKS.

knockout drops. liquid chloral (trichloroacetaldehyde), a hypnotic and sedative, mixed with alcohol, which POTENTIATES its effects.

The result is that the unsuspecting victim who receives the knockout drops sinks into a coma (the effects are similar to BARBITURATE overdosage). The toxic oral dose of CHLORAL HYDRATE, a close relative, is approximately 10 grams. Compare MICKEY FINN.

kratom. [Thailand] a plant, *Mitragyna speciosa,* which is believed to have a narcotic effect, although little is known about it. Compare BEINSA.

K.Y. U.S. Public Health Service (Narcotics) Hospital in Lexington, Kentucky, where addicts go voluntarily or by court sentence to cure addiction.

L l

L. LSD-25.

lady snow. [from the resemblance of cocaine crystals to snow] COCAINE.

La Guardia Report. short title for a study of MARIJUANA ordered by Mayor Fiorello H. La Guardia in 1938, carried out by the New York Academy of Medicine, with the assistance of the New York Police Department. Finally published in 1944 under the official title, *The Marihuana Problem in the City of New York, by The Mayor's Committee on Marihuana.* The study was in two parts: a clinical study of the effects of marijuana and a sociological study of marijuana users in the city.

The clinical study was carried out under the supervision of doctors in Goldwater Memorial Hospital. Experimental subjects (prisoners) were given both natural and synthetic marijuana and subjected to a battery of physiological and mental tests to determine what the drug's pharmacodynamic effects were, whether it caused physical or mental deterioration, and if it possessed any possible therapeutic effects for the treatment of disease or for other drug addictions.

The sociological study was carried out by specially trained members of the police department, who visited places haunted by marijuana smokers in the city in an undercover capacity. The committee's conclusions were as follows:

> Marihuana, by virtue of its property of lowering inhibitions, accentuates all traits of personality, both those harmful and those beneficial. It does not impel its user to take spontaneous action but may make his response to stimuli more emphatic than it normally would be. Increasingly larger doses of marihuana are not necessary in order that the long-term user may capture the original degree of pleasure.
>
> Marihuana, like alcohol, does not alter the basic personality, but by relaxing inhibitions may permit antisocial tendencies formerly suppressed to come to the fore. Marihuana does not of itself give rise to antisocial behavior.
>
> There is no evidence to suggest that the continued use of marihuana is a stepping-stone to the use of opiates. Prolonged use of the drug does not lead to physical, mental, or moral degeneration, nor have we observed any permanent deleterious effects from its continued use. Quite the contrary, marihuana and its derivatives and allied synthetics have potentially valuable therapeutic applications which merit future investigation.
>
> [Mayor La Guardia added this statement in his foreword to the report:] I am glad that the sociological, psychological and medical ills commonly attributed to marihuana have been found to be exaggerated insofar as the City of New York is concerned. I hasten to point out, however, that the findings are to be interpreted only as a reassuring report of progress and not as encouragement to indulgence, for I shall continue to enforce the laws prohibiting the use of marihuana until and if complete findings may justify an amendment of existing laws.
>
> —*The Marihuana Problem in the City of New York, by The Mayor's Committee on Marihuana* (1944)

Although it might be said that one of the main things the report proved was that prisoners given a holiday from jail and allowed to smoke marijuana will be happy, docile, and cooperative indeed under the influence of the drug, the La Guardia Report stands as a landmark study into the physiological effects of marijuana, and its conclusions, especially those about the relationship of marijuana to psychosis and crime, are still cited today, even though the book has been virtually out of print for years.

As a result of its tentatively favorable verdict, the report came to be a sort of marijuana smoker's underground bible, but whether its conclusions warrant legalization of marijuana, as some people claim, is another matter.

laudanum. [from Latin *ladanum,* a yellowish resin] a hydroalcoholic tincture containing 10 percent OPIUM; a solution of opium, first compounded by Paracelsus (1493?–1541). This, the first medicinal form of opium, was used widely for a variety of diseases up through the nineteenth century. It was sold without prescription, and its addictive liability was not clearly understood. As a result, many people who took laudanum for various indispositions became addicted, among them such well-known persons as Coleridge, Poe, Moussorgsky, Mrs. Browning, Swinburne, Chatterton, Francis Thompson, Dante Gabriel Rossetti, James Thomson, Wilberforce, Horace Day, John Randolph, and De Quincey.

> I possess a secret remedy which I call laudanum and which is superior to all other heroic remedies.   —Paracelsus, *Letter* (ca. 1530)

> But I took it; and in an hour, O heavens! What a revulsion! What a resurrection from the lowest depths, of the inner spirit! What an apocalypse of the world within me! That my pains had vanished was now a trifle in my eyes; this negative effect was swallowed up in the immensity of those positive effects which had opened up before me, in the abyss of divine enjoyment thus suddenly revealed. Here was a panacea for all human woes; here was the secret of happiness, about which the philosophers had disputed for so many ages, at once discovered; happiness might now be bought for a penny, and carried in the waist-coat-pocket; portable ecstasies might be had corked up in a pint-bottle; and peace of mind sent down by the mail.
> —Thomas De Quincey, *Confessions of an English Opium Eater*
> (1822)

laughing gas. NITROUS OXIDE.

lay. to smoke OPIUM. *Obsolete.*

lay down. [the price or fee for admission to an OPIUM den; since the 1920s—*EP;* but compare "to recline and smoke opium"—*MM,* 1946] to smoke opium in a reclining position, a practice which may decrease nausea and other undesirable side effects of the drug. *Obsolete.*

layout. [since the 1880s—*EP*] OPIUM-smoking equipment. *Obsolete.*

lay up. having acquired a large supply of drugs, to withdraw from hustling and lie about one's room using the drugs, as in "I used the money to buy a big stash of heroin and decided to just *lay up* for the next couple of weeks."

L.B. a pound. Compare O.Z.

leapers. AMPHETAMINES.

leaving-the-set walk. [from (?) *set*, a stage set] police term describing the characteristic demeanor of an addict after he has bought drugs from a pusher. See SET.

legal high. generic term for a variety of substances that are not prohibited by law, can be obtained without prescription or are available as foods, and are supposed to alter the consciousness. Such substances include AMYL NITRITE, Sominex (see SCOPOLAMINE, see the quotation) various drugs which contain BELLADONNA, cigarette tobacco dusted in aspirin powder, NUTMEG, MACE, cinnamon, CATNIP, lettuce juice, hydrangea leaves, niacin, green pepper (see JACKSON GREEN PEPPER), and dried banana pulp (see BANANA SMOKING). Compare NATCH TRIPS.

lemonade. BLANK.

Leritine. [ANILERIDINE, Merck Sharp & Dohme] a SYNTHETIC OPIATE analgesic somewhat less potent than MORPHINE. Injections of 30 to 40 milligrams give analgesia equivalent to 10 milligrams of morphine. Prolonged administration will produce PHYSICAL DEPENDENCE. WITHDRAWAL SYMPTOMS are milder than those associated with morphine dependence and are more comparable to those of MEPERIDINE dependence. Manufacturer claims that Leritine is a more effective pain reliever than meperidine in equipotent dosages. The dosage is about half that of meperidine: about 50 milligrams initially; 75 milligrams in more severe pain; 100 milligrams in extremely severe pain, up to a total of 200 milligrams over three to four hours. An ungraduated, sudden intravenous injection of Leritine in excess of 10 milligrams is dangerous and may result in fatal respiratory depression. Manufacturer also cautions that direct injection of undiluted Leritine is to be avoided, except in grave emergencies. The product is sold in white tablets and in solution for injection. A CLASS A NARCOTIC.

levallorphan. [*l*-3-hydroxy-*N*-allylmorphinan tartrate] a synthetic drug which reverses the action of MORPHINE and the synthetic morphine drugs and is used to counter acute respiratory depression resulting from overdosage. In persons addicted to narcotics, Levallorphan will trigger severe WITHDRAWAL SYMPTOMS. Compare LORFAN, NALLINE.

Levo-Dromoran. [LEVORPHANOL tartrate, Roche Laboratories] a SYNTHETIC OPIATE analgesic more potent than MORPHINE. Doses of 2 to 3 milligrams of Levo-Dromoran will produce analgesia equal to that produced by 10 milligrams of morphine, lasting four to five hours. After prolonged administration, PHYSICAL DEPENDENCE upon Levo-Dromoran will occur, with WITHDRAWAL SYMPTOMS equal to those of morphine in severity. The recommended clinical dose is 2 milligrams orally or injected subcutaneously. The product is sold in 2-milligram tablets or in solution. A CLASS A NARCOTIC.

levorphanol. a SYNTHETIC OPIATE analgesic composed of the levo isomer of morphan. Dosages of 2 to 3 milligrams produce analgesia equal to that produced by 10 milligrams of MORPHINE, lasting four to five hours. Prolonged administration will result in PHYSICAL DEPENDENCE with WITHDRAWAL SYMPTOMS similar to those of morphine dependence in severity. A CLASS A NARCOTIC. Compare LEVO-DROMORAN.

Lexington. also called K.Y., narco. U.S. Public Health Service (Narcotics) Hospital in Lexington, Kentucky.

Librium. [chlordiazepoxide hydrochloride, Roche Laboratories] a MINOR TRANQUILIZER of the BENZODIAZEPINE group that lies between CHLORPROMAZINE and MEPROBAMATE in potency, Librium is used to treat anxiety, to allay apprehension before surgery, and, in large doses, to alleviate acute panic psychoses, alcoholic anxiety, and paranoid and schizophrenic states. Usual recommended dosages are from 5 to 10 milligrams three to four times daily up to 50- to 100-milligram injections totaling no more than 300 milligrams per day. Other depressant or stimulant drugs such as alcohol, BARBITURATES, phenothiazine derivatives, MONOAMINE OXIDASE (MAO) INHIBITORS, and imipraminelike compounds POTENTIATE Librium's effects, and the danger of fatal respiratory depression is increased. Fatal overdoses of the drug have been rare, however.

Prolonged, excessive use of Librium, i.e., 300 to 600 milligrams daily, or about ten times the normal therapeutic dose, over a period of about five months, will result in PHYSICAL DEPENDENCE, in which case WITHDRAWAL SYMPTOMS will occur if the drug is abruptly stopped. Withdrawal symptoms are similar to those resulting from barbiturate dependence: loss of appetite, aggravation of existing psychopathological states, depression, agitation, insomnia, and convulsions. Since it is thought that Librium produces significantly less euphoria than meprobamate, OPIATE analgesics, or the barbiturates, the danger of PSYCHIC DEPENDENCE may be relatively less, but it does occur. In some persons the drug will produce idiosyncratic or paradoxical reactions, i.e., inebriation, stimulation, loss of bodily coordination, delirium, drowsiness, rage, and confusion.

Librium is sold in capsules or solution for injection. The capsules contain 5 milligrams (green top, yellow bottom, both inscribed "ROCHE 5"); 10 milligrams (brown top, green bottom, both inscribed "ROCHE 10"); and 25 milligrams (green top, white bottom, both inscribed "ROCHE 25"). Subject to the DRUG ABUSE CONTROL AMENDMENT OF 1965.

lid. [from the fact that MARIJUANA used to be sold in pipe-tobacco tins; see CAN] an amount approximately equal to 22 grams (0.77 to 1 ounce) of marijuana; a measure for purposes of sale. The price in 1967 ranged from $10 (West Coast) to $25 (New York City). The term is used mainly in the western United States. About forty marijuana cigarettes can be made from this amount.

lid poppers. AMPHETAMINES.

life, the. the drug addict's characteristic life pattern, revolving around HUSTLING, copping (see COP), the FIX, interaction with fellow addicts, dealing with PUSHERS, and so on. When one is in the life, one is using drugs, of course, and committed to a whole complex of rituals, fraternalisms, lingo, etc., rather like joining a lodge. Compare STREET, ON THE.

light stuff. MARIJUANA or other nonopiate drugs, as opposed to HEAVY STUFF, i.e., HEROIN, COCAINE, other OPIATES. Compare HEAD DRUGS.

> "When I came back, I started to hustle pot—*light stuff,* here and there a few bricks. But no mo' junk. I was gonna stay clean."
> —Piri Thomas, *Down These Mean Streets* (1967)

light up. [since the 1930s] to smoke MARIJUANA. *Obsolete?* Compare BLAST.

> Light up, Gates, Report Finds "Tea" a Good Kick.
> —headline in *Downbeat,* after the publication of the LA GUARDIA REPORT (1944)

line. [from MAINLINE, to inject HEROIN into the large vein of the arm] the main vein in the arm; to "shoot in the *line*" is to inject heroin into this vein.

load. twenty-five to thirty DECKS (packets) of HEROIN stacked and fastened together with a rubber band for delivery.

loaded. [from the sense of *load,* a heavy weight; one who is "carrying a load" is "burdened" by a heavy intoxication] in a state of drug intoxication (not limited to alcoholic intoxication).

loco. MARIJUANA. Compare MEXICAN LOCOWEED.

long con. a major, elaborately plotted confidence game. Compare SHORT CON.

lophophorine. one of the alkaloids found in the hallucinogenic PEYOTE cactus.

Lorfan. [LEVALLORPHAN tartrate, Roche Laboratories] a synthetic NARCOTIC antagonist which acts to reverse the effects of the OPIATE analgesics. Lorfan is customarily injected along with the opiate in order to lessen the danger of respiratory depression from the latter without impairing analgesia. Used alone, Lorfan may itself induce severe respiratory depression; hence, it is recommended that it be administered in conjunction with an opiate except in emergencies. It is also valuable in cases of accidental or deliberate narcotic overdosages resulting in respiratory depression (along with other medical measures). Lorfan is not effective against BARBITURATE-induced respiratory depression. Compare NALORPHINE, NALLINE.

LSD-25. [*d*-lysergic acid diethylamide tartrate 25. For another meaning that puns on this one see IFIF] a hallucinogenic semisynthetic derivative of lysergic acid, an alkaloid found in the rye fungus ergot, *Claviceps purpurea.* The standard laboratory process for making the drug, developed in 1938 by Dr. Albert Hofmann at the Sandoz Laboratories in Switzerland, is to mix the lysergic acid with diethylamide, freeze the mixture, and extract the resulting LSD by fractional distillation with chloroform or benzine or with a vacuum evaporator. The drug's hallucinogenic effects were first experienced by Dr. Hofmann in 1943, when he accidentally ingested some of it and experienced hallucinations.

The drug is one of the most potent known to man: 20 micrograms (1 microgram is one-millionth of a gram) or approximately 1/700,000,000 of the average man's body weight, will produce effects. In experiments the usual dose is 25 to 50 micrograms, though some doctors favor 100 micrograms. In treating alcoholics, when a more profound experience is considered desirable, doses of 300 micrograms are given. Illicit users customarily take amounts ranging from 100 to 700 micrograms, with 2,000 micrograms being the highest known dosage taken. The lethal dose in human beings is not known; rabbits have been given 120 times the average human dose and rats 2,000 without harm, but an elephant given 297 milligrams (297,000 micrograms) of the drug died.

In relation to the other HALLUCINOGENS, LSD is considered 5,000 times as potent as MESCALINE and 200 times as potent as PSILOCYBIN (this is arrived at by the comparative amounts needed to produce full effects in the average adult male weighing 150 pounds). It is said that 1 ounce of LSD will furnish enough for 300,000 individual doses on the illicit market. The drug is usually distributed as a soluble powder (a tartrate of lysergic acid diethylamide) packaged in capsules or as a liquid. In large enough quantities, the liquid drug has a slight bluish or purplish cast; the powder is colorless, odorless, and crystalline.

Sometimes the liquid is soaked up into pieces of blotting paper, chewing gum, sugar cubes, tablets, animal crackers, and heart-shaped candies. The practice of dissolving doses in cubes, once prevalent, gradually faded out, perhaps indicating that a more serious breed of drug takers, who wanted their drug in *drug form,* had made its appearance. It can also be injected, which induces a quicker HIGH but also increases the danger of INFECTION from unsterile needles.

The average price for a single dose (200 to 300 micrograms) on the illicit market in 1967 was between $2.50 and $10. The process of making LSD is fairly simple; however, certain items of laboratory equipment are needed, and the chemicals from which it is derived are difficult to obtain. Chief sources are the homemade LSD on the market, which is of unpredictable potency (due to inaccuracies in mixing the tiny amounts), and smuggled LSD, with Canada, England, Israel, Czechoslovakia, and Switzerland among the primary origins.

The effects of the drug vary widely among individuals and are in part related to the dosage, the mental state of the individual at the time he takes it (SET), and the circumstances in which he takes it (SETTING). The effects also vary with the same individual from time to time; he may have a series of pleasant experiences and then have an extremely unpleasant one. Because of its unpredictability, many HEROIN addicts, who are especially prone to experiment with other drugs, do not like LSD. The drug's effects occur within an hour after ingestion. The initial reaction is a vague anxiety and sometimes nausea. The anxiety may be unrelated to the drug; in one experiment a group of subjects was given an inert substance and told it was LSD; all of them experienced a heightened anxiety. Physiological alterations due to the drug's immediate action are relatively minor. The pupils dilate, the appetite is depressed, blood pressure and body temperature are increased, and insomnia follows upon the waning of its action. Sometimes there is restlessness, paralysis, or a suffocating sensation. The effects last from six to fourteen hours, tapering off into waves of alternating normality and abnormality. In a few cases they last for several days. A not uncommon postdrug experience, especially among long-time users, is *recurrence,* the phenomenon of some external or emotional stimulus setting off a more or less intense LSD experience even though the person has not taken the drug; he may not even be aware he is hallucinating—with disastrous results! This phenomenon can continue for a period of up to eighteen months.

Surprisingly only a small percentage (about 0.01 percent) of the dose taken enters the brain, where it remains twenty minutes, then disappears; a much larger percentage goes to the liver and kidneys. The fact that the amount in the brain remains there only about twenty minutes suggests that LSD's action is indirect; i.e., it either releases or inhibits other substances naturally occurring in the brain, and this imbalance causes the subjective effects. (LSD can be detected in the bloodstream up to two hours after it is taken, but the amount is so tiny that especially sensitive laboratory tests are needed.)

The drug's subjective effects are spectacular if taken in large doses. They are similar to those produced by other hallucinogenic drugs but on a grander scale and include stimulation of the central and autonomic nervous systems, changes in mood (sometimes euphoric and megalomaniac, sometimes fearful, panicky, and anxiety-ridden), a sense of threat to the ego, an intensification of colors so that they seem brighter, intensification of the other senses so that inaudible sounds become magnified or food tastes better or normally unnoticed aspects of things such as the pores in concrete become strikingly vivid, merging of senses (synesthesia) so that sounds are seen as color patterns, a wavelike sense of time so that seconds seem like an eternity, distortions in the perception of space so that surrounding objects seem fluid and shifting, a sense of depersonalization, of being simultaneously both within and without oneself, a closely related feeling of merger (dissolving) with the external world and a loss of personality, a perception of ordinary things as if seen for the first time unstructured by perceptual "sets," hallucinations of flowers, snakes, animals, other people, etc., which the subject usually knows to be hallucinations though he is powerless to stop them, a sense of closeness to, or merger with, other persons in the room as if barriers between individuals had been dissolved, enhanced sensuousness and sexual stimulation (the drug is neither an aphrodisiac nor an anaphrodisiac, but its overpowering mental effects tend to make it more of the latter), vivid swirling colors and shapes when the eyes are closed, an impairment in body coordination and in pain perception, impairment of performance on intelligence tests, sometimes voices commanding the user to do something, and the release from the subconscious of repressed material, sometimes in the form of terrifying, dreamlike, visual symbols and breakdown of conscience and superego restraints.

Since some of these effects are similar to those of schizophrenia, LSD was first thought to produce an "imitation" psychosis and was called a PSYCHOTOMIMETIC drug. However, this term was found to be inaccurate because of many differences, notably that the subject is usually aware, watching himself undergoing the hallucinatory experiences, and generally responsive to others. Nevertheless, one of the chief dangers of the drug is that it will trigger a latent psychosis into activity. This may result from anxiety, panic, and the release of repressed material with which the individual cannot cope, pushing him over the edge into an acute panic psychosis. Often such untoward effects can be headed off by the administration of a strong tranquilizer, such as CHLORPROMAZINE (THORAZINE), which reverses the drug's effects or calms the patient down sufficiently during the aftermath of his drug experience. Such transient panic psychoses, then, clear up more or less spontaneously in a day or so. But the drug has also induced chronic psychoses lasting several months or even longer. It also has induced severe depressions which are sometimes suicidal. (The suicide rate in a controlled group was 0.1 percent, which is low considering they were psychiatric patients.) Fatalities have also resulted from accidents occurring while the individual is under the drug, because his grandiose conception of himself and loss of contact with reality impair his judgment. He may jump out of the window without realizing the hazardousness of his actions. Driving while under the influence of the drug is especially dangerous because of distorted perception.

Aggressive acts committed under the influence of LSD are comparatively rare, yet they have occurred, with sometimes fatal results. Negative reactions to LSD generally occur among the following types of users: (1) unstable persons harboring a latent psychosis or severe neurosis (but who nevertheless may be functioning fairly successfully in everyday life), (2) persons who have been given the drug in large amounts without their knowledge (an extremely dangerous practice), and (3) persons who take the drug in a strange or apparently hostile or nonsupportive environment or take it alone without any proper supervision. (It must be added that negative reactions also occur among persons who have taken care to provide themselves with a congenial environment before using the drug or persons who have taken the drug as many as 100 times without adverse effects.)

Since the number of persons who have taken LSD outside of medical supervision in this country is not known (estimates range from 40,000 to 1 million), it is impossible to say what percentage have psychotic episodes. An analysis of medically supervised experiments with LSD revealed a very low psychosis rate of 0.8 per thousand. It is likely that psychotic reactions among unsupervised users is considerably higher than that figure. Certainly, the number of admissions to hospitals for treatment of such psychoses is steadily increasing as use of the drug becomes more widespread. In New York City, for example, the number of persons admitted to the psychiatric division of Bellevue Hospital with LSD-induced psychoses during the ten-month period from March 1, 1965, to December 31, 1965, numbered sixty-five; previous to that time there had only been a handful of such admissions. During the first six months of 1966, this admission rate roughly doubled (recent figures, however, show a decline in the admissions rate). Figures for California are similar. While this does not represent a public health crisis, it indicates that indiscriminate use of the drug can be dangerous. Since many of the people figuring in these statistics were functioning fairly successfully in society before taking the drug, the drug has obviously changed their lives for the worse.

The majority of users of LSD tend to be young, middle-class, and college-educated or else from the bohemian fringe of society. The number of college students trying LSD has increased and at a few colleges may total 25 percent (University of Illinois) of the student body, but the percentage of users out of the entire college population is probably considerably less than 5 percent, and all such figures are guesses at best. Motives for using the drug include expansion of consciousness; greater psychological insight into one's personality; a desire to change one's personality and become a more loving, "creative" individual; a religious or quasi-religious mystical experience; "kicks" (ranging from the novelty of the LSD state to enhanced experience of sex), improved creativity, solution of intellectual problems, a profound dissatisfaction with one's personality and way of life and a desire to experience something more intense and beautiful than one's daily humdrum. In some individuals LSD does seem to induce profound changes in the personality—whether for the better or the worse is a complex question. Certainly it has proved dramatically effective in treating some alcoholics, with a lower relapse rate than any other treatment for this disease (compare the alleged beneficial effects of PEYOTE on Indian alcoholics).

Whether creativity is enhanced by LSD is problematic; however, experiments with a group of architects suggested that they were better able to solve design problems while under the influence of the drug, but this capacity only exists while the subject is under the drug. For example, a physics major dropout said he could understand the theory of relativity only while under the drug. When asked to explain it when full of the drug, he could not. LSD has also been used with varying success in treating autistic schizophrenic children (it is not so effective with adult schizophrenics), as an adjunct to psychotherapy, in frigidity and homosexuality, and to ease the pains of terminal cancer and put the patient in a state of mind in which he is better able to accept his imminent death. However, LSD is still *a highly unpredictable drug,* and its pharmacology and psychic potentialities are still only dimly understood.

The adverse publicity inspired by the drug caused its only United States manufacturer, Sandoz Pharmaceuticals, to stop making it and withdraw it from the market. As a consequence, supplies on hand were transferred to the federal government, and the number of research projects with LSD dropped from 72 to 12. Current projects are under the supervision of the National Institute for Mental Health and the Veterans Administration, both governmental agencies.

Modern authorities are still not certain as to the nature of the pharmacodynamic action of LSD. One theory postulates that it acts to block the production of SEROTONIN, a neurohormone found in the brain, or replaces it. Apparently, its action causes the normal pattern of communication from various parts of the body to the brain to break down, so that instead of orderly, selective perception and analysis of incoming sensory data, the brain is deluged by a wide variety of undifferentiated external stimuli and subconscious material bubbling up in the consciousness at random and perceived in unstructured and startling ways—what Dr. Harold A. Abramson has called "an emotional storm."

LSD is, so far as is known, nontoxic. It does not cause PHYSICAL DEPENDENCE and there are no WITHDRAWAL SYMPTOMS upon cessation of long-term use. TOLERANCE to the drug occurs very rapidly; usually within three days the original dose will have no effect. This tolerance just as rapidly abates, however. CROSS-TOLERANCE with psilocybin and mescaline also occurs; so that a person who has built up a tolerance to one of these hallucinogens will also be tolerant to LSD, and vice versa. Because the LSD experience is so profound, many users have no desire to repeat it, and others are inclined to use it very frequentlly. Still, PSYCHIC DEPENDENCE does develop among some, who become deeply preoccupied with the drug and persist in its use. Often, this results in an abrupt and radical change in the user's way of life; he becomes more passive, more introspective, more benign and euphoric, and less cognizant of threats and anxiety. He usually gives up his career and becomes a bohemian or enters the world of the LSD cult. He may even withdraw completely from the world and exist in a state of near psychosis or else become a "grandiose paranoid"—a term applied by a psychiatrist to one of the leaders in the PSYCHEDELIC drug movement. The LSD user also risks arrest. Federal law (the Drug Abuse Control Amendment of 1965) makes it a crime to possess, make, sell, or transfer LSD; and several state laws, including California and New York, make possession of LSD a misdemeanor. Some authorities speculate that LSD may cause organic damage to the brain, but there is as yet no conclusive evidence for this. Experiments in which LSD is applied to white blood cells indicate that it may cause chromosome breakage, which could result in defective children if pregnant women use the drug, or, possibly, leukemia among adults, but this is still unproved.

In summary, supervised, directed and goal-oriented use of LSD tentatively suggests some benefits to the community in the areas of mental health, religion, and creative problem solving, but the drug is so unpredictable in its effects that these may be illusory. The chief hazard lies in illicit, unsupervised use in untoward circumstances, which increase the risk of a psychotic break under the influence of the drug, or use by latently psychotic individuals. As usual, passing a law does not eliminate the drug; however, only if the illicit traffic is eliminated will the unsupervised use of the drug stop. Since LSD is colorless, odorless, powerful in minute quantities, soluble in any liquid, fairly easy to manufacture if one has the equipment, and quite easy to smuggle, it appears that the illicit traffic will be difficult to stop. As long as the mystique surrounds the drug, the curious will want to try it, and the adepts will orient their lives around it. There will probably continue to be agitation for the drug's legalization by its advocates. Considered philosophically, such a decision would involve a conscious weighing of the risks involved against the potential benefits of the drug. A drug that can cure cancer might be highly dangerous, resulting in deaths of 50 percent of its users, but society might say that the risks were worth it and there is no alternative. The risks of unregulated LSD would seem to outweigh its benefits, although when used in controlled medical situations there is probably a more favorable balance. But in America, laws are usually passed or repealed at the behest of a pressure group. The pro-LSD pressure group is too incompetent politically and too powerless economically to overcome the counterpressure of the anti-LSD forces. Dedicated LSD users are characteristically, almost compulsively, proselyters for the drug, but it remains to be seen whether their efforts will have any widespread effect in our society, for the meditative, nonaggressive, inward orientation of self associated with the drug runs counter to the values of an extroverted, aggressive, acquisitive society.

Here the notes in the laboratory journal stop. The last words were written down only with great effort. I asked my laboratory assistant to accompany me home, since I believed that events would take the same course as the disturbance on Friday [his first ingestion of LSD]. But even on the way home—by bicycle—it appeared that all the symptoms were more intense than the first time. Already I had the greatest difficulty in speaking clearly, and my field of vision wavered and was distorted like the image in a curved mirror. Also, I had the feeling that I was making no headway, although later my assistant told me that we were traveling at a fast pace. . . .

As far as I can remember, the following symptoms were strongly marked during the height of the crisis, which had already passed when the doctor arrived: dizziness and defective vision; the faces of those present seemed to me like colored masks; strong kinetic disturbances alternating with paralysis; my head, my whole body and limbs seemed at times very heavy, as if filled with lead; cramps in my legs, my hands sometimes cold and numb; a metallic taste on my tongue; my throat dry and contracted; a feeling of suffocation; I was alternately bewildered and in clear understanding of the situation, so that I sometimes stood outside myself as a neutral observer as I shrieked half madly or babbled unintelligible nonsense. . . .

The visual distortions were still pronounced. Everything seemed to waver and be out of proportion, like the reflection in an agitated sheet of water. Moreover, everything was soaked in changing, unpleasant, mostly poisonous shades of green and blue. With my eyes closed, colorful, ever-changing fantastic images invaded my mind continuously. It was especially remarkably how all sounds—for instance, the noise of a passing car—were transposed into visual sensations, so that with each tone and noise a corresponding colored image, changing in form and color like a kaleidoscope was produced.

—Albert Hofmann, in "Mental Changes Experimentally Produced by LSD," *Psychiatric Quarterly* (1952).

A New Yorker made his first trip last November. It was a riot, a carnival of exquisite sensation, exploding color, visions so unspeakably beautiful that he sobbed with joy and said again and again, "Oh, my God, how lovely, how wonderful, how beautiful, how fair." Crystal palaces soared thousands of miles into a velvet void. His body dissolved in honey and quicksilver. He watched a bronze Buddha come alive and listened to a record of Ella Fitzgerald singing "My Ship" that he would give his soul to hear again. He went home and slept and the next day he was certain that the whole world was turned on. A month later he made his second trip. This is his account of how it ended:

"My guide's face changed. It became abstracted, reduced to a series of planes. His eyes were closed. In his expression there was absolute detachment, perfection, peace. An aura of silvery light flickered around his head. Then, between and slightly above the level of his eyes, I saw the third eye, the eye that gazes inward.

"The room darkened and the music faded. I was lying on my back on the floor. Then the room itself vanished and I was sinking, sinking, sinking. From far away I heard, very faintly, the word 'death.' I sank faster, turning and falling a million light years from the earth. The word got louder and more insistent. It took shape around me, closing me in. 'DEATH . . . DEATH . . . DEATH.' I thought of the dread in my father's eyes in his final hours. At the last instant before my own death I shouted, 'No.' Absolute terror, total horror. With immense effort I began to lift myself back to life. It seemed to take an eternity.

"Then the room reappeared and I was standing there shaking. My guide still sat in his chair, perfectly still. Suddenly I knew that he controlled me. There was no escape. No way to explain. I was his slave. His thoughts were my thoughts.

"'Oh, you bastard!' I shouted. 'What have you done to me? What have you done?' From far away I heard another voice. It said, 'You are insane. Totally, finally, irrevocably insane.' My face got cold. I ran in circles in that little room. I scattered the bright stones that I had felt change and grow beneath my fingers a few hours earlier.

"I tried to be calm and think, but I couldn't. I could feel my brain splitting. I never pray, God knows, but I fell to my knees in that chamber of horrors. 'Jesus, help me!' I said. 'Help me! Help me!'

"My guide stood over me. 'Take it easy,' he said. 'You always knew it could end like this.' The way the words reverberated with menace, it was the most frightening thing I had ever heard. He held a white capsule in one hand and a glass of water in the other. 'Take this,' he said. 'It's Thorazine. It will calm you.'

"To me it looked like more LSD. 'Not on your life, you bastard,' I shouted. 'I'm getting out of here.' He stood in front of the door. I picked up a chair and went for him."

—Tom Buckley, *The New Republic* (May 14, 1966)

"I saw the most horrible, slimy snake I have ever seen. It was large and ugly and it curled around me, starting at my ankles, slowly winding up my legs. I tried to get free but I couldn't, my legs seemed to become part of the snake. . . . I knew the snake was swallowing me, bit by bit. I could feel the mucus inside the snake. I was becoming a part of it. I was sick. I screamed and looked for Buddy. He seemed very far away. I thought he was laughing at me. He knew I was terrified of snakes. . . . He held out his hand and his whole arm started to twist and pulsate as if it had no bones. It was another snake. . . . The snake began to swallow my head, all wet and smooth. . . . I was the snake without eyelids, so I had to watch everything."

—student, quoted in John Cashman, *The LSD Story* (1966)

LSM. Lysergic acid morpholide, a chemical congener of LSD-25.

Luminal. [phenobarbital, Winthrop Laboratories] a long-acting, slow-onset BARBITURATE hypnotic and sedative. Like all the phenobarbitals, Luminal is considered especially effective as an anticonvulsant, e.g., in epilepsy and delirium tremens. The hypnotic dose is 100 milligrams; the sedative dose, 25 to 30 milligrams. The average daily intake over a long period of time should not exceed 0.6 grain (36 milligrams). Fatal overdoses of Luminal (ten to twelve times the hypnotic dose) occur, usually in suicides. Because it is a slow-onset, long-acting barbiturate, Luminal is perhaps more dangerous in such attempts. The coma induced is slower in taking effect, deeper, longer lasting once it does take effect, and there is consequently less chance that the patient will be discovered in time to be saved.

Still, the phenobarbitals, which have been in medical use since 1912, are among the most useful of the barbiturates. TOLERANCE to the drug's hypnotic effects builds up over time, so that there is a temptation to increase the dosage in order to continue getting the same effects. After prolonged use in excessive amounts, PHYSICAL DEPENDENCE will occur, with severe WITHDRAWAL SYMPTOMS if the drug is abruptly stopped.

Luminal is sold in purple (16 milligrams), white (32 milligrams), or green (100 milligrams) scored tablets, and as an elixir, hypodermic tablets, powder, and solution. Slang name: purple hearts.

lush. [from an eighteenth-century English term for strong beer or from the German *löschen,* to quench flames or thirst—*EP*] *1.* a heavy drinker. *2.* an alcoholic. *3.* alcoholic beverages, as in "he was on *lush.*" *4.* to drink alcoholic beverages. Compare JUICE.

lysergic acid. a compound close in chemical structure to LSD-25 but without hallucinogenic effects; one of the direct chemical precursors of LSD-25. Sometimes LSD-25 is erroneously called by this name.

lysergide. LSD-25.

M m

M. [since around 1920—*EP*] MORPHINE.

mace. a common spice made from the integuments of NUTMEG and used, mixed with hot water, especially by prisoners, to produce stimulation and light-headed HIGH.

macon. [West Africa] CANNABIS.

maconha. [Brazil] CANNABIS.

made. [from *make the man,* buy drugs—*EP*. Also *to make,* to obtain from by guile or cheating or by purchase; perhaps when one is *made,* one is "had," taken, seduced, beaten. But see MAKE] *1.* exposed; revealed for what you really are, as in "I *made* him as a narco." *2.* purchased narcotics, as in "I *made* him for a nickel bag."

magic mushrooms. see MUSHROOMS, SACRED.

mainline. [from *main line,* a major rail route or "a vein forms a line, and main rhymes vein"—*EP;* since around 1925] *1.* the large arterial (ulnar or median cephalic) vein in the arm, the usual, because most convenient, place for the injection of HEROIN. *2.* to inject heroin or other drugs into this vein. *3.* to inject intravenously.

mainlining. injecting HEROIN into the main vein of the arm or other vein.

main stash. home—*MM,* 1946. *Obsolete.* Compare STASH.

maintenance therapy. legally supplying an addict with a daily ration of drugs, either those to which he is addicted or those of the MORPHINE type, with the intention of preventing WITHDRAWAL SYMPTOMS, winning his confidence, and working with him to break his habit, transferring his addiction from HEROIN to another drug (see METHADONE) and thus weaning from the heroin addict's life pattern, or simply enabling him to continue to function in the community as a supervised drug addict who does not have to acquire his drugs illegally.

In Great Britain addicts can register as such and receive daily dosages legally, under restricted conditions (BRITISH SYSTEM). Because of strict interpretations by the Supreme Court of the HARRISON NARCOTICS ACT in the 1920s, doctors were prohibited from giving narcotics to addicts for relief of withdrawal symptoms, and so in practice maintenance therapy by a private physician became impossible. More recent decisions have reversed those earlier interpretations, but most doctors are still reluctant to give narcotics to addicts on a long-term basis and have no knowledge of how to treat addicts or desire to become involved with them. Instead, medical efforts have been concentrated on maintenance with drugs like methadone or CYCLAZOCINE. The federal BUREAU OF NARCOTICS is opposed to doctors' prescribing for addicts; the few doctors who have done so as part of their treatment of an addicted patient have experienced harassment and forfeiture of their licenses.

majoon. [Arabic *ma'jun,* jam; confection containing cannabis] also majoun. Greenish-black or brown confection of a gummy consistency containing powdered HASHISH or CANNABIS, honey, fruit, nuts, spices, and rancid butter, consumed in North Africa and the Middle East for its hallucinogenic effects. Compare DAWAMESK, GOBLET OF JAM.

> The doctor stood by the side of a buffet on which lay a platter filled with small Japanese saucers. He spooned a morsel of paste or greenish jam about as large as the thumb from a crystal vase, and placed it next to the silver spoon on each saucer. . . . "This will be deducted from your share in Paradise," he said as he handed me my portion.
> —Theophile Gautier, *Revue des Deux Mondes* (1846) (Translation by Polly Kraft, *The Drug Experience,* 1961)

major tranquilizer. a pharmacological and chemical classification (compare MINOR TRANQUILIZER). The major tranquilizers are of the phenothiazine type, chemically, which consists of three subgroups:

1. Dimethylaminopropyl compounds (CHLORPROMAZINE, promazine, triflupromazine)
2. Piperidyl compounds (mepazine, thioridazine)
3. Piperazine compounds (carphenazine, fluphenazine, perphenazine, prochlorperazine, trifluoperazine, thioprozate)

The major tranquilizers are unique in their effectiveness in treating acute and chronic psychotic states, specifically, by calming violent, hyperactive, hyperexcited, fearful patients without any soporific actions. Even large doses will not induce coma or anesthesia, and PHYSICAL DEPENDENCE and PSYCHIC DEPENDENCE are unlikely. Thus, psychotic patients can be calmed without the risk (present with BARBITURATES) of dangerous respiratory depression.

Major tranquilizers can be administered over a prolonged period without addiction, and the patient will be sufficiently alert mentally to respond to other psychotherapeutical measures. It is also possible to return the patient to the community sooner, substituting outpatient for institutional care. The major tranquilizers also lessen the patient's hallucinations and delusions, or at least his fears and anxieties about them. Once the patient is calmed and his mental tortures and delusions brought under control, the possibility of his achieving rapport with others and especially with a psychiatrist is greatly increased; further, if he continues to receive maintenance doses of the tranquilizer after leaving the institution, there is less chance of his having to be rehospitalized.

Some TOLERANCE develops to several effects of the major tranquilizers. Their main danger lies in such untoward side effects as loss of control over muscles of the head, arms, and hands; tremors, shuffling gait, drooling, etc.; skin and liver disorders (jaundice); drowsiness, dizziness, and fatigue, which are usually produced by large doses; and various anticholinergic reactions (see ATROPINE) such as fall in blood pressure or ocular pressure.

majoun. MAJOON.

make. [from *make,* to detect or recognize, since around 1900—*EP.* Also *make,* to steal, burgle, or sell things to a person or at a house, or *make it,* to arrive, to succeed, which is related to a specialization of the convicts' *make it,* to get a parole or pardon, since around 1900; and also the colloquial sense of "to gain a desired point," since the 1880s—*EP.*] *1.* to detect or recognize someone for what they really are. *2.* to purchase drugs from a peddler, as in "I tried to *make* him for some junk." *3.* to flee, leave, "beat it." Compare MADE.

make it. [see MAKE] to do, achieve, accomplish something; specifically, to inject a narcotic and experience a HIGH or to have sexual intercourse.

making a croaker for a reader. [from CROAKER, a doctor, and READER, prescription] bribing a doctor to write an illegal prescription for a NARCOTIC.

man, the. [in Harlem during the 1930s *the man* was the law—*EP.* Also probably taken from *to make the man,* to purchase narcotics from a peddler—*EP.* Current Negro usage has extended *the man* to mean the boss, i.e., the white man] *1.* police, detective, or parole officer. *2.* a connection, a PUSHER, a drug peddler. Compare BIG MAN, the high-level seller, wholesaler, or importer of narcotics.

M and C. [from *Marmon* and *Cadillac,* the motor cars; in turn, from the drugs' initials; the 1920s—*EP.* Also connoting the high prices of the drugs and their relative value to the addict, i.e., the equivalent of a Cadillac to a nonaddict] a mixture of MORPHINE and COCAINE ("usually four parts morphine to one part cocaine"— *EP*). *Obsolete.* Compare SPEEDBALL.

manida. [from (?) Spanish transliteration of *mannite,* milk sugar] MILK SUGAR.

mannite. MILK SUGAR.

MAO inhibitors. MONOAMINE OXIDASE INHIBITORS.

marijuana. [probably a mutilation of Portuguese, *maran guango,* intoxication; first applied to CANNABIS SATIVA in Brazil. Pablo Oswaldo Wolff posits a possible (Mexican) Indian derivation, which is dubious and too complex etymologically to go into here] the flowering tops, stems, and leaves of the female Indian hemp plant, *Cannabis sativa,* dried, shredded, and cleaned of twigs and seeds and ingested for the hallucinogenic effects. Sometimes the name is applied to the plant itself, but hemp or Indian hemp is the correct name, and marijuana more precisely refers to the portions of the plant prepared and used for their hallucinogenic effects.

The name refers to the variety of *Cannabis sativa* grown in the Western Hemisphere and to the manner in which it is customarily taken, i.e., smoked in a pipe or cigarette (occasional users brew a tea from the seeds and twig waste or bake them into cakes or cookies;—the untreated seeds contain the ACTIVE PRINCIPLE of the plant). Unlike the CANNABIS consumed in other countries, the western marijuana is relatively mild from the standpoint of hallucinogenic potency. For example, it is considered about one-tenth as potent as CHARAS or HASHISH (the pure resin of the plant, which contains the active principle (TETRAHYDROCANNABINOL) in concentration), which are used in India and North Africa and the Middle East, respectively. Ordinarily marijuana is not specially cultivated, as it is in the Far East (see GHANJA), where methods of cultivation induce a more copious exudation of the resin when the female plant is mature. (Geographical origin and variety of *Cannabis sativa* are also closely related to potency. Hence, Tunisian cannabis is three times as potent as American varieties.) It is most comparable to the BHANG used in India.

The quality of marijuana sold in the illicit market also varies widely: sometimes the male plant (which has a low amount of the resin) is sold along with the female (which produces a high amount of the resin), with no effort made to separate the flowering tops of the female plant (where the resin is exuded at maturity) and with immature plants of both sexes being sold along with mature plants, which, again, contain the most resin. A hot, dry, upland climate is also considered to produce a more potent plant, and most marijuana consumed in North America is not grown in such a climate. Most American marijuana is grown in Mexico, within the United States —especially the southwest, Iowa, Kentucky, and Pennsylvania, although it grows wild as a weed in most parts of the country—even in vacant lots in large cities (the New York City Sanitation Department has destroyed over 100,000 pounds of the plant growing within the city)—Jamaica, Panama, and Canada.

It varies in potency according to informal, ill-defined "grades," ranging from MEXICAN GREEN or Kentucky blue up to ACAPULCO GOLD. Because of the difficulty in finding sufficient quantities of marijuana of uniform potency, controlled research with the plant is difficult. Apparently, strict federal government regulations and general apathy or hostility to the drug among the medical profession have further crippled research; at any rate, the number of persons registered under the Marijuana Tax Act for permission to use the drug in research, instruction, or analysis fell from a high of eighty-seven in 1948 to seven in 1964. (The most comprehensive research on the pharmacology and use of the drug in this country occurred in the early 1940s, when a commission was appointed by Mayor Fiorello H. La Guardia of New York City to study marijuana. Their report, popularly known as the LA GUARDIA REPORT was published in 1944.)

More reliable for research purposes are the eighty-odd preparations of marijuana synthesized from the oil of the plant, e.g., PYRAHEXYL, or the recently synthesized active principle of the plant, tetrahydrocannabinol. Some experiments were conducted with the semisynthetic derivatives of marijuana in the late 1930s and 1940s in the treatment of severe depression and drug-addiction WITHDRAWAL SYMPTOMS, but professional interest in these clinical applications has declined, and the drugs are not employed now. (It should be added that experiments with the synthetic derivatives of marijuana are only useful as tests of derivatives themselves and do not constitute a study of the effects of marijuana, as used in its traditional form; the synthetics have different, though related effects. In devising, say, a urine or blood test to detect whether a person involved in an accident has smoked marijuana, the drug proper must be used, for that is the form in which it is used most frequently.) What effects synthetic tetrahydrocannabinol (first synthesized at Princeton University in 1966 and in Israel in 1967) will have on marijuana research is difficult to say.

Marijuana smoking was probably introduced into the United States by Mexican laborers in the early twentieth century and by merchant seamen of Latin American descent into New Orleans in the 1920s. The practice was largely ignored by state authorities, although several states had laws against it, until the mid-thirties, when reports of a "crime wave" in New Orleans involving school children high on "muggles" received much publicity. In 1937, goaded by lurid publicity about marijuana-induced crimes and the testimony by the then Commissioner of Narcotics, Harry Anslinger, that marijuana was criminogenic, Congress passed the Marijuana Tax Act modeled after the HARRISON NARCOTICS ACT. Hearings on the bill produced only one witness opposed to the bill (aside from representatives from the birdseed industry—marijuana seeds were used to feed pigeons—who succeeded in having sterilized marijuana seeds excluded from the ambit of the statute), and Commissioner Anslinger's testimony was controlling. The assertion that marijuana use caused criminal activity was later dropped, and in 1951, during the hearings on amendments to United States narcotics laws, Commissioner Anslinger testified that the real danger of marijuana was that its users inevitably proceeded to HEROIN addiction (in 1937 he had said that marijuana users and heroin addicts were entirely different classes).

Despite efforts of the federal Bureau of Narcotics, use of marijuana steadily increased, spreading from Latin American, Negro, and musician subcultures to middle-class users, especially college youths from urban areas. Meanwhile the legitimate cultivation of marijuana in the country rapidly declined from its peak during World War II, when Japanese conquests cut off Asian sources of hemp and stimulated domestic cultivation of *Cannabis sativa* for the fibers obtained exclusively from the male plant. The return of Manila hemp to the domestic market after the war and the increasing use of substitutes such as nylon has displaced the use of *Cannabis sativa* for this purpose, and the plant is no longer legally cultivated.

In the 1950s marijuana use was given a literary boost in the writings of the "beat generation," which effected a sort of literary bridge between marijuana use among the lower classes and jazz musicians and among intellectual, student, and middle-class circles. The use in colleges, and later high schools, increased in the 1960s, becoming a fad, and current estimates are that, varying with the college, anywhere from 5 to 75 percent of the student body has experimented with the drug at least once. Concomitant with this increase in the number of middle-class users (some of whom have been sent to prison for violation of federal or state marijuana laws) a growing body of opinion has urged that the nation's marijuana laws be made less harsh. Chief target of these efforts was the state and federal narcotics laws which placed sale, transfer, or possession of marijuana in the same category as that of OPIATES and COCAINE. (Parallel to this, federal arrests on marijuana possession charges declined, although efforts against traffickers presumably continued unabated.)

Proponents of changes in the laws argued that marijuana could more properly be classified as a HALLUCINOGEN—and a mild one at that. Other arguments for outright repeal (in the extremist wing) or modifications of the law included assertions that marijuana was less dangerous to health than alcohol and cigarettes—and perhaps less habit-forming than the latter; that Commissioner Anslinger's characterization of marijuana use as inevitably leading to heroin addiction was belied by the large percentage of marijuana smokers who do not go on to heroin (estimates of marijuana users in America —i.e., persons who have tried it at least once—range upward of 500,000 persons, while the BUREAU OF NARCOTICS lists about 60,000 known HEROIN addicts in the country); that falsely exaggerating the dangers of marijuana makes youths skeptical of warnings about other drugs, which may be more dangerous; that prohibition encourages the illicit traffic and gives the drug a "forbidden fruit" allure; and that marijuana smoking is a harmless private pleasure in the pursuit of which the government has no business interfering.

Arguments against changing the laws include the Bureau of Narcotics' stubborn claim that 75 to 80 percent of the heroin addicts began their drug use with marijuana; that marijuana is still an intoxicant whose effects are more unpredictable and uncontrollable than alcohol; that our society is already too obsessed with "escape" drugs, whether prescription pills or alcohol, and does not need another intoxicant; that marijuana is not completely innocuous and that habituation (PSYCHIC DEPENDENCE) occurs and heavy usage may be physically harmful; that if marijuana were sold commercially, Madison Avenue advertising techniques like those employed with cigarettes and alcoholic beverages would increase use of marijuana until it reached the scale of a national problem; and, finally, that this country is a signatory to United Nations treaties discouraging the export and import of cannabis and, further, that the WHO is opposed to the use of cannabis, and American prestige, if nothing else, would suffer, aside from the demands of international comity.

The outcome of these arguments is uncertain, though it seems probable that while the traffic in marijuana will continue to be illegal, possession of marijuana will no longer be a felony and will be reduced to the misdemeanor class, with supplementary stricter laws for offenses—especially traffic accidents—committed under the influence of marijuana. (There were, at this writing, no tests to determine the presence of marijuana in the blood or urine, as with alcohol, but research in this area was being carried on at the Albert Einstein Medical College.) In the present and foreseeable future state of public opinion, stronger preparations of cannabis such as charas, ganja, or hashish will undoubtedly continue to be banned, as will the other hallucinogens whose effects they resemble.

Marijuana's effects are on the near end of a continuum with

LSD as its opposite end. Physiological alterations induced by the drug include (within a few minutes of consumption) dizziness, buzzing and cottony sounds, a lightness in the head; followed by dryness of the mouth and throat (probably due to the harshness of the marijuana smoke); unsteadiness in movement, loss of bodily coordination, and a feeling of heaviness in the extremities; hunger and/or a craving for sweets; nausea and vomiting occasionally; sensations of warmth around the head and the body; burning irritation of the eyes; blurring of vision; tightness in the chest; palpitations or rapid beating of the heart; ringing or pressure in the ears; and occasionally an urge to urinate or defecate.

Psychologically they include vague dread or anxiety or fear of bodily harm, especially among inexperienced users, at the outset, followed by disorientation of thinking, which includes fragmentation of thought patterns, disturbance of memory so that things thought or said immediately slip out of one's mind, and frequent and sudden interruptions in the flow of thoughts—blanks or gaps lasting a few seconds (similar to the "epileptic absence"); a wavelike aspect to the flow of perceptions; euphoria; giggling and hilarity ("fatuous euphoria"); perception of some parts of one's body as distorted; depersonalization (double consciousness), the sense that one is both within and outside oneself; spatial and temporal distortion, i.e., far objects seem near (hence the danger in driving a car), a minute seems to stretch elastically; feelings of grandiosity (megalopsia) and mystical insight into the true meaning of life, as well as a detached, amused view of cares and suffering; a heightened sensuousness and perception of colors, music, pictures; a more favorable sense of one's worth and an increased sociability; and sometimes, fear, anxiety, or panic. (Such subjective experiences are not common to all users of marijuana and vary also with the amount taken; indeed, some persons get no pleasant reaction to initial amounts of marijuana at all, or else find it unpleasantly dulling and stupefying.) Because marijuana distorts depth perception and sometimes impairs bodily coordination, driving under its influence can be dangerous.

PHYSICAL DEPENDENCE on the drug, it is agreed, does not occur, and there are no WITHDRAWAL SYMPTOMS. Most of the small samples of users interviewed through the years say that they easily stopped using the drug without any physical symptoms and usually without any strong craving to resume. However, psychic dependence can develop among certain users, usually passive, dependent, perhaps latent schizophrenic types who seek the mental escape the drug provides in preference to their normal state of consciousness. Such heavy users tend to become indolent, dreamy, and negligent of their jobs and personal appearance. (Such types are more often seen among cannabis users in Morocco and India, where, among certain social groups, use is widespread and accepted.) Dr. P. Kielholz, of the Psychiatric University, Basel, Switzerland, termed the habitual heavy marijuana user a "disinhibiting decrement seeker." The increment seeker, e.g., user of alcohol or AMPHETAMINES, seeks to do more; the decrement seeker seeks to do less.

The marijuana user, then, enjoys the release the drug gives to his thoughts and the breakdown of normal patterns of perception, as well as the intensified sensuousness, relaxation, and release from social inhibitions. At the same time, he usually sits quietly saying little and prefers his introspective flights to seeking out new experiences. Hence, a person whose personality structure was withdrawn and introverted might find in marijuana the mental state and well-being that would be vastly superior to the "real world," in which he was chronically dislocated and ill at ease.

Such heavy users of the drug generally smoke from six to ten marijuana cigarettes daily, enough to keep them permanently in a state of HIGH. Probably they could stop the habit with relatively little discomfort, although the result might be mental unease or perhaps the activation of a latent psychosis. Only a tiny percentage of marijuana users in this country use the drug so heavily, although such use has been observed in Morocco and India (see HASHISH). Marijuana causes no bodily damage (occasional cases of conjunctivitis with heavy use have been reported; chronic, long-term use may cause asthma and chronic bronchitis), and there is no known lethal dose. When smoked, marijuana has a kind of built-in safety factor, for the smoker regulates his intake, finds too much unpleasant or, after taking large amounts, sinks into a deep sleep. To a large degree, pleasurable use of marijuana is a learned technique. Not only is the novice instructed in inhaling the smoke and holding it in his lungs, he "learns" what he should feel; hence, many novices who experience no feeling at all or feel anxiety and dysphoria may pretend to be high until they have learned to recognize and enjoy the drug's pleasurable effects. The mystique associated with the drug, the experiences recounted by users face to face or in literature, and the desire to be at one with an admired ingroup are usually sufficient for the novice to desire and achieve a positive experience. Perhaps mainly for this reason (rather than any physiological changes induced by continuous use of the drug), only a slight TOLERANCE develops; which is to say that the veteran user will not get so high on so little as the novice will because he is thoroughly familiar with the drug's effects (see DRAGGED).

In this country, acute or chronic psychoses and panic reactions triggered by smoking marijuana appear to be relatively rare, probably at a much lower percentage of incidence than among users of LSD and other of the stronger hallucinogens. Perhaps an indication of their rarity is that no sensational cases have been reported in the press, unlike LSD (and unlike the situation in the 1930s, when use of marijuana in the United States first achieved notoriety through publicization of a New Orleans crime wave among school children attributed to marijuana smoking). When the number of LSD-induced chronic psychoses observed at Bellevue Hospital in New York was increasing during 1966 (see LSD), there were no cases of marijuana psychoses. Again, this factor probably reflects the relatively mild nature of marijuana's effects and also that it is not a new and strange drug (stimulating underlying uneasiness in some users) and the customary ingestion by smoking enables the user to control his intake (while he swallows LSD and experiences its effects in a sudden onrush); if he smokes a large amount, he will probably fall asleep. Then, too, the socioeconomic level of the majority of users is high, and they perhaps tend to be more educated, stable individuals. Also, the large majority are experimenters and infrequent users. This is not to say that chronic psychoses do not or have not occurred. The studies leading to the La Guardia Report in New York in the early 1940s recorded nine psychotic breaks, of varying duration, among a sample of 200 studied intensely. Most of these were found to be cases of already psychotic personalities, and one of the psychiatrists involved in the study wrote, in 1942, "Marijuana will not produce a psychosis *de novo* in a well-integrated stable person." The team who observed New York's marijuana smokers of the period found them to be a rather passive, peaceful, and friendly group, distinctly not prone to violence (though above average perpetrators of petty crimes).

In countries where the use of cannabis, and especially hashish, is more widespread, clinical studies have shown the occurrence of psychotic breaks, sometimes accompanied by acts of violence and usually associated with a toxic overdose, among a relatively small minority of users. Similarly, criminal acts attributed to cannabis use have been reported in several countries over the years, but most authorities (the federal Bureau of Narcotics excepted) agree that marijuana plays a very minor role as a cause of major crimes, both in this country and abroad. As for long-term psychoses attributed to marijuana use, again, there is little evidence of this in the United States, although investigators in Morocco have identified, among mental patients, a "KIF psychosis." A survey made in 1963 concluded, "The prevalence of *major* mental disorder among cannabis users appears to be little, if any, higher than that in the general population."

Finally, the contention that marijuana smoking in some mysterious fashion "leads" to addiction to opiate drugs is at best a partial truth. The large majority of marijuana users do not use narcotics, either because they have no desire or no opportunity. Younger marijuana smokers often have a contempt for narcotics users or fear of the well-known dangers of ADDICTION and look upon it as "square" or sick (see SICKIE). Marijuana is the most readily available drug on campus, followed by the other hallucinogens, pep pills, and miscellaneous drugs. After college, the students lose their connections and probably their interest. The general prognosis for the heavy marijuana user is that after about twelve years, if he does not get involved with stronger drugs, and otherwise survives the emotional turmoil of adolescence and young adulthood, he will no longer desire marijuana. However, the slackening of motivation attendant to regular use will cause the loss of twelve years out of his life— enough to blight his entire career. A more complex relationship between marijuana and narcotics addiction is related to the way of life that use of marijuana introduces the young user into—a life where a variety of illegal drugs are acceptable (why not the ultimate, the BOSS drug, heroin?) and available, or else, especially in slum areas, where use of drugs is related to a need to escape from one's environment and the heroin pusher stands always available on the nearest corner. Such slum users apparently are initiated to drugs with marijuana (though it often is glue sniffing) at a very young age (perhaps because it is cheaper: around 50 cents a cigarette as opposed to $5 for a bag of heroin). Then, in the classic sense, they "graduate" to heroin when they are older, when marijuana seems an inadequate escape mechanism, and heroin promises a stronger—

a boss—high, and many of their contemporaries are similarly disposed or already using. Perhaps this is analogous to the "good boy" who begins reading comic books, finds them inadequate, and "graduates" to adventure novels, and finally to works of literature—instead of a set of WORKS. For the middle-class boy it would be the world of reading, for the slum boy the world of HARD NARCOTICS. Both worlds have gradations of pleasure and demands. When that middle-class boy who reads has deep personality problems, when drugs become available and an "in" thing, when an obsession with them in all their varieties comes to dominate his life so that the various kinds become almost interchangeable, and to be really sophisticated one leaves the "kid stuff" and goes on to heroin, the ultimate, super-drug, *then* marijuana is usually a link in the chain clipped at its nether end to the plummeting weight of addiction.

About 4:30 PM, September 23, I took most of this extract [a tincture of the powdered leaves of male hemp plants grown in the vicinity of Lexington, Kentucky, and "obtained for me by R. B. Hamilton, Esq. to whom my thanks are due for the trouble taken by him to aid my investigation"] which a druggist estimated to contain from 20 to 30 grains. No immediate symptoms were produced. About 7 PM a professional call was requested and forgetting all about the hemp, I went out and saw my patient. Whilst writing the prescription, I became perfectly oblivious to surrounding objects but went on writing, without any check to or deviation from the ordinary series of mental acts, connected with the process, at least that I am aware of. When the recipe was finished, I suddenly recollected where I was and looking up, saw my patient sitting quietly before me. The conviction was irresistible that I had sat there many minutes, perhaps hours and directly the idea fastened itself that the hemp had commenced to act and had thrown me into a trance-like state of considerable duration, during which I had been stupidly sitting before my wondering patient.

I hastily rose and apologized for remaining so long, but was assured I had only been a very few minutes. About 7:30 PM I returned home. I was by this time quite excited, and the feeling of hilarity now rapidly increased. It was not a sensuous feeling, in the ordinary meaning of the term; it was not merely an intellectual excitation, it was a sort of *bien-être*—the very opposite *malaise*. It did not come from without; it was not connected with any passion or sense. It was simply a feeling of inner joyousness; the heart seemed buoyant beyond all trouble; the whole system felt as though all sense of fatigue were ever banished; the mind gladly ran riot, free constantly to leap from one idea to another, apparently unbound from its ordinary laws. I was disposed to laugh; to make comic gestures—one very frequent recurrent fancy, was to imitate with the arms the motions of the fiddler and with the lips the tune he was supposed to be playing. There was nothing like wild delirium nor any hallucinations I can remember. At no time had I any visions, or at least any that I can now call to mind; but a person, who was with me at that time, states that once I raised my hand and exclaimed, "Oh the mountains! The mountains!" Whilst I was performing the various antics, already alluded to I knew very well I was acting exceedingly foolishly but couldn't control myself. . . . [About 8] my skin to myself was warm, in fact the whole surface felt flushed; my mouth and throat were very dry; my legs put on a strange foreign feeling as though they were not a part of my body. . . . A foreboding, an undefined, horrible fear, as of impending death now commenced to creep over me . . . [There were] periods when all connection seemed to be severed between the external world and myself . . . wild reveries. . . . The mind seemed freed from all its ordinary laws of association so that it passed from idea to idea, as it were, perfectly at random. . . . I now entirely lost my power of measuring time. Seconds seemed hours; minutes seemed days; hours seemed infinite. . . . The oppressive feeling of impending death became more intense. It was horrible. Each paroxysm would seem to have been the longest I had suffered: as I came out of it, a voice seemed constantly saying, "You are getting worse—your paroxysms are growing longer and deeper—they will overmaster you —you will die."

I felt as if some evil spirit had control of the whole of me, except the will power, and was in determined conflict with that, the last citadel of my being. I have never experienced anything like the fearful sense of almost hopeless anguish and utter weariness which was upon me. Once or twice during a paroxysm, I had what might be called nightmare sensations; I felt myself mounting upwards, expanding, dilating, dissolving into the wide confines of space, overwhelmed by a horrible, rending, unutterable despair. Then with tremendous effort I seemed to shake this off and to start up with the shuddering thought next time, you will not be able to throw this off, and what then!"

—Dr. Horatio C. Wood, "On the Medical Activity of the Hemp Plant as Grown in North America," American Philosophical Society Prize Essay (1869)

After I finished the weed I went back to the bandstand. Everything seemed normal and I began to play as usual. I passed a stick of gauge around for the other boys to smoke, and we started a set.

The first thing I noticed was that I began to hear my saxophone as though it was inside my head, but I couldn't hear much of the band in back of me, although I knew they were there. All the other instruments sounded like they were way off in the distance; I got the same sensations you'd get if you stuffed your ears with cotton and talked out loud. Then I began to feel the vibrations of the reed much more pronounced against my lip, and my head buzzed like a loud speaker. I found I was slurring much better and putting just the right feeling into my phrases—I was really coming on. All the notes came easing out of my horn like they'd already been made up, greased and stuffed into the ball, so all I had to do was blow a little and send them on their way, one right after the other, never missing, never behind time, all without an ounce of effort. The phrases seemed to have more continuity to them and I was sticking to the theme without ever going tangent. I felt I could go on playing for years without running out of ideas and energy. There wasn't any struggle; it was all made-to-order and suddenly there wasn't a sour note or a discord in the world that could bother me. . . .

It's a funny thing about marijuana—when you first begin smoking it you see things in a wonderful soothing, easygoing new light. All of a sudden the world is stripped of its dirty gray shrouds and becomes one big bellyful of giggles, a special laugh, bathed in brilliant, sparkling colors that hit you like a heat-wave. Nothing leaves you cold any more; there's a humorous tickle and great meaning in the least little thing, the twitch of somebody's little finger or the click of a beer glass. All your pores open like funnels, your nerve ends stretch their mouths wide, hungry and thirsty for new sights and sounds and sensations; and every sensation, when it comes, is the most exciting one you've ever had. You can't get enough of anything— you want to gobble up the whole goddamned universe just for an appetizer. Them first kicks are a killer, Jim. . . . You know how jittery, got-to-be-moving people in the city always get up in the sub-way train two minutes before they arrive at the station? Their nerves are on edge; they're watching the clock, thinking about schedules, full of that high-powered mile-a-minute jive. Well, when you've picked upon some gauge that clock just stretches its arms, yawns, and dozes off. The whole world slows down and gets drowsy. You wait until the train stops dead and the doors slide open, then you get up and stroll out in slow motion, like a sleep walker with a long night ahead of him and no appointments to keep. You've got all the time in the world. What's the rush, buddy? Take-it-easy, that's the play, it's bound to sweeten that way. . . . . .

(Before I go any further I want to make one thing clear: I never advocated that anybody should use marijuana, and I sure don't mean to start now. Even during the years I sold the stuff . . . I sold it to grown-up friends of mine who had got to using it on their own, just like I did. . . . Sort of everybody to their own notion, that was the whole spirit. I laid off five years ago, and if anybody asks my advice today, I tell them straight to steer clear of it because it carries a rap. That's my final word to all the cats: today I know of one very bad thing the tea can do to you—it can put you in jail. 'Nuff said.) —Mezz Mezzrow and Bernard Wolfe, *Really the Blues* (1946)

mary. MORPHINE. *Obsolete.*

mary ann. [variation of MARY JANE. Since the 1920s—*EP*] MARIJUANA. *Obsolete?*

mary jane. (the English of the folk-lore interpretation of marijuana; since the 1920s—*EP;* i.e., marijuana was sometimes mispronounced with a hard *j*, from which mary *jane*.) MARIJUANA. *Obsolete?*

mary warner. [also from the phonetic resemblance to marijuana, soft *j*]. MARIJUANA. *Obsolete?*

mary weaver. [compare MARY WARNER] MARIJUANA. *Obsolete.*

mash Allah. [Arabic, gift of God] OPIUM. Called by this name by eighteenth-century Tartars who used it to sustain themselves and their horses over long journeys.

matchbox. [probably from the use of a large empty kitchen matchbox to measure lots of MARIJUANA for sale; penny matchboxes were also used]

". . . he gave us a cut-rate price, a tobacco tin full-up with muta for two dollars or a Diamond *matchbox* full for four or five"—*MM*. 1946

a measure of marijuana for sale; about 1/5 ounce, enough for rolling five to eight cigarettes. Compare CAN, LID, NICKEL BAG.

medical hype. [from *hypodermic,* and HYPE, a drug addict] *1.* one who has become accidentally addicted to MORPHINE during medical treatment. 2. one who obtains drugs, through a legal prescription, from a doctor or a hospital.

meet. [shortening (?) of *meeting*] the appointment between an addict and his PUSHER, always used as a noun, as in "I made a *meet* with him for six."

megahallucinogen. [journalese] STP.

mellow yellow. [from the song, "Mellow Yellow"] *1.* dried banana fibers prepared for smoking and packaged for sale (see BANANA SMOKING). *2.* slang for bananas used for smoking.

Mepergan. [MEPERIDINE hydrochloride and promethazine hydrochloride, Wyeth Laboratories] a synthetic narcotic analgesic containing meperidine. Manufacturer's rationale for the combination with promethazine is that the latter strengthens the analgesia of the meperidine and consequently a smaller dosage is needed. Thus, addiction is less likely. Whether this is true or not, PHYSICAL DEPENDENCE upon the meperidine will occur if Mepergan is used continuously over a prolonged period. Manufacturer's recommended dose: one capsule every four to six hours. Capsules contain 50 milligrams of meperidine hydrochloride and 12.5 milligrams of promethazine, or, as Mepergan Fortis, 50 milligrams of meperidine and 25 milligrams of promethazine. A CLASS A NARCOTIC. Compare SYNTHETIC OPIATES.

meperidine. [ethyl-1-methyl-4-phenylpiperidine-4-carboxylate] a synthetic narcotic analgesic which, despite its structural dissimilarity to MORPHINE, has many similar pharmacological effects when given in equipotent doses. Meperidine was introduced in 1939 and first employed as a substitute for ATROPINE; however, it was soon discovered that the two drugs were unlike in their actions, and meperidine's chief medical use is as an analgesic. Dosages of 80 to 100 milligrams injected intramuscularly give analgesia equivalent to that of 10 milligrams of morphine. The duration of the action is two to four hours, as compared with four to five hours for morphine. Most therapeutic doses range between 50 and 200 milligrams.

The drug has several advantages over morphine, which account for its frequent medical use, especially in obstetrics. It does not usually produce constipation or urinary retention and does not induce respiratory depression. The danger of ADDICTION is also considered less, for reasons discussed below. Meperidine occasionally produces such undesirable side effects as nausea and vomiting (probably less than morphine), giddiness, vertigo, and faintness. In toxic doses meperidine causes excitement of the central nervous system, resulting in tremors, muscle twitches, disorientation, hallucinations, palpitating heart, and convulsive movements.

Large doses of the drug can be taken safely; although the lethal dose is not specified, in one case a dose of 2,000 milligrams was survived, while in another a dose of 1,200 milligrams was fatal. The drug also has a sedative action, although this is apparently brief, the sleep marred by dreams, and large doses are necessary. Meperidine does not produce so much euphoria as morphine and in a pain-free patient may produce dysphoria.

PHYSICAL DEPENDENCE and PSYCHIC DEPENDENCE upon meperidine do occur, however, although most addicts vastly prefer morphine or HEROIN and most subjectively cannot differentiate among them. Addiction is most common among hospital personnel (some of whom erroneously believe it to be nonaddictive), and though some may have a euphoric reaction to the drug, many seem to use it for analgesic-sedative effects or simply because it has no "dope addict" stigma.

TOLERANCE to meperidine's analgesic action develops slowly, so that patients can be kept on the same dosage for months; however, tolerance to its sedative and other effects occurs more rapidly. Tolerance developing to the excitatory effects of the drug also induces the addict to increase his dosage. On the other hand, tolerance to side effects of meperidine, such as muscle twitching and tremors, may be incomplete, and the user will continue to experience them, with the result that his efficiency is impaired. Some meperidine addicts are able to take 3,000 to 4,000 milligrams of the drug a day, although the usual amount is less. One reason meperidine was not at first thought to be addictive is that WITHDRAWAL SYMPTOMS resulting from abrupt cessation of the drug after physical dependence has developed are much less severe than those of morphine. Though dissimilar in degree, however, these symptoms are similar in kind to those of morphine dependence. The symptoms reach their peak eight to twelve hours after the last dose, then subside and are completely gone in four to five days. Meperidine addiction also differs from morphine addiction in that the pupils are not pinpointed. Also, a meperidine addict will not respond to the NALLINE TEST, which indicates addiction by inducing withdrawal symptoms in an addict, unless he is using over 1,600 milligrams per day. Ketbemidone, a derivative of meperidine, is thirty times as potent; hence, the addiction liability is much greater, and ketbemidone is not used in medicine. Meperidine is usually known as DEMEROL in the United States; it is called pethidine in Great Britain. Compare ALPHAPRODINE.

Demerol [meperidine] is probably less addicting than morphine. It is also less satisfying to the addict, and less effective as a pain killer. While a demerol habit is easier to break than a morphine habit, demerol is certainly more injurious to the health and specifically the nervous system. I once used demerol for three months and developed a number of distressing symptoms: trembling hands (with morphine my hands are always steady), progressive loss of coordination, muscular contractions, paranoid obsessions, fear of insanity. Finally I contracted an opportune intolerance for demerol—no doubt a measure of self preservation—and switched to methadone. Immediately all my symptoms disappeared. I may add that demerol is quite as constipating as morphine, that it exerts an even more depressing effect on the appetite and the sexual functions, does not, however, contract the pupils. I have given myself thousands of injections over a period of years with unsterilized, in fact dirty, needles and never sustained an infection until I used demerol. Then I came down with a series of abscesses one of which had to be lanced and drained. In short demerol seems to me a more dangerous drug than morphine.

—William Burroughs, *Naked Lunch* (1965)

meprobamate. [2-methyl-2-*n*-propyl-1,3-propanediol dicarbamate] a nonbarbiturate sedative and muscle relaxant classified as a MINOR TRANQUILIZER. Meprobamate, under a variety of commercial names (the most prominent of which is MILTOWN), is used with varying effectiveness in the treatment of anxiety states, muscular tremors arising from several conditions, and minor epilepsy. As with the other TRANQUILIZERS, PSYCHIC DEPENDENCE, or habituation, to meprobamate occurs, especially among patients to whom it becomes a psychic "crutch," producing a state of lethargy and indifference to the stresses endemic to their lives without touching the underlying neurosis. When the daily dosage is abruptly stopped, these patients suffer a reemergence in magnified degree of symptoms formerly masked by the drug, such as insomnia, anxiety, and loss of appetite.

Prolonged heavy use can result in PHYSICAL DEPENDENCE with physical WITHDRAWAL SYMPTOMS when the drug is suddenly stopped, rather than gradually tapered off. Meprobamate withdrawal symptoms include tremors, insomnia, gastrointestinal upset, hallucinations, serious epilepticlike convulsions, and sometimes death. The usual daily dosage is 400 milligrams; total dosages above 2,400 milligrams are not recommended.

Since its introduction, meprobamate has been used in a number of suicide attempts, although fatalities have been rare. Amounts of 20,000 to 40,000 milligrams have been survived; however, alcohol in large amounts may POTENTIATE meprobamate's effects, and the danger of death from respiratory depression is correspondingly increased. Overdosages cause drowsiness, loss of bodily coordination, lethargy, stupor, shock, coma, and, rarely, fatal respiratory collapse and death. Meprobamate preparations are subject to the DRUG ABUSE CONTROL AMENDMENT of 1965, because of their depressant effect on the central nervous system and potential for abuse and habituation. The Food and Drug Administration lists the following brand names for meprobamate preparations:

Apascil	Mepavlon	Perquietil
Atraxin	Meproleaf	Pertranquil
Biobamat	Meprosin	Placidon
Calmiren	Meprospan	Probamyl
Casil	Meprotabs	Quanil
Cirpon	Miltown	Quilate
Cyrpon	Nervonus	Sedabamate
Ecuanil	Neuramate	Sedazil
Equanil	Pameco	Urbil
Equanil L-A	Panediol	Viobamate
Harmonin	Perequil	

mesc. MESCALINE.

mescal. *1.* PEYOTE (compare MESCALINE). *2.* an intoxicating beverage distilled from the maguey plants.

mescaline. [from *mescal,* the surface tops (mescal buttons) of the PEYOTE cactus] the hallucinogenic alkaloid (3,4,5,-trimethoxyphenylethylamine) extracted from the peyote cactus, *Lophophora williamsii,* or synthesized in the laboratory. The alkaloids in the cactus were first identified in 1886 by Louis Lewin, a German pharmacologist. Like the AMPHETAMINES, mescaline belongs to the amine group. Its chemical structure distantly resembles norepinephrine, which is, in turn, a close relation of adrenalin (epinephrine). Both are mind-altering chemicals which are manufactured in the body and which have activating effects upon certain tissues and organs.

Mescaline induces a variety of alterations of consciousness, sense distortions, and hallucinations rather like in kind to those produced by LSD. Because it generates less nausea, vomiting, and other unpleasant side effects than the peyote cactus, it is preferred, both by illegal drug users and researchers. (Other hallucinogenic drugs which produce no nausea are available.) It is usually ingested in the form of a soluble crystalline powder, which is dissolved, or in a capsule. The standard human dosage of mescaline (producing full effects in a person weighing 150 pounds) is 500 milligrams; the effects appear within two to three hours and last for four to twelve hours or more. (Doses above 1,000 milligrams may provoke toxic reactions.)

TOLERANCE develops to the drug, although more slowly than to LSD. There is also CROSS-TOLERANCE between LSD, mescaline, and psilocybin; i.e., one who has developed a tolerance to one of those drugs will be tolerant to the others. PHYSICAL DEPENDENCE with WITHDRAWAL SYMPTOMS does not occur. PSYCHIC DEPENDENCE may develop, with the user craving a repetition of the drug's mental effects in a pattern similar to that of the habitual user of LSD. Other dangers of the drug to the individual's mental health are similar to those of LSD, but it is not known what, if any, organic damage the drug may cause.

STP, a close chemical relative of mescaline said to produce more violent and prolonged psychic effects, has been reported in use, while illicit mescaline use is relatively rare. Mescaline and its derivatives are subject to the DRUG ABUSE CONTROL AMENDMENT OF 1965, and several states make possession of it a misdemeanor.

> My ideas of space were very unusual [under the influence of mescaline]. I could see myself from head to foot as well as the sofa on which I was lying. All else was nothing, absolutely empty space. I was on a solitary island floating in the ether. No part of my body was subject to the laws of gravitation. On the other side of the vacuum— the room seemed to be unlimited in space—extremely fantastic figures appeared before my eyes. I was very excited, perspired and shivered, and was kept in a state of ceaseless wonder. I saw endless passages with beautiful pointed arches, delightfully colored arabesques, grotesque decorations, divine, sublime and enchanting in their fantastic splendour. These visions changed in waves and billows, were built, destroyed and appeared again in endless variations, first on one plane and then in three dimensions, at last disappearing in infinity. The sofa-island disappeared; I did not feel my physical self; an ever-increasing feeling of dissolution set in. I was seized with passionate curiosity, great things were about to be unveiled before me. I would perceive the essence of all things, the problems of creation would be unravelled. I was dematerialized.
>
> Then the dark room once more. The visions of fantastic archi-

tecture again took hold of me, endless passages in Moorish style moving like waves alternated astonishing pictures of curious figures. A design in the form of a cross was very frequent and present in unceasing variety. Incessantly the central lines of the ornament emanated, creeping like serpents or shooting forth like tongues towards the sides, but always in straight lines. Crystals appeared again and again, changing in form and colour and in the rapidity with which they came before my eyes. Then the pictures grew more steady, and slowly two immense cosmic systems were created, divided by a kind of line into an upper and a lower half. Shining with their own light, they appeared in unlimited space. From the interior new rays appeared in more luminescent colours, and, gradually becoming perfect, they assumed the form of oblong prisms. At the same time they began to move. The systems approaching each other were attracted and repelled. Their rays were broken into infinitely fine molecules along the middle line. This line was imaginary. This image was produced by the regular collision of the rays against one another. I saw two cosmic systems both equally powerful in appearance and the difference of their structure, and in perpetual combat. Everything that happened in them was in an eternal flux. At the beginning they moved at a giddy speed which gradually changed to a quiet rhythm. I was possessed with a growing feeling of liberation. This is the solution of the mystery, it is on rhythm that the evolution of the world is finally founded. The rhythm became more and more slow and solemn and at the same time more strange and indescribable. The moment drew near when both the polar systems would be able to oscillate together, when their nuclei would combine in a tremendous construction. Then everything would become visible to my eyes. I would experience everything, understand all, no limits would bind my perceptions. A disagreeable trismus tore me away in this moment from the supreme tension. I gnashed my teeth, my hands perspired and my eyes burnt with seeing. I experienced a very queer muscular sensation. I could have detached separately every single muscle from my body. I felt great unhappiness and profound discontent. Why had physical sensations torn me from the supremacy of my soaring soul?

However, I had one unshakable conviction: Everything was ruled by rhythm, the ultimate essence of all things is buried in rhythm, rhythm was for me a medium of metaphysical expression. Again the visions appeared, again the two cosmic systems, but at the same time I heard music. The sounds came from infinity, the music of the spheres, slowly rising and falling, and everything followed its rhythm. Dr. B. played music, but it did not harmonize with my pictures and disturbed them. It came again and again, that mighty tension of the soul, that desire of solution, and then each time at the decisive moment the painful cramping of the muscles of the jaw. Crystals in a magic light with shining facets, abstract details of the theory of knowledge appeared behind a misty vaporous veil which the eyes sought to pierce in vain. Again forms appeared fighting one another; in concentric circles, from the middle Gothic, from the outside Romanesque forms. With an increasing jubilation and daring the Gothic pointed arches penetrated between the Romanesque round arches and crushed them together. And again, shortly before the decision, the gnashing of teeth. I was not to penetrate the mystery. I was standing in the midst of the evolution of the universe, I experienced cosmic life just before its solution. The impossibility of understanding the end, this refusal of knowledge was exasperating. I was tired and experienced bodily suffering.

—"an unprejudiced physician who was under the influence of the substance [mescaline]," in Louis Lewin, *Phantastica: Narcotic and Stimulating Drugs* (1964)

meserole. [corruption or misspelling of *mezzrole,* from *Mezz's roll;* Mezz Mezzrow, jazz musician and Harlem MARIJUANA peddler in the 1940s, gave his name to the type of marijuana cigarettes he sold, which were supposed to contain highly potent marijuana in generous amounts] a fat marijuana cigarette. Compare MEZZROLE, MEZZ. *Obsolete?*

messerole. MESEROLE.

methadone. [4,4-diphenyl-6-dimethylamino-3-heptanone] a SYNTHETIC OPIATE analgesic completely dissimilar in chemical structure to MORPHINE but having similar actions. The drug was synthetisized by German chemists and made available in the United States after World War II. It is used in medicine as an analgesic, to suppress the cough reflex, in treatment of heroin or morphine WITHDRAWAL SYMPTOMS, and in maintenance therapy with addicts (the "methadone treatment"; see below).

As an analgesic, methadone is slightly more potent than morphine; doses of 7.5 to 10 milligrams produce relief of pain equal to that of 10 milligrams of morphine, lasting for three to five hours. Methadone produces somewhat less respiratory depression than morphine and, unlike morphine, is nearly as effective in oral doses as in injections. It does not produce so much sedation or euphoria as morphine; however, in pain-free individuals, the drug does have a pronounced euphoric effect in injections of 10 to 20 milligrams. This effect lasts longer than morphine-induced euphoria and is potentially just as significant in producing PSYCHIC DEPENDENCE. Consequently, addicts sometimes use methadone, producing a nodding, dozing state akin to a HEROIN NOD. Some users report unpleasant side effects, including pains in the bones and muscles, nausea, constipation, mental sluggishness, hallucinations, and impotence.

PHYSICAL DEPENDENCE upon methadone occurs after continuous administration, with WITHDRAWAL SYMPTOMS less severe than those of morphine dependence but more prolonged. When methadone is substituted for heroin and the addict gradually withdrawn from the drug, he will undergo withdrawal symptoms of methadone, rather than those of heroin. For this reason methadone is used in hospitals to withdraw addicts. Addicts also use it, usually in the form of pills (DOLOPHINE, or "dollies") as self-medication for withdrawal symptoms, e.g., when they are unable to obtain heroin, or their heroin habit has grown too expensive to support. However, withdrawal symptoms can be severe, and include diarrhea and pains in the stomach, hot and cold flashes, insomnia, and sweating. One addict reported: "The pain was excruciating. The marrow of my bones screamed." After the physical symptoms have passed (after about two weeks), the addict may continue to experience lethargy, insomnia, and loss of appetite for months. Narcotic antagonists such as NALLINE will induce more severe withdrawal symptoms in the methadone addict than simple gradual withdrawal of the drug does.

TOLERANCE to methadone's effects develops through continued usage. Because methadone is effective orally, it is given in this form in maintenance therapy—the so-called "methadone treatment." The purpose is to wean the patient from heroin by substituting another addiction under medical supervision, thus enabling him to break out of the conditioned life pattern of the heroin addict. Addicts in the program report once daily for their dosage, usually 100 to 180 milligrams in orange juice. Taking it orally, the addict is no longer dependent upon injections; the use of the needle itself —and the entire ritual known as FIXING—may be one factor of addiction. The methadone assuages the addict's subjective craving for heroin and serves as a reasonably satisfactory substitute for it. (Addicts report that the subjective effects of 300 to 900 milligrams of methadone equal those of 5 to 9 grains, or 300 to 540 milligrams, of morphine.) In such massive doses, a large tolerance to all opiate drugs is built up in the addict; further, these large doses are effective for as long as twenty-four hours. Thus a shot of HEROIN taken while undergoing methadone therapy, especially in the highly diluted amounts available on the STREET, will probably give no pleasurable effects, and the addict therefore has no motive to continue using heroin. After he has functioned free of heroin for a sufficiently long time, secured steady employment, and otherwise readjusted his life away from the addict's characteristic life pattern, he theoretically can be withdrawn from the methadone and go forth to live a drug-free life. Whether this last step can be accomplished is still unproved and awaits the results of long-term experiments now in progress.

Another type of maintenance therapy based on the narcotic-blocking drug CYCLAZOCINE is also being tested. Critics of the methadone program say that it is doubtful that the addicts will ever be withdrawn from methadone and that the addict will always remain an addict, albeit, a methadone addict. Although defenders of the program say that the methadone addict is able to function normally in the community (and engages in less crime than he did before methadone), other critics say that methadone addicts report being in a drugged state and complain about various side difficulties, such as sexual impotence. Lastly, advocates of the various psychological group-therapy programs (such as SYNANON) say that methadone therapy does not attack the roots of the addict's problems, which lie in basic defects of character; hence, he has no chance to change himself and is condemned to a perpetual life on drugs, which, these critics hold, is both psychically and morally an abnormal life, inferior to a life without drugs. In sum, the methadone treatment is primarily a chemical therapy, aimed at breaking the vicious circle of conditioned responses upon which the addict's habit feeds and enabling him to live a life free of heroin by substituting a legal and controlled addiction on a semiclinical or outpatient basis for an illegal and patently self-destructive one. If the only aim of the treatment is to make the addict drug-free, then it may well be a failure. But if the aim is to rehabilitate the addict and enable him to hold a job and function in society, then it has been very successful. Methadone is a CLASS A NARCOTIC.

We got shots four times a day and an additional barbiturate sedative at night. They gave us a synthetic horror called Dolophine [metha-

done], which was invented in Germany under the Nazis and named after the great Adolph! The ward physician, another polite and good-natured young man, who visited us every morning, told me that it was easier to get off Dolophine than regular opiates. I'm sure he was convinced of it. Everybody not addicted to drugs was convinced of it.

Day by day my dosages were decreased. I felt real discomfort and anxiety only about half an hour before each shot was administered. Sometimes the hack was late in dealing out the medications, and this caused real suffering—pain in the knee joints, eyes out of focus, shortness of breath, palpitation, sweat gushing out of every pore, and too many other calamities to list properly. . . .

After seven days they stopped giving me even Dolophine and I instantly caught a cold. This is a standard development, as is vomiting, diarrhea and sleeplessness.

I stayed thirty days in Lexington and I never slept more than half an hour a night. The nights of the recently weaned drug addict are a special horror, because even after a few minutes' sleep his pajamas and his sheets are soaked with cold sweat. . . .

After vomiting for about ten days I was so dehydrated that I passed out in our room one day, so I was shipped back to the infirmary and . . . I was put to bed and given intravenous glucose, and I was sure that nobody in the whole world had ever been so deathly sick.   —Alexander King, *Mine Enemy Grows Older* (1958)

Methadone is completely satisfying to the addict, an excellent pain killer, at least as addicting as morphine.
                              —William Burroughs, *Naked Lunch* (1959)

methamphetamine. METHEDRINE.

Methedrine. [methamphetamine hydrochloride (*d*-desoxyephedrine hydrochloride), Burroughs Wellcome & Co.] a central nervous system stimulant, methamphetamine, of which Methedrine is a brand name, was first used widely during World War II by the German army to counter fatigue among the troops engaged in prolonged missions with little sleep possible.

Chemically, methamphetamine is closely related to AMPHETAMINE and norephedrine. It is considered a more potent central nervous system stimulant than amphetamine sulfate (BENZEDRINE) and *d*-amphetamine sulfate (DEXEDRINE). The manufacturer recommends Methedrine as an appetite depressant for loss of weight, in cases of depression, as an analeptic (awakener) in BARBITURATE overdose, and to raise abnormally low blood pressure, e.g., in anesthetized patients. Recommended doses range from 2.5 milligrams three times a day, working up, over a period of weeks, to 30 milligrams a day (for cases of chronic depression). The drug produces euphoria, excitability, feelings of power, aggressiveness, and insomnia. Excessive doses can cause talkativeness, pupil dilation, nervousness, hyper-excitability, insomnia, dryness of the mouth, rapid heartbeat, violent actions, or paranoid delusions. The drug is considered dangerous for patients with high blood pressure, irregular heartbeat, and various cardiac disorders.

Methedrine is a favored drug among habitual amphetamine users, who frequently take it by intravenous injection, which produces an almost instantaneous onset of the drug's euphoric properties (the FLASH or RUSH), which many Methedrine users compare to a sexual orgasm (the drug also acts to delay orgasm in sexual intercourse). Such use can produce a particularly persistent form of PSYCHIC DEPENDENCE; the user keeps injecting, until after several days without sleep (the RUN), he sinks into an exhausted coma (FALLING OUT or CRASH) lasting three to six days. After recovery, he tends to return to using the drug for its euphoric properties; apparently, he does not require sedation from barbiturates to damp down the excitative effects of the Methedrine. Nor does he seek the lulling, narcotizing follow-up effects of HEROIN, like the heroin addict who injects amphetamines mixed with heroin for a heightened initial thrill followed by a NOD (though he may take them at the end of the run in order to sleep; compare BOMBITA, SPEEDBALL).

Amounts taken range from 1,200 to 3,600 milligrams a day over three to six days and may engender acute or chronic psychoses, loss of memory and powers of concentration, or possibly brain damage in the habitual user. Other adverse effects are loss of weight and malnutrition (due to the drug's appetite-depressant effects), and various INFECTIONS from unsterile needles. The user may also engage in violent or self-destructive acts. TOLERANCE to the drug also develops, so that the dose must be markedly increased to achieve enphoria.

Methedrine is sold as 5-milligram scored tablets and ampuls for injection containing 20 milligrams each. Subject to the DRUG ABUSE CONTROL AMENDMENT OF 1965. Slang names: meth, speed.

Speed kills   —hippie slogan (1967)

meth freak. [from FREAK, *freakish*, bizarre, unpredictable behavior which the drug induces] a frequent, habitual user of METHEDRINE.

methyldihydromorphinone. also known as METOPON. A semisynthetic analgesic derived from MORPHINE, methyldihydromorphinone is considerably more potent than morphine: 3.5 milligrams produces analgesia equivalent to that produced by 10 milligrams of morphine, lasting four to five hours. Hence, it is of the same potency of HEROIN, but its use among addicts is rare (heroin dominates the illicit market, and the illicit market supplies most addicts). Prolonged use will result in TOLERANCE, PSYCHIC DEPENDENCE, and PHYSICAL DEPENDENCE, with WITHDRAWAL SYMPTOMS at least as severe as those produced by morphine dependence. A CLASS A NARCOTIC.

methyprylon. a nonbarbiturate hypnotic and sedative derived from piperidinedione and chemically similar to GLUTETHIMIDE (DORIDEN), methyprylon is used as a daytime sedative or a hypnotic to induce sleep in insomnia, especially when the patient is allergic to BARBITURATES. Since it is less potent than the barbiturates, larger amounts must be taken, but large doses can cause respiratory depression and death. The drug has been used in suicide attempts. Similarly, prolonged usage can result in TOLERANCE and PHYSICAL DEPENDENCE with severe WITHDRAWAL SYMPTOMS (major epileptic, or grand mal, convulsions and delirium) upon abrupt cessation of the drug. Chronic intoxication, similar to alcoholic intoxication, can also result from heavy use. Subject to the DRUG ABUSE CONTROL AMENDMENT OF 1965. Compare NOLUDAR 300.

metopon. METHYLDIHYDROMORPHINONE.

Mexican brown. [from the color; presumably indicating a more mature or longer cured plant than MEXICAN GREEN] a grade of MARIJUANA.

Mexican green. [from the color; presumably indicating low resin content] perhaps the commonest grade of MARIJUANA, emanating from Mexico.

Mexican locoweed. [term prevalent in the southwestern United States; the locoweeds proper, e.g., *Astragalus mollissimus,* cause intoxication in animals] MARIJUANA.

Mexican mushroom. hallucinogenic mushroom, *Psilocybe mexicana.* See MUSHROOM, SACRED.

mezz, the. [from Mezz Mezzrow, jazz musician and Harlem MARI-

JUANA peddler; since the 1940s] he claimed that the quality of his marijuana was so high that his name became synonymous with any good marijuana and, by extension, anything fine or good. *Obsolete.*

mezzrole. [from Mezz Mezzrow (see MEZZ) and Mezz's roll, i.e., the way Mezzrow rolled his MARIJUANA, hand-rolled, in fat cigarettes, with the ends tucked in.—*Really the Blues* (1946).] *Obsolete.* Also: MESEROLE, MESSEROLE.

mickey. MICKEY FINN.

mickey finn. [from a notorious saloonkeeper in Chicago circa 1896, a synonym for a double drink; a drink containing KNOCKOUT DROPS or drugged liquor—*EP*] liquid chloral, often in capsule form, mixed with alcohol and given to an unwitting drinker to cause unconsciousness. Compare CHLORAL HYDRATE.

mike. a microgram (one-millionth gram), usually as a measure of LSD for purposes of sale or consumption.

> [LSD] sells for between a half-cent to as much as two cents a microgram and you usually take anywhere from 250 to a 1,000 *mikes* a trip.
> —"Ric," "Confessions of a Campus Pot Dealer," *Esquire* (September, 1967)

milk sugar. also mannite. Crystals of lactose with a sweetish taste, closely resembling HEROIN in appearance and hence used for CUTTING it prior to sale to addicts. Quinine is also often added to imitate heroin's bitter taste, so that the addict, who knows the drug is diluted, is still unable to estimate how much heroin he is actually getting.

milligram. one-thousandth gram; an aspirin tablet is 5 grains, or 300 milligrams.

Miltown. [MEPROBAMATE, Wallace Laboratories] a MINOR TRANQUILIZER used in alleviating nonpsychotic anxiety and tension states, as a muscle relaxant, and as an anticonvulsant. Manufacturer's recommended dose is one or two 400-milligram tablets three times daily; total dosages above 2,400 milligrams a day are not recommended, though they have been administered by researchers in cases of severe convulsions, spasm, or anxiety.

Miltown's main action is to depress the central nervous system, hence its calming effects. Like other minor tranquilizers, Miltown does not produce drowsiness or significant respiratory depression in small doses. Massive overdosages, while sometimes resulting in coma, shock, respiratory depression, and death, are less likely to be fatal than those of the BARBITURATES.

PSYCHIC DEPENDENCE upon Miltown can develop among patients who seek its sedative effects, both as an adjunct to sleep and to blur the stresses and strains of normal living. Excessive (1,600–2,400 mg. daily), prolonged use results in PHYSICAL DEPENDENCE, accompanied by WITHDRAWAL SYMPTOMS when the drug is abruptly discontinued, including vomiting, tremors, muscle twitching, and epilepticlike seizures. They can be as serious as those produced by barbiturate dependence.

Miltown is sold as a white scored 400-milligram tablet inscribed with a "W," as a white 200-milligram sugar-coated tablet, and as 400-milligram white coated tablets called Meprotabs. Subject to the DRUG ABUSE CONTROL AMENDMENT OF 1965. Compare EQUANIL.

mind detergent, the. LSD.

mind trippers. youths seventeen to twenty-two who use drugs for self-therapy, introspection, self-awareness, in the vaguely defined hope of becoming more creative, aware, loving, etc., human beings.

minor tranquilizer. a pharmacological and chemical classification (compare MAJOR TRANQUILIZER). The minor tranquilizers are generally not effective in serious psychoses and are used mainly in treating mild to moderate anxiety and tension and undue stress in response to outside pressures. They are commonly divided into three types, determined by their effects (other than the common one of depressing the central nervous system without causing sleep):

1. Those which act mainly on the central nervous system but also relax the skeletal muscles and have anticonvulsant actions (chlordiazepoxide, chlormezanone, diazepam, emylcamate, hydroxyphenamate, mephenoxalone, meprobamate, oxanamide)
2. Those which have antihistiminic and antinausea action (hydroxyzine, buclizine) and are useful in allergy and motion sickness
3. Those which do not belong in type 1 or type 2, have a calming effect, but differ widely in both chemistry and pharmacological action.

The first category, which includes such well-known commercial preparations as LIBRIUM, VALIUM, EQUANIL, and MILTOWN, is the most widely used, with varying degrees of success, both in treating anxiety and as skeletal-muscle relaxants in a variety of therapeutic situations. Often a BARBITURATE will give better results in small "daytime sedative" doses than the minor tranquilizers. Further, experiments have shown that often a placebo is just as effective as the tranquilizer, creating the suspicion that the drug's effectiveness is often due to the patient's faith in what his doctor says it will do.

Nevertheless, the minor tranquilizers are somewhat safer than the barbiturates in that deep coma and fatal respiratory collapse, an ever present hazard with hypnotics and sedatives, come only after much larger doses. Undesirable side effects include drowsiness, loss of coordination, dizziness, stomach upset, rash, chills, fever, etc. Taken in excessive amounts over long periods of time, the tranquilizers of types 1 and 2 induce PHYSICAL DEPENDENCE with WITHDRAWAL SYMPTOMS equal in severity to those associated with barbiturate dependence, including convulsions and delirium.

PSYCHIC DEPENDENCE upon their mildly euphoric and sedative effects (roughly similar to psychic dependence upon alcohol) also occurs, leading to habitual excessive use. Although they are safer than the barbiturates, large doses can lead to death, and suicide attempts with them have been successful. The major tranquilizers, and to a lesser degree the minor tranquilizers, POTENTIATE the effects of other central nervous system depressants such as alcohol and barbiturates and when used in conjunction with them, magnify the dangers of fatal respiratory collapse; i.e., the lethal dose of alcohol and barbiturates is lowered. Compare RESERPINE.

miss emma. [from morphine. M, em, emma, Miss Emma; since around 1925—*EP*] MORPHINE.

M.J. [from MARY JANE] MARIJUANA. *Obsolete?*

MMDA. [trimethoxyamphetamine (3-methoxy-4,5-methylenedioxy-amphetamine)] an AMPHETAMINE synthesized from ELEMICIN MYRISTICIN, which is believed to be the hallucinogenic alkaloid of NUTMEG and VIROLA. Dosages in the ratio of 2 milligrams to 1 kilogram of body weight produce hallucinations, according to a single experimenter. The drug's potency is calculated to be greater than that of TMA and nearly three times that of MESCALINE.

mojo. [from a "disguise" or codeword for morphine, a play with *morph* which is more obscure; since around 1930—*EP;* another theory has it that *mojo* is a voodoo word for magic; drugs are magic] HEROIN, COCAINE, or MORPHINE.

monkey. [from MONKEY ON (HIS, MY) BACK, addicted to a drug] an addict's drug dependence, regarded as so independent of his will as to be a separate person living inside him.

> The addict needs more and more junk to maintain a human form . . buy off the *Monkey.*
> —William Burroughs, *Evergreen Review* (1960)

monkey on (his, my) back. [from *monkey,* a Chinaman, since around 1912—*EP;* and perhaps a variation of the phrase have a *Chinaman on one's back,* meaning to have a drug habit, have WITHDRAWAL SYMPTOMS. Chinese immigrants to the United States in the nineteenth century frequently used opium and became associated with the opium habit] *1.* to be physically dependent upon OPIUM, MORPHINE, or HEROIN. *2.* to undergo OPIATE WITHDRAWAL SYMPTOMS.

monoamine oxidase (MAO) inhibitors. central nervous system stimulants, related chemically to the AMPHETAMINES and used as psychic mood elevators. The stimulation these drugs produce is indirect and thought to arise from their inhibitory action on the flow of monoamine enzymes (compare SEROTONIN). There are four main types of MAO inhibitors in current medical use: isocarboxazid (Marplan), nialamide (Niamid), phenelzine dihydrogen sulfate (Nardil), tranylcypromine (Parnate), and pargyline hydrocholoride (Eutonyl).

The drugs are employed in psychotic depressive states where other drugs and electric-shock treatments have not proved effective. The MAO inhibitors are potent, unpredictable drugs, capable of producing a variety of side effects. They are particularly dangerous, and deaths have resulted from administration in conjunction with the following drugs, whose effects they POTENTIATE: ALCOHOL, AMPHETAMINES, and other stimulant drugs, NARCOTIC and other depressant drugs, antihistamines, sedatives, anesthetic drugs, and insulin. Also, deaths have been caused by eating cheese while taking MAO inhibitors. They may also have toxic effects on the liver, brain, and cardiovascular system. Other complications include cerebral hemorrhage, convulsions, tremors, insomnia, excessive perspiration, hallucinations (rare), confusion (rare), and high blood pressure, sometimes followed by death. Because of their myriad dangers, the MAO inhibitors are administered only under conditions of constant medical supervision.

moocah. [variation of (?) MUTA or (?) MU] MARIJUANA. *Obsolete?*

moon. *1.* PEYOTE; the circle of lumps, or buttons, making up the top of the peyote cactus. *2.* a cake of HASHISH, the form in which hashish is sold in bulk on the illicit market.

moota. [variant spelling (?) of MUTA] MARIJUANA. *Obsolete?*

mooters. [from MUTA] MARIJUANA cigarettes. *Obsolete?*

mootie. [from MUTA] MARIJUANA; a marijuana cigarette. *Obsolete?*

morning glory seeds. the seeds of certain members of the large bindweed family (Convolvulaceae) have been used for centuries in America for their hallucinogenic effects. The Aztecs called the active varieties OLOLIUQUI or TLITLILTZEN. The former is believed to be the morning glory *Rivea corymbosa,* and the latter a morning glory of the genus *Ipomoea.* Both species are still used by Mexican Indians.

The seeds, which are either brown or black, are ground until reduced to a flour, which is soaked in cold water for a set period of time. Then the water containing the drug is strained through a cloth and drunk. Like their forebears, the Indians use the drug for divination, religious ceremonies, and healing (the content of the visions is analyzed and the cure determined). In the United States the seeds are available commercially, and trade names include Heavenly Blues, Flying Saucers, and Pearly Gates.

Analysis (by Albert Hofmann, discoverer of LSD-25) has shown the seeds to contain amides of lysergic acid, *d*-isolysergic acid amide, chanoclavine, and clymoclavine, all of which are also found in the fungus ergot, *Claviceps purpurea,* from which Hofmann first synthesized LSD. Hence, the ACTIVE PRINCIPLE in the seeds is quite similar to LSD and about 1/10 as potent; 300 Heavenly Blue seeds give the effects of about 200 to 300 micrograms of LSD-25.

The seeds are ingested after grinding them up more or less as the Indians did; by eating the seeds whole (seedsmen claim to have added a nauseating ingredient to the seeds, which makes this method extremely unpleasant; even without the ingredient, some nausea is produced) ; or by extracting the active principle chemically, using such highly toxic chemicals as wood alcohol. The seeds have also been used as the source of lysergic acid in the illicit manufacture of LSD-25 in home laboratories, along with other chemicals.

Cases of acute, chronic psychotic reactions, similar to those caused by LSD, following ingestion of morning glory seeds have been reported, although their use among illicit drug users is probably relatively rare, since LSD or MARIJUANA is preferred.

A suicide related to the morning glory seed psychosis was studied by Dr. Sidney Cohen. A student chewed 300 Heavenly Blue seeds and experienced the characteristic depersonalization, pseudo hallucinations, feelings of wonderment and self-transcendence, and grandiose fantasies for about twenty-four hours; then, for the next three weeks, he found himself sliding into a disassociation state at frequent intervals. These states were very unpleasant, and he feared he was going crazy. Despite sedation the condition persisted. One morning, feeling himself going off balance again, he became overwrought, dressed, got into his car, and drove down a hill at a speed estimated at 90 to 100 miles an hour, deliberately crashing to his death into a house at the bottom.

> When it is drunk, it provokes lasciviousness. . . . The priests of the idols used to eat of this plant when they wanted to deal with the devil and to have answers to their doubts. They became mad and saw a thousand phantoms that appeared to their eyes. . . . It is not a great mistake to leave unsaid where it grows because it is not important. . . . that the Spaniards know the plant.
> —Hernandez on the use of morning glory seeds among the Indians, *Historia plantar. Novae Hispaniae* (1721)

This patient first learned of the hallucinogenic effects of *morning glory seed* ingestion through a newspaper article cautioning against the use of the seeds. He first tried the Heavenly Blue variety (*Rivea corymbosa*), but later preferred the Pearly Gates variety (*Ipomea* [sic] *violacea*) because they provided more dramatic effects. After finding that four ingestions (using approximately 200 to 300 seeds) did not produce a "high" quickly enough, he prepared an injectable dose. By boiling 200 seeds in water, he developed a brown, oily fluid containing many small particles. Using a 10 cc. syringe, he drew the fluid up through a wad of cotton which he used as a filter. Frightened by the appearance of the liquid, he used only 0.5 cc. instead of the 10 cc. he had originally intended.

The results were dramatic. Within seconds he was stiffened and "jolted back" in his chair. He experienced a feeling of "nothingness" and "negate thought." He repeatedly asked himself, "Am I high?," but could not decide. He became fascinated with his bodily movements and desired to move very slowly, imagining himself doing a primitive African tribal dance. There seemed to be "more substance" to his head than to the rest of his body, and his head seemed detached from his shoulders. He moved the rest of his body carefully under his head to prevent it from falling on the floor.

He said he felt "very human," i.e., no longer estranged from others; "very compassionate," i.e., optimistic and loving everyone and everything. About ten minutes after injection of the solution, he developed a "catatonic feeling" and desired to remain completely still. He felt pain if he moved rapidly. While in this state he noticed that shadows on a marble wall about 60 feet away seemed to be "undulating" or "creeping across the wall."

He thought that he could make a darkened doorway light up as if a searchlight had been turned on it, and he began to experiment with this, believing himself to be very powerful. Within a few moments, the light fixtures in the ceiling and one end of a balcony began to droop. He could make them bend but only to a certain point, after which they reassumed their "reality positions."

During this time, he was not frightened, because he knew that the changes in perception and sensation were not real and would not occur unless he made himself "receptive" to them. One half hour after the injection, he suddenly developed nausea, vomiting, diarrhea, and chills. He craved sugar, and obtained a soft drink which nauseated him. He was unable to see clearly. Subsequently, he developed frank shock with a drop in blood pressure to 60/40 mm. Hg.

He was taken to an accident ward. After supportive treatment for shock, his condition improved promptly, except for blurring of vision, which persisted for several hours.

One month later the patient reported that the perceptual distortions recurred when he was fatigued or distracted. He believed he had permanently damaged his brain. Four months following the original injection, the patient reported that he was powerfully attracted to the drug, that the sensations could be made to return at will, that at times the sensations returned against his will, and that despite this, he planned to continue the use of psychotomimetic drugs.

—P. J. Fink, M. J. Goldman, and I. Lyons, *Archives of General Psychiatry* (1966)

morning shot. WAKE-UP.

morph. MORPHINE.

morphine. [from Morpheus, god of dreams] a natural alkaloid in OPIUM, occurring in proportions of about 10 percent of the total weight, with analgesic properties. Morphine was first isolated from opium in 1803 by Sertürner, who named it, and first received widespread use in this country during the Civil War (see ARMY DISEASE). It was used in Hong Kong as a "cure" for opium addiction, until it was discovered that morphine was even more addictive. It is still considered one of the most useful drugs in the medical armamentorium for the relief of nearly all kinds of pain (in sufficient doses), especially continuing, dull pain. Morphine acts directly on the central nervous system and also on the bowel muscles (hence its constipating effect).

The usual dosage in mild to moderate pain is 5 to 10 milligrams, producing an analgesia that lasts four to five hours, and no sedation. In severe pain doses of 15 to 20 milligrams, sometimes higher, are given. Injected intravenously, morphine reaches its peak within twenty minutes, but the analgesia is shorter in duration. The preferred method of administration is by subcutaneous injection, with analgesia occuring after sixty to ninety minutes and lasting the maximum amount of time. Taken orally, morphine is not so potent, though the analgesia lasts longer; 60 milligrams orally produces a peak analgesia somewhat inferior to 8 milligrams injected.

Physiological effects produced by the drug include constipation, nausea, sometimes vomiting, constriction of the pupils, heaviness of the limbs, itchiness of the face and nose, yawning, warmth in the stomach, respiratory depression, sweating, flushing of the skin, and fall in body temperature (occurrence of these effects varies with the individual). The drug's psychological effects include analgesia, drowsiness, impairment of mental and physical performance, especially complex learned behavior, reduced sex and hunger drives, changes in mood, mental clouding, sometimes excitation, inability to concentrate, sometimes apathy, euphoria. This last effect is attributed to the drug's action in dramatically relieving pain, discomfort, worry, and anxiety. (Given to a person free of pain, the drug's effect may be unpleasant.) Although morphine's precise pharmacological action within the body to relieve pain is not known, the drug does seem to depress a pain center in the cortex and does so without affecting the other senses of touch, taste, hearing, etc. Psychologically, it seems to operate to raise the perceived threshold of pain (especially if given before the pain, or preoperatively) ; i.e., the patient cannot feel a degree of pain he would have perceived without morphine. Second, the drug relieves the anxiety and fear associated with pain, so that while the pain is known to be there, it can be regarded with equanimity and detachment. Although in small doses morphine does not induce sleep, in larger doses it will; this, in turn, can operate as an effective antidote to pain. Hence, morphine differs from general anesthesias in that it (1) produces analgesia without inducing sleep and (2) depresses the respiratory center, while anesthetics stimulate it. It differs from hypnotics and sedatives in that (1) it has no anticonvulsant action and (2) it does have an analgesic action, which sedatives do not have.

As the dosage increases to the 15- to 20-milligram range, drowsiness increases, followed in time by a deep sleep; the euphoria is also intensified, as is the vomiting reaction. Respiratory depression becomes more marked, and indeed death from respiratory failure is the chief hazard of morphine, aside from addiction. An overdose of morphine, then, results in a magnification of the symptoms seen in lesser doses: profound coma, very slight respiration, markedly constricted pupils, marked fall in body temperature, cold and clammy skin, shock, and flaccid skeletal muscles. The lethal dose of the drug varies from individual to individual; in the pain-free, nonaddicted adult, however, an oral dose of less than 120 milligrams or injected dose of less than 30 milligrams will not cause any serious toxic reactions. Where TOLERANCE has developed, this allowable dosage will of course go much higher.

Tolerance develops specifically to the depressant effects of the drug on the nervous system but not to some of its other effects, such as constipation, constriction of the pupils, and excitation. Tolerance to the depressant effects usually develops after two to three weeks of daily dosages; it develops more rapidly if a clockwork regularity of dosage is followed or if relatively large doses are administered. (As an interesting sidelight to the development of tolerance, it has been shown that the morphine antagonist NALLINE will precipitate WITH-DRAWAL SYMPTOMS in a person who has been taking 15 milligrams of morphine three or four times a day after only three days, which indicates that the mechanisms of PHYSICAL DEPENDENCE are already at work, even though the addict will not be aware of them for weeks or months.)

Once tolerance has set in, the user can take rapidly increasing doses without adverse effects, and cases of addicts taking 4,000 to

5,000 milligrams a day, or nearly 200 times the dose that is dangerous to the normal, pain-free adult, have been reported. This tolerance is not unlimited, however, and as a general rule, the longer the time and the greater the amount of the drug used, the more severe the physical dependence and resultant withdrawal symptoms when the drug is discontinued.

Since the advent of HEROIN, a semisynthetic derivative of morphine, the use of morphine among the addict underworld has declined. The subjective effects of the two drugs in equipotent doses are almost identical. The differences seem to be in potency, mode of ingestion, and what the addict is used to. Heroin is more potent—three or four times as potent as morphine, analgesically; i.e., less is needed to produce analgesia. It also produces more euphoria and excitation than any other OPIATE drug. Also, heroin is more potent when it is injected intravenously (the favored mode of the addict because it produces the quickest effect and thus the way he habitually experiences the drug) than when it is injected subcutaneously (although, paradoxically, it produces less euphoria). Just the opposite is true with morphine, which may explain why addicts offered a choice between the two with which they have been injected intravenously, without knowing which drug they are getting, tend to choose heroin even when both drugs are given in equipotent doses.

The total amount of illegal morphine seized by the Bureau of Narcotics in 1964 was 140 grams, compared with 45 kilograms of heroin. When used by addicts, morphine is most commonly in the form of a salt, e.g., morphine sulfate (the origin of M.S., a slang term for morphine), which is soluble in water and hence injectable. Pure morphine is only slightly soluble in water. The drug is also swallowed in capsules, taken through the rectum in suppositories, drunk in solution, or heated and inhaled.

Experiments have shown that *d*-AMPHETAMINE injected with morphine counteracts the depression, weakness, and dizziness usually caused by morphine while enhancing its analgesic action; addicts have discovered this medical fact for themselves and hence the frequent combination of the two drugs (also amphetamines with heroin or COCAINE with morphine or heroin). Morphine is a CLASS A NARCOTIC.

morpholinylethylmorphine. PHOLOCODINE.

mota. [Mexican, MUTA] MARIJUANA.

mother. a drug peddler, or PUSHER.

M.S. MORPHINE sulfate. *Obsolete?*

mu. [from (?) MUTA] MARIJUANA.

muchamor. [Siberian Indian] FLY AGARIC.

muggles. [from (?) smuggle—*EP;* since around 1930] MARIJUANA cigarettes.

multihabituation. also called PANADDICTION. Using two or more drugs interchangeably in an attempt to counteract the adverse effects of one with the other or to POTENTIATE the effects of one with the other, so that an interdependent habit requiring both is formed. The heavy drinker who habitually uses BARBITURATES to relieve his hangover, so that he becomes dependent upon both, has a multi-habituation. More common is the combined use of AMPHETAMINES and barbiturates or the two with alcohol. The barbiturate-dependent person may begin increasing his dose as tolerance builds up, in order to sleep; this increased dose leads to a morning-after barbiturate hangover, and so he begins taking amphetamines to counteract the morning drowsiness and enable him to function in society. The increased use of amphetamines may in turn so overstimulate him that he requires more barbiturates to sleep, increasing the morning-after hangover, and so on in a vicious circle. Methamphetamine (METHEDRINE) addiction has become common. The addict tries to correct every defect in his life with this and sedative drugs—a "lift" in the morning, a sedative during the day, another lift, another seda-tive, etc. The HEROIN user may become multihabituated—or ad-dicted—to barbiturates because the weak doses of heroin on the market do not give him the NOD he wants, and he supplements it with barbiturates, with the result that he develops a PHYSICAL DEPENDENCE on barbiturates that may have graver WITHDRAWAL SYMPTOMS than those caused by his heroin dependence.

muscarine. an alkaloid found in the hallucinogenic mushroom FLY AGARIC, *Amanita muscaria*. Muscarine may be the hallucinogenic ACTIVE PRINCIPLE in the mushroom; other authorities claim that it is BUFOTENINE, which in turn is closely related to the hallucinogen dimethyltryptamine (DMT) and PSILOCYBIN.

Muscarine is a deadly poison which acts to slow the heartbeat and dilate the blood vessels. In lethal amounts (usually as a result of eating the mushroom), death ensues within a few hours; toxic symptoms (weeping, salivation, sweating, constriction of the pupils, severe abdominal pain, vertigo, watery and painful bowel movements, coma, occasionally convulsions, etc.) occur within two minutes to two hours. ATROPINE is an effective antidote to muscarine poisoning if administered in time and is effective in the majority of cases. More deadly is the related mushroom *Amanita phalloides,* which contains a different, slower-acting, yet more uniformly fatal alkaloid.

mushrooms, sacred. various species of fungi growing in the Western Hemisphere with hallucinogenic actions. The mushrooms were used by the Aztecs for the visions and hallucinations and as a sacrament in religious ceremonies (they called it *teonanactl,* God's flesh) and are used still today by Mexican Indians for divination and religious worship. Several species of mushrooms with hallucinogenic properties were identified by R. Gordon Wasson and Roger Heim, in 1953, and there are probably others still unclassified.

The most widely used and studied of all these is *Psilocybe mexicana,* a small tawny mushroom which grows in marshy pastures, often in cow pats. Other species include *Conocybe siliginoides, Psilocybe aztecorum, P. zapotecorum, P. caerulescens,* and *Stropharia cubensis.* Albert Hofmann, discoverer of LSD-25, analyzed *P. mexicana* and in 1958 isolated its hallucinogenic alkaloid, PSILOCYBIN (the phosphoric acid ester of 4-hydroxydimethyltryptamine, a close relative of BUFOTENINE and SEROTONIN and with an indole position identical with LSD-25). Hofmann also synthesized psilocybin. The alkaloid has since been found in *Stropharia cubensis* and in other species of *Psilocybe.*

Indians who use the mushroom in religious rites usually ingest (by eating) twelve of the mushrooms, which have an unpleasant bitter taste and an acrid odor. The initial reactions are nausea, muscular relaxation, coldness of the limbs, dilation of the pupils, and then abrupt mood changes, often characterized by wild hilarity. After this comes the visions—brilliant colors, shapes, geometric patterns, and myriad scenes sometimes perceived as if from a lofty height, as well as aural hallucinations. They last four to five hours and are followed by lassitude, mental and physical depression, and a loss of time and space perception.

[The visions] were in vivid color, always harmonious. They began with angular art motifs, such as might decorate carpets or wallpaper or the drawing board of an architect. Then they evolved into palaces with courts, arcades, gardens—resplendent palaces all laid over with semiprecious stones. Then I saw a mythological beast drawing a regal chariot.

Later it was as though the walls of our house had dissolved and my spirit had flown forth, and I was suspended in mid-air viewing towering landscapes of mountains, with camel caravans advancing slowly across wide slopes, the mountains rising tier above tier to the very heavens. . . . They were sharply focused, the lines and colors so sharp that they seemed more real to me than anything I had ever seen with my own eyes. . . .

The Senora stood up in the darkness where there was an open space in our room and began a rhythmic dance with clapping or slapping. . . . The claps or slaps were always resonant and true. So far as we know she used no device, only her hands against each other or possibly against different parts of her body. . . . We think the Senora faced successively the four points of the compass, rotating clockwise, but we are not sure. One thing is certain: this mysterious percussive utterance was ventriloquistic, each slap coming from an unpredictable direction and distance, now close to our ears, now distant, above, below, here and yonder, like Hamlet's ghost."

—R. Gordon Wasson, in *The Drug Takers* (1965)

muta. [from (?) Spanish *mudar,* to change—*EP*] MARIJUANA.

myristicin. also called ELEMICIN. Hallucinogenic substance in NUTMEG. See MMDA.

N n

nab. an arresting officer, policeman.

nail. [variant of SPIKE] hypodermic needle; addicts usually affix it to a medicine dropper and use the rubber bulb to inject the drug.

nail-polish remover. adolescents sometimes inhale the fumes for their intoxicatory effects. Compare BENZINE, CARBON TETRACHLORIDE, CLEANING FLUID, GLUE SNIFFING.

Nalline. [nalorphine hydrochloride (*N*-allylnormorphine hydrochloride), Merck, Sharp & Dohme] a semisynthetic derivative of MORPHINE, first synthesized in 1941, which has no analgesic action and which acts to reverse the effects of morphine and other synthetic and semisynthetic opiates. Its primary action is to counter the depression of the central nervous system and especially that of the respiratory system induced by OPIATE drugs. Hence, it is valuable in cases of NARCOTIC overdoses (but not in BARBITURATE- or other drug-induced respiratory depressions). In conjunction with morphine or other opiates, Nalline acts to prevent respiratory depression and promptly abolishes already existing respiratory depression. Usually respiration is restored to normal in two to three minutes. Dosages of 5 to 10 milligrams are usually effective; larger doses (30 to 40 milligrams) more completely reverse the action of the narcotic drug.

In persons who have not taken any narcotics, small doses of Nalline produce relaxation and drowsiness, similar to that from whiskey or MARIJUANA; larger doses cause slurred speech, racing thoughts, panic, anxiety, lethargy, hallucinations, pallor, nausea, heaviness of the limbs, and respiratory depression. Thus, nalorphine is a depressant drug itself, yet it acts to antagonize other depressant drugs of the opiate type. In addicts, Nalline precipitates WITHDRAWAL SYMPTOMS, which is the basis for the NALLINE TEST. Nalline does not cause PHYSICAL DEPENDENCE or withdrawal symptoms upon discontinuance after long-term administration. A CLASS M NARCOTIC. Compare LEVALLORPHAN.

Nalline test. a test using NALLINE to ascertain whether a paroled addict who has been withdrawn from narcotics has returned to using them. Since it is a narcotic antagonist, Nalline reverses the effects of any narcotic present in the system; hence it precipitates WITHDRAWAL SYMPTOMS by reversing the depressant action of the narcotic. This serves to unleash the symptoms of PHYSICAL DEPENDENCE just as if the addict had abruptly stopped taking his drug.

The severity of the withdrawal symptoms is directly proportional to the amount of Nalline administered (and also varies somewhat with the drug addicted to). Hence, to avoid precipitating severe withdrawal distress, the Nalline test is begun with a small dose (3 milligrams), which usually precipitates a minor syndrome; if none is observed, the dosage may gradually be increased. The California Department of Correction uses a circumscribed form of the Nalline test on all paroled or outpatient addicts. A dosage of 3 milligrams is injected, and if the pupil dilates (the addict's pupils will be constricted before the injection) by 1/2 millimeter, the patient is presumed to have become readdicted. (In nonusers Nalline constricts the pupils.) If the California test is positive, urine tests are made to establish the actual presence of the narcotic in the system. Nalline precipitates unusually strong withdrawal symptoms in METHADONE addicts, stronger than the normal syndrome; it has no effect on MEPERIDINE addicts unless they are taking more than 1,600 milligrams of the drug a day (sixteen to twenty times the usual analgesic dose). Its effectiveness in detecting CODEINE addiction is not known. Compare LEVALLORPHAN.

nalorphine. NALLINE.

narc. a federal, state, or local narcotics officer.

narco. *1.* U.S. Public Health Service (Narcotics) Hospital, Lexington, Kentucky. *2.* any narcotics treatment center to which the addict may be committed. *3.* a federal, state, or city narcotics policeman.

narco fuzz. a federal, state, or city narcotics officer.

narcotic. [from Greek *narkotikos,* benumbing.] *1.* any drug that numbs the senses, induces lethargy and drowsiness or coma in large doses, and relieves pain. As defined by United States narcotics laws: addictive drugs, including OPIUM, MORPHINE, and CODEINE; their derivatives; SYNTHETIC OPIATES; and COCAINE and ECOGNINE (although the last are not addictive in the sense of causing PHYSICAL DEPENDENCE.) Compare ADDICTION, CLASS A NARCOTICS, CLASS B NARCOTICS, CLASS M NARCOTICS, and CLASS X NARCOTICS.

narghile. [Turkish] a water pipe used for smoking tobacco or CANNABIS, especially HASHISH. The smoke is bubbled through the water, thus cooling it and alleviating the harshness characteristic of cannabis smoke. Compare HOOKAH.

nark. NARC.

natch, on the. [from *natch,* natural] not using drugs; leading a natural life as opposed to a life centered around chemicals.

natch trips. [from *natural*] HIGHS produced by natural substances such as NUTMEG, banana pulp, MACE, cinnamon, green peppers, wild rice, or peanut skins. Smoking or drinking in hot water are the preferred modes of consumption. These substances are usually of low or dubious psychopotency.

nateema. [South American Indian] BANISTERIOPSIS CAAPI.

nebbie. NEMBUTAL capsule.

needle. hypodermic needle used for injecting drugs.

needle park. a traffic island at Sherman Square, corner of West 71st Street, junction of Broadway and Amsterdam Avenue, that is a meeting place and hangout for drug addicts in New York City.

Nembutal. [pentobarbital sodium, Abbott Laboratories] a short-acting BARBITURATE hypnotic and sedative. The sedative dosage is 30 to 50 milligrams two to three times a day; the recommended hypnotic dose is 100 milligrams. TOLERANCE to the drug's action, especially its hypnotic action, builds up over a period of continuous use. PSYCHIC DEPENDENCE upon the drug's hypnotic and sedative (and sometimes euphoric or excitatory) effects can occur. PSYSICAL DEPENDENCE occurs after prolonged usage in amounts several times the hypnotic dose.

Since pentobarbital is eliminated through the liver, taking it when the liver is impaired means danger of acute intoxication and possibly fatal respiratory depression. Nembutal is sold in 30-milligram all-yellow capsules bearing a symbol representing a lowercase *a;* 50-milligram capsules with yellow cap and white bottom, *a* symbol on the white part; and 100-milligram all-yellow capsules bearing the *a* and the word "ABBOTT" on the cap.

Slang names: nebbies, nemmies, nemish, yellow jackets.

nemish. NEMBUTAL capsules.

nemmies. [since around 1938—*EP*] NEMBUTAL capsules.

Neurosine. [sodium, potassium, ammonium, and zinc bromides in combination with other ingredients, including hyoscyamus and BELLADONNA, Dios Chemical Company] a nonbarbiturate hypnotic, sedative, and anticonvulsant. Recommended dosage is 1 to 2 teaspoonfuls a day, which manufacturer says is 33 3/4 grains of bromides, equal in combination to 45 grains of any bromide separately. Overdosages or prolonged use can result in bromism (rash and mental disturbances).

nickel. *1.* five dollars. *2.* a NICKEL ($5) BAG. *3.* five-year sentence, as in "the judge gave me a nickel at K.Y." Compare DIME.

nickel bag. *1.* a $5 measure of heroin diluted to roughly 3 percent with quinine and/or MILK SUGAR; total weight is roughly 1/100 ounce, or 310 milligrams, or 5 grains. In times of heroin shortage (PANIC) a nickel bag may sell for $10 or more. *2.* a $5 packet of MARIJUANA, roughly 1/5 to 1/7 ounce and yielding five to eight marijuana cigarettes depending upon how CLEAN it is, i.e., how free it is of waste material (seeds, twigs, stems). Compare CAN, DECK, DIME, LID, MATCHBOX, PAPER.

nimby. NEMBUTAL, a BARBITURATE.

nitrous oxide. also called nitrogen monoxide. A general-acting inhalant anesthetic. It was discovered in 1776 by Priestley, but use as an anesthetic did not come until the mid-nineteenth century. The gas's primary action is on the central nervous system to effectively obliterate the perception of pain. Nitrous oxide does not depress the central respiratory center, however, like MORPHINE; in fact, it stimulates it. Its action is clearly anesthetic and does not arise from asphyxiation. It is most effective analgesically as a general anesthetic in medical practice. Because it does not induce sufficient muscle relaxation for major surgery, has a low anesthetic potency, plus danger of anoxia, it is often used in minor surgery, in childbirth, as a preinduction anesthetic (followed by ether), or in conjunction with other analgesic drugs.

Nitrous oxide is sometimes used nonmedically for its consciousness-altering effects. Such use, or abuse, suggests the possibility of PSYCHIC DEPENDENCE (see the quotation below), but occasional use is probably the rule, and undoubtedly harmless. The chief danger of nitrous oxide and its harmful effects arise from the anoxia produced by sustained inhalation unaccompanied by adequate oxygen. When the pure gas is inhaled, anoxia will set in after about two minutes and can result in death from oxygen deprivation, from heart failure, or more pulmonary edema ("drowning" due to bodily fluid accumulating in the lungs), or in organic brain damage resulting in personality change and psychosis. Anoxia is usually accompanied by cyanosis (blueness of the skin), although not in anemic persons. Cyanosis is accompanied by slow pulse, rise in blood pressure, twitching of the muscles, and violent respiration; then respiration becomes shallow and irregular and finally ceases altogether. The heart continues to beat after respiration has stopped, so that resuscitative measures are usually successful, although permanent brain damage may occur. Reawakening from normal anesthesia is rapid—within one to three minutes—and the gas is completely out of the system within five to ten minutes. Nitrous oxide alone is not considered useful as an anesthetic.

A Grand Exhibition of the Effects Produced by Inhaling Nitrous Oxide, Exhilarating or Laughing Gas!

Men will be invited from the audience, to protect those under the influence of the Gas from injuring themselves or others. This course is adopted so that no apprehension of danger may be entertained. Probably no one will attempt to fight. The effect of the gas is to make those who inhale it either: Laugh, Sing, Dance, Swear or Fight—according to the leading trait of their character. They seem to retain consciousness enough not to say or do that which they would have occasion to regret.

N.B. The Gas will be administered only to gentlemen of the first respectability. The object is to make the entertainment in every respect a genteel affair.   —broadside, dated 1845

High on Laughing Gas
I've been here before
the odd vibration of
the same old universe

the nasal whine of the dentist's drill
        singing against the nostalgic
                piano Muzak in the wall
insistent, familiar, penetrating
        the teeth, where've I heard that
                asshole jazz before?

The universe is a void
in which there is a dreamhold
The dream disappears
        the hole closes

It's the instant of going
into or coming out of
existence that is
important—to catch on
to the secret of the magic
        box

Stepping outside the universe
        by means of Nitrous Oxide
anesthesizing mind-consciousness
        the chilicosm was an impersonal dream—
one of many, being mere dreams.

the sadness of birth
and death, the sadness of
changing from dream to dream,
the constant farewell
of forms . . .
saying ungoodby to what
didn't exist
The many worlds that don't exist
all which seem real
all joke
all lost cartoon
—Allen Ginsberg, "Laughing Gas," *Kaddish and Other Poems*
(1961)

A chemist gradually acquired the habit of inhaling every day a small quantity of nitrous oxide (laughing gas). At the beginning the sweetish smell of the gas was very unpleasant, but he slowly became used to it. In order to be able to inhale the gas at all times he fitted a small apparatus to the reservoir from which he could easily take a whiff. This gave rise to a permanent state of inebriety, the source of extremely pleasant sensations. He had wonderful dreams in which he saw beautiful landscapes, marvellous figures and scenes. The young man soon began to neglect his duties, but could not renounce his passion. He went mad and ended in an asylum.
—Louis Lewin, *Phantastica: Narcotic and Stimulating Drugs* (1964)

no-art. [from pop, op, etc., art; also meaning not what is conventionally thought to be art], name coined for PSYCHEDELIC ART.

nod. [from the characteristic lolling of the head], a drowsy, dreamy dozing state following the injection of an opiate drug and due to its sedative action. Most HEROIN addicts seek this effect and take enough to achieve it if possible. Compare GOOFING.

It is, first of all, useful to see that there are three levels of the *nod* corresponding to the unconscious, pre-conscious, and conscious levels in the Freudian topography of the mind. In the very deep nod there is true oblivion; then, moving up, there is the less intense nod in which a man is vaguely aware of the life both inside and outside himself; finally, there is the superficial nod in which he is fitfully awake and asleep, and often falsely conscious of what is happening around him. In the deep nod the man loses touch with the reality outside, and in the superficial nod he is easily irritated into angry awareness.
There is no doubt that the nod is valued as such by addicts. They

prefer to nod rather than to sleep. Sleeping, they say, keeps a man from enjoying the nod.

The nod is therefore the culmination of the shot and represents the narcotization and apparent stimulation which the addict craves. It represents the end of striving, the cessation in varying degrees of all troubled reflection as well as the abandonment of all other projects except that of the quest for apparent euphoria and homeo-stasis.

The nod produces anguish because its standards are ever escalat-ing beyond the capacity of the addict to be satisfied. In the nod, at any of its levels, the addict experiences an expectation of a certain stimulus, and it is in the nature of heroin addiction that as time goes on the nod becomes harder and harder to achieve. This is a Sisyphian task, doomed to failure and anguish, this attempt to meet the internalized expectations of the nod.

—Seymour Fiddle, *Portraits from a Shooting Gallery* (1967)

nodding. In a state of NOD, the head lolling forward, slowly jerking up and down.

nod, on the. going off into a NOD.

Noludar 300. [METHYPRYLON, a piperidine derivative (3,3-diethyl-5-methyl-2,4-piperidinedione), Roche Laboratories] a nonbarbiturate hypnotic and sedative. Manufacturer recommends for insomnia in doses of 200 to 400 milligrams, with 400 milligrams per day the maxi-mum taken. In conjunction with alcohol, Noludar may lower resist-ance to the latter and POTENTIATE its effects. It also dulls mental alertness, so that driving a car or operating machinery should be avoided after taking it. As with the BARBITURATES, PSYCHIC DE-PENDENCE upon the sedative effects of the drug can occur. PHYSICAL DEPENDENCE with WITHDRAWAL SYMPTOMS similar in severity to those associated with barbiturate dependence can occur after pro-longed, excessive use. Death has occurred from overdoses of Noludar. Sold as 300-milligram capsules, with an amethyst top and white bot-tom bearing the word "ROCHE" and also as 50- and 200-milligram scored tablets, bearing the word "ROCHE." Subject to the DRUG ABUSE CONTROL AMENDMENT OF 1965.

noscapine. a natural alkaloid of OPIUM in the benzylisoquinoline group, similar to PAPAVERINE. It is nonaddictive and unlike members of the phenanthrene group (MORPHINE, CODEINE, etc.), has no anal-gesic, gastrointestinal or central nervous system depressant actions.

Because of its mild suppressive action on the cough reflex, it is used in cough medicines. A CLASS M NARCOTIC. Compare CONAR, THEO-NAR.

number two sale, the. [narcotics police term]. the second conviction for narcotic sales, which carries a much severer penalty (under federal law it is ten to forty years, compared with five to fifteen for the first sale).

Numorphan. [OXYMORPHONE (dihydrohydroxymorphinone) hydrochloride, Endo Laboratories] a semisynthetic derivative of MORPHINE with analgesic action. Oxymorphone has a more potent analgesic effect action than morphine. A dose of 1 to 1.5 milligrams results in analgesic equivalent to that produced by 10 milligrams of morphine. PHYSICAL DEPENDENCE occurs after continuous, frequent use. WITHDRAWAL SYMPTOMS are similar to those associated with morphine dependence in severity. Numorphan is sold in solution for injection, rectal suppositories, and in 10-milligram tablets. A CLASS A NARCOTIC.

nutmeg. the dried seeds of the East Indian evergreen tree, *Myristica fragrans,* family Myristicaceae, to which the hallucinogenic-snuff-producing genus VIROLA also belongs. Taken in powdered form, nutmeg has mind-altering properties. A dose of 10 grams (1/3 ounce) can produce a mild, brief euphoria, accompanied by light-headedness, floating feelings, and central nervous system stimulation—an effect very roughly akin to that produced by one MARIJUANA cigarette. Sometimes tension and fear are also experienced. Over 10 grams will often produce unpleasant results, including rapid heart beat, excessive thirst, agitation, anxiety, and sometimes acute panic. Hallucinations are rare.

The ACTIVE PRINCIPLE is believed to be ELEMICIN (MYRISTICIN), which is chemically close to the HALLUCINOGEN TMA. Other authorities state that nutmeg contains a compound of the dimethoxy group related to STP and MESCALINE. Nutmeg is commonly used as a drug substitute by prisoners (perhaps because it can be stolen from the kitchen), who drink it or MACE in hot water, and by teen-agers seeking a substitute for illegal drugs. See MMDA.

> I recently got a visit from a "beatnik" acquaintance who smokes marijuana frequently and has tried other drugs. I asked him if he had heard that *nutmeg* was a narcotic, and he replied, "We've known

about that for years!" He explained that he and many of his friends had tried nutmeg several times, taking it both as snuff and by mouth. They didn't think it was very good, however, because "you either get very sick or have a horrible experience." He said that people who blow pot sometimes take nutmeg when they can't get marijuana.

—student, quoted by Dr. Andrews T. Weil, "The Use of Nutmeg as a Psychotropic Agent," *Bulletin on Narcotics* (1967)

O. OPIUM.

O.D. OVERDOSE, whether fatal or nonfatal, of an opiate drug, producing a coma.

O.D.-ing. exhibiting symptoms of an OVERDOSE of an opiate drug.

off artist. a TAKE-OFF ARTIST, a thief.

ololiuqui. [Nahuatl, round thing, pellet] Aztec name for the hallucinogenic seeds of *Rivea corymbosa*.
See MORNING GLORY SEEDS.

on. [from *turned on;* or, simply, *on drugs*] using drugs.

"I wish I had me some stuff."
"You *on*, man?"   —Piri Thomas, *Down These Mean Streets* (1967)

on the needle. injecting narcotics.

opiate. a natural or semisynthetic derivative of the juice in the unripe seed pods of the OPIUM poppy, *Papaver somniferum,* such as MORPHINE, HEROIN, CODEINE. Compare SYNTHETIC OPIATES.

opioid. synthetic substance with pharmacological action similar to that of MORPHINE. Compare SYNTHETIC OPIATES.

opium. [from Greek *opion,* poppy juice]. the milky exudate of the incised, unripe seed pods of a poppy, *Papaver somniferum,* which is dried in air to form a brownish gummy substance. The effects of opium (dulling of pain, euphoria, detachment from the anxieties of existence) have been known to man since prehistoric times. The opium poppy was probably first cultivated in Asia Minor and used medically in Egypt, whence its use spread to Greece. The first reference to its pharmacology occurs in the writings of Theophrastus in the third century B.C. In the *Odyssey* Homer may have meant it by "The drug of sleep and forgetfulness" (our word nepenthe). Arab traders carried it to India and China, where it was used medicinally (to suppress dysentery) and for pleasure. Opium addiction spread rapidly in China, while in Turkey soldiers commonly used it before going into battle in the belief that it gave them added courage and endurance.

In the eighteenth century, the Chinese government attempted to prohibit the importation, sale, and use of opium, so harmful had the the habit become. The British, however, who were conducting a profitable trade in opium grown in India, opposed the ban, an action which led to the Opium War (1839 to 1842). One result was the legalization of opium in China and its cultivation by the Chinese government. Many Chinese emigrants carried the opium habit with them wherever they settled and introduced the practice of opium smoking into the United States.

Meanwhile, the medical use of opium to relieve pain, suppress coughing, act as sedative, and counter diarrhea grew apace. In the early part of the sixteenth century the physician Paracelsus had compounded tincture of opium called LAUDANUM, which became a standard drug. Dover's powder, concocted by the English physician Thomas Dover as a remedy for gout in 1732, and the "brown mixture" (opium and licorice), compounded by the American Dr. Barton, in 1814, were two other staple remedies containing opium. A variety of patent nostrums containing opium followed, and by the end of the nineteenth century it was estimated that 1 in 400 Americans (mainly housewives) were addicted to it.

Doctors awoke to the problems of ADDICTION, and laws were passed making opium available only through a doctor's prescription. In 1914 the HARRISON NARCOTICS ACT placed opium under federal regulation. With the advent of MORPHINE (1803) and HEROIN (1897) opium smoking in the addict underground gave way to consumption of these more powerful alkaloids and semisynthetic derivatives. Opium smoking is practiced mainly in China, Hong Kong, and Southeast Asia. Crude opium becomes much more valuable when it is converted to heroin, and hence its movements in the illicit drug traffic (see TRAFFIC, DRUG) are mainly to this end. Opium is grown in Burma, Turkey, Mexico, Communist China, Thailand, Lebanon, Laos, and Cambodia. The raw opium gum is converted to smoking opium by a simple heating process. It is sometimes eaten but mainly smoked, the smoker characteristically lying down (to lessen nausea and stupor) on a pallet furnished by the owner of the establishment —the "opium den" of lurid journalism.

In the United States, the illicit use of opium is confined to such standard remedies as PAREGORIC (opium and camphor) and opium tincture (laudanum), which addicts use when they cannot obtain heroin. (Nonaddicts sometimes mix opium with HASHISH or smoke ordinary cigarettes which have been soaked in paregoric and dried out.) Since opium's chief actions on the central nervous system and the bowel muscles are caused by its natural alkaloid morphine, the latter is most widely used in medical practice because it can be standardized and made soluble for injection. In medical opium morphine must make up 10 percent of the total weight; consequently, 60 milligrams of opium will give analgesic effects equivalent to 6 milligrams of morphine. The PHYSICAL DEPENDENCE which results from long-term use of opium of course results from the actions of morphine. Other alkaloids found in opium are as follows:

class	alkaloid	average percent weight in opium
phenanthrene	morphine	10.0
	codeine	0.5
	thebaine	0.2
benzylisoquinoline	papaverine	1.0
	narcotine (noscapine)	6.0
	narceine	0.3

Only the phenanthrene class of alkaloids is significant in producing opium's characteristic narcotic actions and in inducing addiction. Opium addiction produces WITHDRAWAL SYMPTOMS comparable to those produced by morphine dependence in severity; the addict's inexorably increasing TOLERANCE to opium, necessitating inexorably increasing doses, means that he will take anywhere from 20 to 40 grams of the drug a day, or 200 to 400 milligrams of morphine, enough for a very severe habit.

In 1921, the chief medical officer of New York City estimated that more than 750,000 pounds of opium were used for medical purposes. In 1963, according to federal BUREAU OF NARCOTICS figures, 539,207 pounds were imported. The total amount of illegal opium seized by the Bureau in 1964 was 62.81 pounds.

outfit. addict's equipment for injecting drugs, especially HEROIN, i.e., needle, syringe or medicine dropper, COOKER, strap, etc. Compare COOKING, FIX, GIMMICKS, WORKS.

overdose. ingestion of an OPIATE or hypnotic-sedative drug in larger amounts than the system has acquired TOLERANCE to. Since such drugs act to depress the central nervous system, the result of an overdose is often coma and death from respiratory depression and cessation of breathing or such complications as pneumonia or heart failure. Deliberate BARBITURATE overdose is one of the leading methods of suicide in the United States. Accidental overdose through DRUG AUTOMATISM or combination of a sedative drug with alcohol, which will POTENTIATE the depressant effects of the sedative, are also signicant causes of fatalities. Although the lethal doses of barbiturates for the prolonged user who has acquired tolerance and for the nonaddict are similar in quantity, the HEROIN or MORPHINE addict acquires a tolerance to the respiratory depressant effects of those drugs to a much greater degree, so that he is taking without ill effects ten to twenty times what would be a lethal dose for a nontolerant person. Nevertheless, fatal heroin or morphine overdose is a leading hazard in the addict's life.

From 1954 to 1965, over 2,000 deaths were caused by narcotics overdose in New York City alone (250 in the year 1965). It has been estimated that 1 percent of the nation's total addict population dies *every day* of an overdose. According to Dr. Donald B. Louria, Chairman of the New York County Medical Association's Sub-committee on Narcotics, overdosage most frequently occurs in the following situations:

1. A beginner, imitating a veteran addict, injects the same amount of heroin but without his tolerance to the drug.
2. An addict who has been withdrawn from narcotics in a hospital or jail, thus losing his accumulated tolerance, injects his former usual dose, which is now in excess of his tolerance.

3. A pusher deliberately supplies an addict suspected of being a police informer with a dose containing a much higher percentage than the usual 3 to 5 percent of heroin to which the addict's system is accustomed.

4. In order to escape the threat of imminent arrest, a pusher dumps relatively undiluted heroin on the market, and the unsuspecting addict takes a dose that is five to twenty times as potent as his usual dose.

5. Fluctuating measures are sold to the addict. Since heroin cutting is often done haphazardly, the percentage of pure heroin in the purchased bag may vary widely. The addict has no way of estimating the amount of heroin in his dose, until after he has injected it, when it is too late. Any mixture containing more than 20 percent heroin is likely to cause a severe overdosage.

Symptoms of opiate overdose include extreme sleepiness, frequent yawning, coma, pinpointed pupils, lung congestion, cyanosis (blue skin), gasping as if something were caught in the throat, shock, and either deep, extremely slow respiration or very rapid, shallow respiration. Overdosage can be immediately arrested by the use of a narcotics antagonist such as NALLINE or LEVALLORPHAN. Addicts, to whom such drugs are usually not available, resort to a variety of home remedies such as icy baths, placing snow in the genitals, walking the victim around and the injection of milk or salt solutions. Such measures are sometimes effective because they keep the patient awake and reverse the fatal respiratory depression.

overjolt. OVERDOSE.

over the hump (go). [since around 1930—*EP*. Sometimes meaning, in women, achieving orgasm] to feel the full exhilaration of a narcotic. *Obsolete?*

oxycodone. also called dihydrohydroxycodeinone. A semisynthetic derivative of MORPHINE, oxycodone is close to it in potency: an injection of 10 to 15 milligrams will produce analgesia equal to that of 10 milligrams of morphine and lasting four to five hours. Prolonged use will produce PHYSICAL DEPENDENCE, with WITHDRAWAL SYMPTOMS comparable to those of morphine dependence in severity. A CLASS A NARCOTIC. Compare EUCODAL, PERCOBARB, PERCODAN.

oxymorphone. also called dihydrohydroxymorphinone. A semisynthetic derivative of MORPHINE which is a much more potent analgesic than the latter. A dose of 1.0 to 1.5 milligrams injected subcutaneously produces analgesia equal to that produced by 10 milligrams of morphine, lasting four to five hours. Oral doses of 10 milligrams and intravenous doses of 0.5 milligram produce similar results. Oxymorphone has 100 times the analgesic potency of MEPERIDINE (DEMEROL). PHYSICAL DEPENDENCE occurs after prolonged use, with WITHDRAWAL SYMPTOMS equal to those of morphine dependence in severity.

O.Z. an ounce.

P p

P. PEYOTE.

pad. [from the mats upon which OPIUM smokers lie, since around 1930—*EP;* also, perhaps from similar pads used by MARIJUANA smokers in the Harlem tea pads of the 1940s] room used for taking narcotics or marijuana, usually in a private residence. (Now the specialized drug-taking meaning seems to have been replaced by the more general slang sense of one's room, house, or apartment.)

Palfium. [DEXTROMORAMIDE bitartrate or hydrochloride] a SYNTHETIC OPIATE.

Pall Mall and paregoric. cigarettes soaked in PAREGORIC, dried out, and then smoked, producing a mild OPIATE euphoria. (Not to be identified with any one brand of cigarette.)

panaddiction. MULTIHABITUATION.

Panama. PANAMA GOLD.

Panama (Panamanian) gold. [from origin and color] local variety of MARIJUANA grown in Panama and highly valued by marijuana users, who consider it more potent than varieties grown in the United States.

Panama red. also called P.R., red. Local variety of MARIJUANA.

grown in Panama and considered more potent than varieties grown in the United States.

panatella. [from its size, i.e., a large cigarette, like a cigar compared with a cigarette; since the 1930s] bigger, fatter, more potent MARI-JUANA cigarette made of Central or South American marijuana.

panic. [connoting the addict's state of anxiety, as his WITHDRAWAL SYMPTOMS begin to occur, and he does not know where his next supply of drugs will come from] a shortage of HEROIN in a general area, due, usually, to arrests of key suppliers and/or interception of a large supply being smuggled into the country.

Pantopon. [hydrochlorides of alkaloids of OPIUM, Roche Laboratories] an opium preparation containing all its alkaloids in their natural percentages but with inert gums and resins removed. Manufacturer recommends as an analgesic in place of MORPHINE on the theory that 20 milligrams of Pantopon, thanks to the synergistic action of the several alkaloids in combination, gives analgesia equal to 15 milligrams of morphine (Pantopon is one-half morphine; hence 20 milligrams would contain only 10 milligrams of morphine). Goodman and Gilman, however, report in their book *The Pharmacological Basis of Therapeutics* that the analgesia is not greater than would be expected for the amount of morphine. The usual dosage is 20 milligrams. Pantopon is sold in ampuls or hypodermic tablets and administered only by subcutaneous or intramuscular injection. A CLASS A NARCOTIC.

papaverine. a naturally occurring alkaloid of OPIUM of the benzylisoquinoline class, which acts mainly to depress the heart and smooth muscles. Unlike MORPHINE and CODEINE, alkaloids of the phenanthrene class, it has no analgesic, euphoric, or other central nervous system effect, and PHYSICAL DEPENDENCE is not produced by prolonged administration. Papaverine has limited use in medicine in treating cardiovascular system diseases and as a cough suppressant. A CLASS M NARCOTIC. Compare NOSCAPINE.

paper. folded piece of paper containing narcotics.

> He opened his fly and extracted a rectangular paper packet—the junkie fold, with one end fitting into another. Inside the packet were two smaller packets, each similarly folded. He placed the *papers* on the table.　　　　　　　　—William Burroughs, *Junkie* (1953)

parahexyl. PYRAHEXYL.

Paral. [PARALDEHYDE, Fellows Testagar] a nonbarbiturate hypnotic and sedative. Paraldehyde use can produce PSYCHIC DEPENDENCE and PHYSICAL DEPENDENCE, with WITHDRAWAL SYMPTOMS similar to delirium tremens. Sold in 15-grain (1-gram) capsules. In the liquid form 1 cubic centimeter (1/5 teaspoonful) contains 15 grains of paraldehyde. Manufacturer's recommended dosage is one to two capsules or, by injection, one to four cubic centimeters.

paraldehyde. [a polymer, i.e., fusion of molecules, of acetaldehyde] a fast-acting, nonbarbiturate hypnotic and sedative, somewhat less potent and toxic than CHLORAL HYDRATE and somewhat more potent and toxic than ETHYL ALCOHOL. Discovered in 1829 and first introduced into medicine in 1882, paraldehyde has been largely replaced today by the BARBITURATES, although it is considered quite as effective as a hypnotic.

Paraldehyde is a colorless, inflammable liquid with a strong odor and a bitter, burning, unpleasant taste, which has made its use unpopular, although it is often masked with various flavoring agents. On the other hand, this unpleasant flavor makes the drug less habit-forming than the barbiturates, which are tasteless and easy to administer, and for this reason authorities recommend its more widespread use. It is frequently given to alcoholics in a state of delirium tremens to induce sleep; and, of course, it may be used as a substitute for barbiturates when a patient is allergic to them.

When 4 to 8 milliliters (1/7 to 2/7 ounce) is taken, sleep ensues within ten to fifteen minutes. Larger doses of 15 to 30 milliliters are frequently given to calm psychiatric patients. The lethal dose is not known, and the drug has a wide margin of safety when taken orally (injected, it is much more dangerous); doses of 150 and 240 milliliters have been survived. However, fatalities have occured due to respiratory depression and collapse of the cardiovascular system. Sometimes these fatalities have been related to liver damage or hepatitis in the patient.

Despite its unpleasant taste and its capacity to burn the mucous membranes when swallowed, PSYCHIC DEPENDENCE upon paraldehyde has occurred—frequently among former alcoholics treated with the drug who acquired a liking for it. Chronic paraldehyde intoxication resembles chronic alcoholism, including WITHDRAWAL SYMPTOMS similar to those of alcohol dependence, i.e., delirium tremens, auditory and visual hallucinations, convulsions, psychoses, etc. Subject to the DRUG ABUSE CONTROL AMENDMENT OF 1965.

paranoia. the drug user's pervasive, perhaps exaggerated fear that the police have him under watch and may arrest him at any time. Drug user's paranoia implies taking elaborate precautions (see STASH, HOLDING) so as not to be caught possessing or dealing in drugs. The term also connotes that his fears, though possibly imaginary, like those of the paranoid psychotic, may well be based on fact; certainly, they arise out of the central fact that his drug use involved breaking the law, and so he theoretically is subject to arrest at any time. Thus, though the term is half ironic, it refers to a real and oppressive state of fear which drug users sometimes experience.

> Even Paranoids Have Real Enemies   —Hippie slogan (1967)

paregoric. tincture of OPIUM in combination with camphor, first prepared in the early eighteenth century and used medicinally ever since largely in the control of diarrhea (from the constipating action of the opium). The usual mixture contains 4 percent tincture of opium, of which one-tenth (0.4 percent) is MORPHINE. The usual dose is 4 milliliters (about 1/7 ounce), which is equivalent to 16 milligrams of opium or 1.6 milligrams of morphine. Addicts often resort to paregoric (obtainable in some locales without a prescription) if HEROIN is not available. They either drink it (usually around a quart per day is taken for the desired effects; this would contain roughly 350 milligrams of morphine) or inject it, after first boiling it to remove the camphor, which causes abscesses when injected. Paregoric is considered a rather old-fashioned preparation today, containing several superfluous ingredients.

> Shooting PG is a terrible hassle, you have to burn out the alcohol first, then freeze out the camphor and draw this brown liquid off with a dropper—have to shoot it in the vein or you get an abscess, and usually end up with an abscess no matter where you shoot it. Best deal is to drink it with goof balls.
> —William Burroughs, *Naked Lunch* (1959)

parica. [Yekwana Indian] hallucinogenic snuff prepared by Venezuelan Indians from bark of trees belong to the genus VIROLA, a member of the same family as the NUTMEG. Compare YAKEE.

partying. enjoying HEROIN sociably; sharing it with others.

pass. a transfer of drugs, as in "I paid him, and we arranged a place to make the *pass*."

PDR. [*Physicians' Desk Reference*] the BOOK.

peaches. BENZEDRINE tablets.

pearls. see AMYL NITRITE.

pellets. LSD capsules.

Pentothal Sodium. [thiopental sodium, Abbott Laboratories] a very short-acting BARBITURATE hypnotic and sedative. When administered intravenously, Pentothal induces sleep rapidly and suddenly; hence, it is used, alone or in combination with other drugs, as an anesthetic for minor and brief surgery; it is also administered before a general anesthetic to place the patient in a receptive state.

Along with other barbiturates, Pentothal is used as an adjunct to psychotherapy (narcoanalysis or narcotherapy). In amounts too small to induce anesthesia, the drug lowers the patient's inhibitions, makes him communicate more freely repressed emotional conflicts, and increases his responsiveness to suggestion by the therapist. Like AMYTAL, the drug is used in an analogous way as a so-called "truth serum" by law-enforcement agencies, especially as an aid to total recall of an event or conversation which the subject cannot remember in a normal conscious state. Naturally, the suggestibility induced by the drug makes the "truth" elicited heavily dependent upon the interrogator's skill in avoiding planting any suggestions in the subject which would cause him to alter his memories in a way he thinks would please the interrogator.

Overdosage of Pentothal Sodium can cause fatal respiratory depression and paralysis. It is sold only in solution and ampuls for injection intravenously and should be administered only by a trained anesthetist with emergency equipment such as oxygen, in case respiratory depression does occur. Subject to the DRUG ABUSE CONTROL AMENDMENT OF 1965. Compare NITROUS OXIDE.

people. [used mainly in New Orleans] the police. *Obsolete?*

pep pills. [popular slang] AMPHETAMINE pills.

Percobarb. [OXYCODONE hydrochloride and hexobarbital, with other ingredients, Endo Laboratories Inc.] a semisynthetic derivative of MORPHINE combined with a BARBITURATE and used as a hypnotic, sedative, and analgesic. Manufacturer recommends in cases of mild to moderate pain causing sleeplessness, e.g., headache, bursitis, neuralgia. Prolonged excessive use can result in PHYSICAL DEPENDENCE upon both the oxycodone and the hexobarbital. When physical dependence develops, the WITHDRAWAL SYMPTOMS are close to those of morphine dependence is severity. Percobarb is sold in blue and yellow capsules, each containing 4.5 milligrams of oxycodone hydrochloride and 100 milligrams of hexobarbital, and as blue and white capsules, each containing one-half as much oxycodone and hexobarbital. Recommended dosage: one tablet every six hours. A CLASS A NARCOTIC.

Percodan. [OXYCODONE hydrochloride and other analgesic ingredients, Endo Laboratories Inc.] similar to PERCOBARB except that it contains no BARBITURATE. Sold as yellow scored tablets, each containing 4.50 milligrams of OXYCODONE, and pink scored tablets containing one-half as much oxycodone. A CLASS A NARCOTIC. Percodan has reportedly found popularity among addicts in California. Compare EUCODAL.

peter. CHLORAL HYDRATE, a sedative.

pethidine. [international generic name] MEPERIDINE.

peyote. [from Nahuatl *peyotl*, silk cocoon or caterpillar's cocoon; from the white, woolly tufts growing out of the surface part of the cactus] a small gray-brown cactus, *Lophophora williamsii*, with small spineless heads, or BUTTONS, barely protruding from the earth (resembling mushrooms) and a long carrot-shaped root. The hallucinogenic properties of peyote were known to the Aztecs, who considered it divine. In remote areas Mexican Indians descended from the Aztecs continue to use it as a divine cure, in religious worship, and as a vehicle for communicating directly with divine spirits.

In the latter part of the nineteenth century Indians in the United States learned of peyote's properties during forays into Mexico and brought it back to their homelands. They used it in religious rites and to heal the sick, and gradually a cult grew up around the cactus. This cult, which incorporated elements of Christianity, was formally organized as the First-born Church of Christ, later the Native American Church. The church and the peyote rite spread among North American Indians regardless of tribal barriers, so that today the Native American Church claims 200,000 members from all tribes in the United States and Canada.

At first the Bureau of Indian Affairs attempted to discourage the use of peyote by the Indians, with the tacit cooperation of several state governments which considered peyote in the class with alcohol for Indians (actually, use of the drug may cut down alcoholism), but it gradually became recognized that peyotism as practiced by the Indians was a sincere religion, and the courts have upheld it as such under the Bill of Rights. Peyotism does not interest all Indians, most of whom prefer either the white man's Christianity or a revival of their own native religions. Those who practice it have faith in its efficacy as a cure-all and a true belief—indeed a worship of the cactus itself—in the sacred character of the altered states of consciousness, especially visions, induced by the drug.

In the traditional peyote rite, the cactus is prepared by cutting off the tops of the plant (though one tribe consumes the root also), slicing them into disks (the mescal buttons), which are dried in the sun and then either crushed and boiled in water to make a tea or eaten raw, sometimes chewed until softened and swallowed whole. The buttons have a bitter taste, which has been compared to that of dried orange rind, and a nauseating odor. Nausea usually accompanies ingestion.

Characteristic physiological effects include dilation of the pupils, chills, and vomiting. Subjective effects include anxiety, terror, minor intensifying of sensual impressions, heightened auditory acuity, dislocation of visual perspective, depersonalization (the breaking down of distinction between self and other), mental stimulation and heightened clarity of thought, intensification of colors of surrounding objects and brilliantly colored visions of shifting, nonobjective shapes, often, but not necessarily, perceived with the eyes closed (and perhaps related to phosphenes). Peyote contains at least eight active alkaloids, but it is MESCALINE that causes the hallucinations.

Peyote does not induce PHYSICAL DEPENDENCE, and there are no WITHDRAWAL SYMPTOMS upon discontinuance of use. Among the Indians, some cases of apparent PSYCHIC DEPENDENCE or repeated, habitual use have been observed, but by far the majority of the Indians use it infrequently and only during their religious ceremonies, which are held informally upon weekends, usually sponsored by a family as a partly social occasion. A limited TOLERANCE probably develops to the effects of peyote, since it does to the active alkaloid mescaline; however, this has not been documented, and cases of regular use, over a span of weeks, have been reported. If so, it would follow that there would be a CROSS-TOLERANCE to LSD-25 and PSILOCYBIN.

> The visions never resembled familiar objects; they were extremely definite, but yet always novel; they were constantly approaching, and yet constantly eluding, the semblance of the known things. I would see thick, glorious fields of jewels, solitary or clustered, sometimes brilliant and sparkling, sometimes with a dull rich glow. Then they would spring up into flower-like shapes beneath my gaze, and then seem to turn into gorgeous butterfly forms or endless folds of glistening, iridescent, fibrous wings of wonderful insects; while sometimes I seemed to be gazing into a vast hollow revolving vessel, on whose polished concave mother-of-pearl surface the hues were swiftly changing. I was surprised, not only by the enormous profusion of the imagery presented to my gaze, but still more by its variety.
>
> —Havelock Ellis, *The Contemporary Review* (1898)

> The technichimekas (the genuine Chichimekas) know herbs and roots, their properties and their effects. They also know of peyotl. Those who eat peyotl take it instead of wine, as well as the poisonous mushroom nanacatl [teonanacatl]. They assemble somewhere in the prairie, dance and sing all day and all night. The next day they meet again and weep to excess. With their tears they wash their eyes and clear their brains (i.e., return to reason, see clearly again). . . . The plant peyotl, a kind of earth nopal, is white, grows in the northern parts, and produces in those who eat or drink it terrible or ludicrous visions. This inebriety lasts two to three days and then disappears. The Chichimekas eat considerable amounts of the plant. It gives them strength, incites them to battle, alleviates fear, and they feel neither hunger nor thirst. It is even said that they are protected from every kind of danger.
>
> —Sahagun, *Historia general de las cosas de Nueva España* (seventeenth century), in Louis Lewin, *Phantastica: Narcotic and Stimulating Drugs* (1964)

> The white man goes into his church house and talks *about* Jesus; the indian goes into his tepee and talks *to* Jesus.
>
> —J. S. Slotkin, *The Peyote Religion,* The Free Press of Glencoe, New York (1956)

> Some of them, they say that the great teacher *Peyote* teaching forever, the Peyote. That's the way they find out, the Peyoters, old Peyoters. Even next meeting I go, I'll find something; next one, I'll

find something. Keep on going like that; you'll never get to end. There's no end to it; it is forever.
—J. S. Slotkin, *Transactions of the American Philosophical Society*
(1952)

peyotl. PEYOTE.

P.G. PAREGORIC.

phenadoxone (CB-11). a SYNTHETIC OPIATE analgesic, equivalent to MORPHINE. An injection of 10 to 20 milligrams produces analgesic effects equal to those produced by 10 milligrams of morphine, lasting one to three hours. PHYSICAL DEPENDENCE results after prolonged use, with WITHDRAWAL SYMPTOMS less severe than those of morphine dependence. A CLASS A NARCOTIC.

phenazocine. a SYNTHETIC OPIATE analgesic somewhat more potent than MORPHINE. A dose of 3 milligrams injected subcutaneously gives analgesia equal to that produced by 10 milligrams of morphine, lasting four to five hours. PHYSICAL DEPENDENCE occurs after prolonged use, with WITHDRAWAL SYMPTOMS between those of METHADONE and morphine dependence in severity. A CLASS A NARCOTIC.

phenos. phenobarbital, possibly other kinds of BARBITURATES, e.g., SECONAL, or red birds, with phenos used as a generic name in the illicit traffic.

We also dealt for red capsules of *phenos,* two of which, with hot water, produce a forgetting high.
—Piri Thomas, *Down These Mean Streets* (1967)

pholocodine. (also called morpholinylethylmorphine) a semisynthetic derivative of MORPHINE, which is more effective orally. A dosage of 10 to 15 milligrams taken orally gives analgesia equivalent to 10 milligrams of morphine injected, lasting four to five hours. PHYSICAL DEPENDENCE occurs after prolonged use, but the WITHDRAWAL SYMPTOMS are less severe than those of CODEINE dependence. A CLASS A NARCOTIC.

physical dependence. physical dependence occurs with certain drugs whose pharmacodynamic action after prolonged administration in sufficient dosages induces an adaptive alteration in the body which erupts in a stereotyped set of WITHDRAWAL SYMPTOMS, peculiar to the drug, when its ingestion is stopped. These withdrawal symptoms may also be set off, in the case of certain drugs, by another drug which antagonizes the action of the original one. The withdrawal symptoms will remain dormant as long as the drug or its analog is administered in sufficient quantities.

Physical dependence unaccompanied by PSYCHIC DEPENDENCE can occur. In the case of certain of both physical- and psychic-dependence-producing drugs, TOLERANCE to some or all of the drug's effects, including the lethal dose, may develop, so that the user has to increase the dosage in order to obtain the effects of previous dosages. If the drug is one which causes physical dependence, the user must also increase the dosage to avoid withdrawal symptoms as his tolerance increases.

DRUGS PRODUCING PHYSICAL DEPENDENCE

morphine type (Tolerance develops to all actions, including the lethal dose if the increase in intake is carefully regulated.)

barbiturates (Tolerance to the sedative effects but not the lethal dosage develops.)

alcohol (A slight degree of tolerance develops; withdrawal symptoms, such as delirium tremens, are similar to those of the barbiturates, which are effective in alleviating them, just as alcohol partially relieves barbiturate withdrawal symptoms.)

picked up. smoked MARIJUANA, as in "when you've *picked up* gauge and feel great."

piece. *1.* [a share, hence a ration of NARCOTICS, since the 1930s; also, an underworld term for ounces since the 1930s—*EP*. A piece is a measure, but in the HEROIN traffic no measure is undiluted, and it thus is also a symbolic share of a monetary pie, cut up by importers, wholesalers, and PUSHERS and hence the slang phrase "a *piece* of the action"] one ounce of heroin, diluted one-third with quinine and MILK SUGAR, and purchased by the pusher or by the wholesaler who dilutes it more and packages it for sale to addicts. Usually ½ kilogram (1.1 pounds) of heroin makes up fifteen pieces. Each piece yields thirty to thirty-six ½ teaspoons of heroin, which in turn are diluted and put into packages (see BAG, CLEAN, CUTTING, DECK UP). Of course, the amount the piece is diluted determines how much the pusher can further dilute it and in turn how many packages he can make and sell, and thus his profits. The heroin the average pusher buys from a wholesaler with direct access to the high-level source of supply is today diluted much more than it was ten years ago, and so he can convert it to fewer packages. *2.* a gun.

"A lot of the junk today I could either put in my coffee or on a cake 'cause it's mostly sugar and quinine. The stuff is very weak. It's not like it used to be. Like when I first started, the purest you could get was 97.6 or something close to that, and a *piece* of that stuff, if you could get that, by the time it went through all the channels, being cut all them times, you could still cut it maybe seven to one or eight to one, like make eight pieces out of one piece. And then at that time, for a piece, you'd pay maybe $200. Now today, if you buy your piece, you'd be very lucky if you could get a three-to-one cut, make three pieces out of one for $500 or $600. It's that weak. Today if you were buying an ounce and cutting it and bagging it, a $5 bag would actually cost you, I mean me, maybe $2. So there's a $3 profit on each bag you sell. So if you get a hundred bags, that's $300 profit, plus you still have your money to recop with. And I could sell in a day maybe close to two hundred bags, maybe more, sometime less. On a good night I could sell maybe a piece, a piece and a half." —pusher in James Mills, *The Panic in Needle Park* (1966)

pilde. South American Indian name for Banisteriopsis caapi.

pill. [pellet of opium, also called "yen pox"—*MM*, 1946. The opium is heated to melt it, and the resulting pellet can be placed in a pipe. *Obsolete*. Now popular slang for prepared, proprietary remedies with an invidious connotation] barbiturate or amphetamine tablets or capsules, as in "on *pills*." Compare pillhead.

pillhead. [from *hophead,* an opium addict; see head] a habitual, heavy user of barbiturates or amphetamines (usually by implication opposed to marijuana, lsd, heroin, etc.).

piminodine. a synthetic opiate analgesic, slightly more potent than morphine. A dose of 7.5 to 10 milligrams injected subcutaneously produces analgesic effects equal to those of 10 milligrams of morphine, lasting two to four hours. Repeated, regular use can result in physical dependence, with withdrawal symptoms less severe than those of morphine dependence and similar to those of meperidine dependence. A class A narcotic.

pin. [usually rolled thinner than an ordinary cigarette] a marijuana cigarette.

pinks. Seconal, a barbiturate.

pinned. constricted; used of the pupils of the eye. Constriction is characteristic of use of heroin, morphine, etc. The opposite effect is produced by HALLUCINOGENS, such as LSD-25, and by MARIJUANA and AMPHETAMINES. The medical term for constriction of the pupils is *miosis* and for enlarged pupils is *mydriasis*. Pupillary action is controlled by the parasympathetic and sympathetic nervous systems of the autonomic chain.

Piper methysticum. see KAVA.

pipiltzintzintli. [Nahuatl] Aztec name for a mint, SALVIA DIVINORUM, said to have hallucinogenic properties.

Piptadenia. a hallucinogenic snuff is made by South American Indians by pulverizing the seeds of the legumes *Piptadenia peregrina, P. colubrina,* and *P. macrocarpa,* belonging to the mimosa family (Leguminosae). Among different tribes it is known variously as yopo, niopo, cohoba, and huilca. These tribes are centered in the Orinoco basin of Colombia and Venezuela and in the Peruvian Andes, where huilca, *P. macrocarpa,* is thought to be used as a hallucinatory snuff, though little is known of it. Piptadenia intoxication produces convulsive movements and uncontrolled dancing, inability to control the movements of the limbs, and stimulation of the senses. These may be followed by periods of madness, or the users sink into a deep, nightmare-filled sleep. The Indians use it in orgies, to heighten their physical courage, for divination of the future, and to give them prowess in battle. Chemical analysis of the snuff has identified its chief alkaloid as BUFOTENINE. Piptadenia may also contain DMT.

pit. the main vein leading to the heart, considered the "original main line" and the best vein to inject by some addicts.

pituri. a shrublike plant, *Duboisia hopwoodii,* belonging to the potato family (Solanaceae), whose leaves are chewed by Australian aborigines and which contains the alkaloid SCOPOLAMINE. The leaves must first be mixed with ashes of an acacia, *Acacia salicina,* which acts chemically, when chewed, to release the alkaloid in the pituri. The leaves have a stimulating effect, at first, which the natives prize, because it enables them to travel long distances without food; later it produces stupefaction and narcosis. Not to be confused with Australian tobacco, which the aborigines also chew.

place. the setting or locale, whether favorable or hostile, of an LSD TRIP.

Placidyl. [ETHCHLORVYNOL, Abbott Laboratories] a nonbarbiturate hypnotic and sedative used to treat insomnia and as a TRANQUILIZER in anxiety and tension states. Manufacturer's recommended dosage: 100 to 200 milligrams per day, for daytime sedation; 500 milligrams at bedtime for sleep. Sold as maroon coated 100- and 500-milligrams (capsule-shaped) tablets. Subject to the DRUG ABUSE CONTROL AMENDMENT OF 1965.

plant. *1.* a hiding place or a cache. *2.* to place narcotics or other drugs in premises belonging to a suspected addict or user, then raiding them, a practice sometimes employed by narcotics police.

plastic hippie. a part-time or weekend HIPPIE; one who pretends to be a hippie without committing himself completely to the hippie way of life.

plata. [Spanish *plata,* silver] money.

poison. HEROIN.

poison people. poison (HEROIN) addicts.

> She had a bent-up spoon that she cooked stuff (heroin) in for the *poison people.*
> —Claude Brown, *Manchild in the Promised Land* (1965)

poke. [variant (?) of TOAK] a puff of a MARIJUANA cigarette.

pop. [from *pop,* to fire a pistol, cause a shot or bang; a *shot* of a drug—*EP* from around 1925] *1.* to shoot HEROIN subcutaneously. *2.* to swallow a PILL. Compare BANG, DROP.

popped. to be picked up by the police, as in "I got *popped* last week."

poppers. small vials containing AMYL NITRITE, which are broken in a handkerchief and inhaled. Compare PEARL.

> The law [in California] refuses liquor to anyone under twenty-one, but permits eighteen-year-olds to buy amyl nitrite for cardio-sexual stimulation. —John Sherlock, "The Hollywood Bachelor Observed," *Cosmopolitan* (August, 1967)

popping. [short for SKIN POPPING since around 1946—*EP*] injecting drugs subcutaneously.

population. at the U.S. Public Health Service (Narcotics) Hospital,

Lexington, Kentucky, the inmates. To be "in *population*" is to be allowed to mix normally with the other inmates, following withdrawal from the drug and "orientation" (counseling).

pot. [from Mexican Indian *potaguaya,* marijuana; since the 1950s] MARIJUANA.

potentiate. [from Latin *potentia,* power] to make a drug more effective or more powerful, usually by means of a second drug. Alcohol potentiates the effect of many drugs.

potlikker. a tea brewed from MARIJUANA waste, i.e., seeds and stems, which users say gives them a satisfactory HIGH (the seeds contain the plant's ACTIVE PRINCIPLE in small quantities).

potsville. using pot (MARIJUANA).

> *Potsville* leads to mainline.   —narcotics agent (1966)

pound. five dollars.

P.R. PANAMA RED.

Preludin. [phenmetrazine hydrochloride, Geigy Pharmaceuticals] central nervous system stimulant similar to an AMPHETAMINE, used in dieting to depress the appetite. The drug promotes a stimulated state and a feeling of well-being and is sometimes used in excess for these effects. Manufacturer's recommended dosage is 50 to 75 milligrams per day. Sold in the form of pink scored 25-milligram tablets or Endurets, round pink delayed-release 75-milligram tablets. Jack Ruby was reportedly using these pills excessively at the time he murdered Oswald, though no connection between this use and the shooting was officially established. Subject to the DRUG ABUSE CONTROL AMENDMENT OF 1965.

Prinadol. [PHENAZOCINE, Smith Kline & French Laboratories] a SYNTHETIC OPIATE. Manufacturer recommends as a narcotic analgesic, adjunct to anesthesia, for relief of postoperative pain, and in acute and chronic pain. Continued, regular use will lead to PHYSICAL DEPENDENCE. Recommended single dose is 2 milligrams. A CLASS A NARCOTIC.

Prolixin. [fluphenazine hydrochloride, E. R. Squibb & Sons] a phenothiazine derivative, classified as a MAJOR TRANQUILIZER and used in severe anxiety and tension states and severe mental disorders. In tension and anxiety states, manufacturer's recommended oral dosage is 1 to 2 milligrams daily; in severe mental disorder, 2.5 to 10 milligrams daily, with 20 milligrams daily the maximum. It is claimed to have longer-lasting action than CHLORPROMAZINE and to have fewer hypotensive (lowering of the blood pressure) and sedative effects than the other phenothiazines, to which it is otherwise similar. Supplied in coated pink 1-milligram, yellow 2.5-milligrams and green 5-milligram tablets with trademark inscribed and as an orange-flavored elixir and in solution for injection.

Prunicodeine. [CODEINE, terpin hydrate, and other ingredients, Eli Lilly and Company] cough syrup. Each 30 cubic centimeters (about 6 teaspoonsful) contains 60 milligrams (1 grain) of codeine sulfate and 175 milligrams of terpin hydrate (120 milligrams of codeine provides analgesic effects equal to those of 10 milligrams of MORPHINE). Prolonged use can result in both PSYCHIC DEPENDENCE and PHYSICAL DEPENDENCE, with WITHDRAWAL SYMPTOMS much less severe than morphine. Recommended dosage: 1 teaspoonful every three hours. Sold without prescription in many states, but federal Narcotic Registry number and record of sale required.

psilocybin. hallucinogenic alkaloid in certain mushrooms. Average hallucinogenic dose is 20 to 60 milligrams. Subject to the DRUG ABUSE CONTROL AMENDMENT of 1965. Compare MUSHROOMS, SACRED.

psychedelia. artifacts, crafts, dress, and music associated with the PSYCHEDELIC drug cult.

psychedelic. [Greek, *psyche,* soul, and *delos,* visible, evident] mind-manifesting; consciousness-expanding; introducing new, strange, or dramatically altered perceptions, sensory experiences, illusions, visions, and subconscious material into the conscious mind, thus "expanding" it in ways that are beyond the capacity of ordinary experience. Drugs such as LSD, MESCALINE, PSILOCYBIN, DMT, and CANNABIS have this effect. See HALLUCINOGEN.

psychedelic art. *1.* art which seeks to evoke or imitate the hallucinogenic experience by employing a bombardment of sensory stimuli produced by mixed-media devices such as stroboscopic lights, movies, slide projections, shadows, colors, shapes, music, and scents, which so surround the spectator that his habitual modes of perception and feeling are overborne and his consciousness "expanded" in a manner similar to the effects of a PSYCHEDELIC drug, or HALLUCINOGEN. *2.* a painting or poster suggested by, or evocative of, the distortions of perception, color patterns, "centering" of consciousness produced by the hallucinogenic drugs.

psychedelic peanut. peanut skins, crushed and smoked in a cigarette, and alleged to produce hallucinogenic effects.

psychedelphia. [coined by Herb Caen, San Francisco newspaper columnist] San Francisco, specifically the HAIGHT-ASHBURY district.

psychic dependence. a craving for the pleasurable mental effects produced by a drug, such as euphoria, elation, stimulation, sedation, hypnosis, hallucinations, sensory acuity, etc., and a strong psychological need or craving for this drug-induced state in preference to the normal state, so that a drug user finds its repetition necessary to his well-being. Withdrawal of psychic-dependence-producing drugs, especially central nervous system stimulants, while it produces no specific physical symptoms, may result in a serious depression, so unpleasant to the user that he may continue increasing his dose to forestall it, eventually triggering a psychosis with severe irruption of symptoms the drug had suppressed.

With mild hallucinogenic drugs, e.g., MARIJUANA, sudden withdrawal generally produces neither mental nor physical symptoms, but if the heavy use is related to underlying anxieties or a desire to retreat from reality, these psychoneurotic symptoms may return in aggravated form because, unmasked by the drug, they are more keenly perceived in the "normal" state. Similarly, there are no physical or psychic WITHDRAWAL SYMPTOMS per se from more powerful hallucinogenic drugs; however, under the influence of these drugs the user's subconscious sometimes releases unpleasant or terrifying matter previously repressed, which continues to exist at the conscious level after the user's normal state is restored and which he may find extremely unpleasant. This released unconscious material may drive him to suicidal urges or push him into a psychotic state. Of course, readministration of the drug will probably not help, and he does not desire it (it is stretching the original definition to say that one or a few ingestions of a drug constitute dependence), but the drug has altered his mental state in such a way that when its effect has passed, the user experiences a specialized and continuing kind of "withdrawal symptom" and often must receive medical and psychiatric care until he recovers. More commonly, psychic dependence on hallucinogenic drugs occurs, arising out of continuing pleasurable experiences with them, a growing preoccupation with self and loss of interest in the real world, and a recurrent desire to return to the mental state produced by the hallucinogenic drug and obsession with it as the preferred mental state.

A radical alteration in personality may also occur, with the user becoming vastly egotistical and so preoccupied with what he believes to be the "higher reality" of the hallucinogenic state that he wrecks his career and turns his back on social condemnation. Such dependence on hallucinogenic drugs appears to be the exception rather than the rule; the majority of experimenters with these drugs have no desire to repeat the experience, or repeat it quite infrequently (but this is true with any drug). Compare PHYSICAL DEPENDENCE.

DRUGS PRODUCING PSYCHIC DEPENDENCE
BUT NO PHYSICAL DEPENDENCE

cocaine (no tolerance develops; severe depression and/or psychotic symptoms may accompany withdrawal after prolonged heavy use)

marijuana (insignificant tolerance develops)

hashish (some degree of tolerance may develop; some degree of physical discomfort upon withdrawal after prolonged use has been observed)

amphetamines (tolerance develops to a considerable degree, but it is selective; i.e., insomnia and hyperexcitability caused by the drug continue, while increasing doses are necessary to sustain the drug's euphoriant effects. If use has masked symptoms of fatigue, abrupt withdrawal will often be accompanied by exhaustion and severe depression)

khat (not known)

LSD (complete tolerance develops after only three days.)

psilocybin (tolerance develops rapidly)

mescaline (tolerance develops rather more slowly)

morning glory seeds (not known)

psyching. [from *psychological* and *psycho,* insane; moderated to mean using psychology on another or causing him temporarily to lose his mental composure] shrewdly sizing up and detecting weaknesses in others in order to manipulate or victimize them.

psychoactive. altering the subjective state; altering perception and consciousness.

psychotogenic. producing hallucinations and psychotic behavior.

psychotomimetic. *1.* imitating a model psychosis. *2.* descriptive of drugs whose effects were thought to produce model psychosis. Since the drug experience is in some ways different from a psychosis, though in other aspects resembling one, the word is not favored, and HALLUCINOGENIC and PSYCHEDELIC are now used to describe those drugs.

> There are considerable differences between LSD-induced and schizophrenic symptoms. The characteristic autism and dissociation of schizophrenia are absent with LSD. Perceptual disturbances due to LSD differ from those due to schizophrenia and, as a rule, are not true hallucinations. Finally, disturbances of consciousness following LSD do not resemble those occurring in schizophrenia.
> —B. Manzini and Saraval, in *Delysid* (*LSD-25*), *Annotated Bibliography Addendum No. 3*, Sandoz Pharmaceuticals (1961)

psychotropic. [Greek *psyche,* soul, and *trope,* a turning] changing the consciousness; opposite of CEPHALOTROPIC.

public pot smoker. one who smokes MARIJUANA in public places, at public gatherings, often mixing the marijuana with tobacco or tobaccolike scent so that the smell is disguised.

pure. [circa 1940] relatively undiluted HEROIN.

> Old "Weeping" fell dead outside a shooting gallery in Saint Paul. Musta' shot some *'pure,'* cause a lookout on the sidewalk heard him mumble before he croaked. "Well kiss my dead mammy's ass if this aint the best 'smack' I ever shot."
> —"Iceberg Slim," *Pimp. The Story of My Life* (1967)

purple hearts. [from their color and rounded diamond shape] *1.* LUMINAL tablets. *2.* in Great Britain, Drinamyl (see DEXAMYL), a combination of a BARBITURATE and an AMPHETAMINE.

push. [from PUSHER, since around 1920—*EP*] to peddle drugs.

pusher. [from *pusher,* a passer of counterfeit money; since around 1920—*EP*] a low-level peddler of narcotics who sells directly to the addict in the street. The pusher buys his drugs from a wholesaler, who in turn gets his from the importer via courier. Also, a seller of MARIJUANA, LSD, PILLS, etc., but not HARD NARCOTICS, frequently called a DEALER or the SOURCE.

pushing. *1.* peddling narcotics. *2.* peddling MARIJUANA, LSD, PILLS, etc., but not NARCOTICS. See DEALING.

put his (your) trip. preaching the superiority of one's own LSD experience and, by implication, oneself and one's philosophy, as in "Timothy Leary is out of favor with the HIPPIES because he's trying too hard to *put his trip* on everybody else"; i.e., a rebellion against another person's structuring or defining one's own LSD experience by holding his up as a model.

put on a crosstown bus. "put someone in a dilemma."
—Seymour Fiddle, *Portraits from a Shooting Gallery* (1967)

put somebody on. give him some MARIJUANA to smoke—*MM*, 1946. Compare TURN ON.

pyrahexyl. also called parahexyl, synhexyl. Derivative of the ACTIVE PRINCIPLE of CANNABIS. When it is swallowed in capsule form, the effects are similar to those of cannabis. It has been used experimentally in the treatment of drug withdrawal and depressive states.

Q q

q'at. KHAT.

quarter bag. about 1 ounce of MARIJUANA, worth $25.

quill. folded matchbook cover used to sniff a drug. The drug (HEROIN or COCAINE) is placed in the fold and then inhaled through the nose. Compare SCOOP.

R r

rainbow. [from the capsule, blue at one half, red at the other, and dark red where the two overlap] TUINAL capsule.

rainy-day woman. MARIJUANA cigarette.

rap. [from *rap,* to perjure oneself, to swear a false oath, around the seventeenth century; hence, *rap,* to speak, to acknowledge someone, since the 1870s—*EP.* Not from *rapport* (see RAPPING), although its use among drug users of middle-class origins, who know the meaning of rapport, may have given it a subtle shift from its meaning among criminals and narcotic addicts] *1.* to talk, especially to talk the jargon of the addict's life. *2.* to gossip, converse. *3.* talk, used as a noun, as in "while I'm going through my *rap,*" i.e., while I'm speaking my piece (under the influence of drugs).

rapping. ["Achieving rapport with random talk"—*Time* (1967); but see RAP] *1.* talking. *2.* random free-form conversation.

rat. an addict who is working as a police informer.

Rauwolfia serpentina. a small climbing shrub of the family Apocynaceae, indigenous to India and neighboring countries, known in English as snakeroot. In India, the root is ground into powder and used medicinally for snakebite, hypertension, insomnia, and insanity. Its tranquilizing effects have been known there for 2,500 years. It is now used by Western medicine as a TRANQUILIZER, rarely in its powdered form, usually in the chemical derivative (RESERPINE).

reader. [prescription for narcotics since around 1925—*EP*] prescription for narcotics, usually obtained from a doctor illicitly by an addict. Compare MAKING A CROAKER FOR A READER, SCRIPT.

red and blues. [from the two-colored capsule] TUINAL capsules.

red birds. [from the color] SECONAL capsules.

red devils. [from the color] SECONAL capsules.

red dirt marijuana. MARIJUANA growing wild.

reds. [from the color] SECONAL capsules.

reefer. [since around 1925; usually plural—*EP*. Perhaps from GREFA, (Mexican), marijuana] MARIJUANA cigarette.

reserpine. one of the alkaloids found in RAUWOLFIA SERPENTINA. It is employed in a variety of preparations as a TRANQUILIZER to alleviate anxiety, combat tension, and calm patients with severe psychoses. The drug is said to exercise its calming effect unaccompanied by loss of motor control and disequilibrium. Unlike some tranquilizers, it has no anticonvulsant or antihistaminic effects. Nevertheless, it is used rather rarely, the phenothiazine derivatives currently being preferred in medical and psychiatric practice. Dosages range from 0.5 to 1.5 milligrams daily in hypertension and anxiety to 5 milligrams daily in psychoses. Compare SANDRIL.

righteous bush. MARIJUANA—*MM*, 1946. *Obsolete.*

ripped. intoxicated by drugs.

Rivea corymbosa. plant of the bindweed family (Convovulaceae) the seeds of which have hallucinogenic properties. See MORNING GLORY SEEDS.

roach. ["In the jargon of the marijuana addict (*sic*) a man who has smoked half a cigarette is called a 'cucaracha' which literally means cockroach"—Pablo Oswaldo Wolff, 1949. Perhaps from the wriggling motion of the cockroach and also the size, shape, and brownish color resembling a cockroach] butt of a MARIJUANA cigarette. In order not to waste any marijuana the smoker puffs down to as short a butt as possible, holding it with a toothpick or inserting it in one end of a tightly rolled match folder, or a ROACH HOLDER, when it is too hot for the fingers. Some even eat the remaining marijuana to destroy evidence and because they believe the ACTIVE PRINCIPLE is concentrated in the end. When the butt can no longer be smoked, it is torn open, and the remaining marijuana is put back in the smoker's supply for reuse. Compare COCKTAIL.

> La cucaracha, la cucaracha,
> Ya no puede caminar,
> Porque no tiene, porque no tiene
> Marijuana que fumar.   —Mexican folk song

roach holder. a thin pronged instrument, often elaborately decorated, upon which a ROACH is skewered for smoking purposes. Compare CRUTCH, STEAMBOAT.

roach pick. ROACH HOLDER.

root. [see JOINT] a MARIJUANA cigarette.

rose maria. [Mexico] CANNABIS.

roses. BENZEDRINE tablets.

run. *1.* period of addiction, as in "then I got hooked and had a three-year *run.*" *2.* a period of continuous, heavy AMPHETAMINE use, usually by injection, lasting three to five days and ending when the user sinks into protracted, exhausted sleep (CRASH).

rush. the initial onset of euphoria and physical well-being immediately after the drug has been injected; distinguished from the HIGH, the continuing state of relaxation and well-being while the drug is effective. Intravenous injection produces the quickest, most intense rush. Compare FLASH, FLUSH.

> Then you just take off the strap and squeeze it in. Then you feel that *rush* all over your body and you got your high.
>   —addict, quoted in Jeremy Larner and Ralph Tefferteller
>   *The Addict in the Street* (1964)

S s

sacred mushrooms. MUSHROOMS, SACRED.

salt shot. an injection of a saline solution to an addict who is unconscious from an OVERDOSE. This treatment, an addict's home remedy not medically sanctioned, may have some merit, being similar to treatment sometimes administered to patients in shock in a hospital. The object, of course, is to counteract respiratory depression by restoring the victim to consciousness.

Salvia divinorum. a plant with hallucinogenic properties belonging to the mint family. It is used primarily by the Mazatec Indians of Mexico, usually when hallucinogenic mushrooms are not available. The leaves are chewed directly or crushed, steeped in water, and drunk. Their effects are said to be similar to those of the hallucinogenic mushrooms, but less sweeping and shorter lasting. The ACTIVE PRINCIPLE of the leaves is not known. Compare MUSHROOMS, SACRED.

Sandril. [RESERPINE, Eli Lilly and Company] a MINOR TRANQUILIZER. Recommended by manufacturer in treating mild to moderate hypertension (high blood pressure) and in anxiety and tension states. Recommended dosages range from 0.25 milligram twice daily up to 5 to 10 milligrams per day in psychiatric treatment. Overdosage can result in depression of the central nervous system, sometimes followed by stimulus to the point of convulsions; death results from cessation of respiration.

Sansert. [methysergide maleate (1-methyllysergic acid butanolamide maleate), Sandoz Pharmaceuticals] a SEROTONIN inhibitor, chemically related to LSD-25. It is used medically as a preventive treatment for chronic migraine headaches. Manufacturer's recommended average daily dosage is two to four tablets or 4 to 8 milligrams. Illicit users have discovered the drug, which they tout as a substitute for LSD, producing similar effects. One claimed that 16 milligrams of Sansert gave effects equivalent to 100 micrograms of LSD. The drug is available only by prescription. Supplied in bright yellow sugar-coated 2-milligram tablets.

sassfras. [from (?) the physical resemblance to the sassafras tree]

MARIJUANA cigarette, made from marijuana grown in the United States and therefore not so potent as the imported kinds—*La Guardia Report,* 1944. *Obsolete.*

scag. HEROIN.

scars. traces left by healing needle marks; black or blue spots. See TRACKS.

> Now people would ask you if you knew someone by describing their *scars.*   —Claude Brown, *Manchild in the Promised Land* (1965)

scene. social patterns of drug use in a particular area, usually referring to a college or high school.

> The drug *scene* at Harvard is normally played in private. . . . The pusher takes you around campus, to the places where "the scene" happens. (i.e., where students turn on).
>   —Richard Goldstein, *One in Seven: Drugs on Campus* (1966)

schmack. [corruption of Yiddish SCHMECK, to sniff] *1.* HEROIN or COCAINE. *2.* by extension, all drugs.

schmeck. [Yiddish, to sniff; from the practice of sniffing drugs, especially heroin; since the 1940s] HEROIN.

schmecker. a HEROIN user.

schoolboy. CODEINE.

scissors. [local at Shimer College, Mt. Carroll, Ill.] MARIJUANA. Compare HAIRCUT.

> Can I borrow your *scissors,* means "I want to buy any pot you can sell me."
>   —Richard Goldstein, *One in Seven: Drugs on Campus* (1966)

scoff. [from tramp's term for food; to take narcotics orally (?); since around 1920—*EP*] *1.* food. *2.* to eat.

scoff back. eat a lot—MM, 1946. *Obsolete.*

scoop. *1.* a folded matchbook cover. *2.* to sniff COCAINE or HEROIN through a rolled or folded matchbook cover.

> I taught him how to *scoop* cocaine. . . . before I could get the matchbook scoop up to my nostril again.
>   —Claude Brown, *Manchild in the Promised Land* (1965)

I felt something thrust into my hand and saw a cap and a piece of match-book cover folded into a V-shaped *scoop.*

"Snort, man," Waneko said. "It's H."

—Piri Thomas, *Down These Mean Streets* (1967)

scopolamine. also called hyoscine. A nonbarbiturate hypnotic, sedative, and involuntary-muscle relaxant. Scopolamine is the active alkaloid of henbane (*Hyoscyamus niger*); it is also found in *Scopola carniolica* and the Australian shrub, PITURI, all of the potato family (Solanaceae), whose members include BELLADONNA and DATURA. They contain the alkaloids ATROPINE and HYOSCYAMINE, which have pharmacological effects similar to scopolamine. In toxic doses, scopolamine, like atropine, can cause excitation, hallucinations, delirium, and other bizarre mental effects.

Scopolamine in large doses can be deadly, and it was known for such properties by the ancient Greeks and Romans. In the Middle Ages, the henbane and belladonna plants were used in the manufacture of salves and potions for necromancy and witchcraft. Some authorities believe that the illusions accompanying such rites, e.g., having intercourse with the Devil, were produced by belladonna or henbane intoxication.

In the twentieth century, scopolamine has been employed as a so-called "truth serum." Subjects in a state of hypnosis or "twilight sleep" produced by the drug are more pliable to interrogation, as they are under such BARBITURATES as PENTOTHAL SODIUM. Since the drug can also induce amnesia, it is not frequently used today. In modern medicine scopolamine is used occasionally as a TRANQUILIZER with mental patients; as a preanesthetic tranquilizer, with morphine, to allay anxiety and fear and induce anesthesia; and as an antispasmodic in gastrointestinal disorders and peptic ulcers, because of its action in immobilizing the smooth muscles of the intestine (for further discussion see ATROPINE). Scopolamine has approximately twice the depressant effect on the central nervous system that atropine has; hence it is a more effective sedative and is found (as scopolamine hydrobromide) in a variety of nonprescription sedatives on the market such as Sominex, Sleep-eze, and Compoz. The usual effects of the average medical dose of scopolamine (0.5 milligram) are drowsiness, euphoria, amnesia, and dreamless sleep. Occasionally, bizarre reactions to such small doses will occur, especially when the patient is in pain. Scopolamine also acts to inhibit bodily secretions (saliva, tears, sweat, etc.), to dilate the pupils, and to stimulate the central respiratory system.

Scopolamine is thought to be more toxic than atropine, although this is not certain. Toxic reactions progress, with increase of the dosage, from slight slowing of the heartbeat, dryness of the mouth, rapid heartbeat, dry skin, dilated pupils, and restlessness combined with fatigue, to loss of coordination, extreme restlessness, loss of memory, excitement, flushed skin, hallucinations, delirium, and coma. Doses of above 10 milligrams will almost certainly produce these major toxic effects. When death occurs, it is due to paralysis, coma, and resultant respiratory failure. The toxic symptoms may continue for a period of days. With scopolamine, a period of depression and hypnosis may follow the psychotic symptoms. TOLERANCE develops if it is used over a period of time. Some patients take doses of 5 milligrams three times a day, and one taking 54 milligrams a day was reported. The fatal dose is sometimes given as roughly 100 milligrams; a dose of 500 milligrams has been survived.

PHYSICAL DEPENDENCE upon scopolamine with WITHDRAWAL SYMPTOMS does not occur; presumably PSYCHIC DEPENDENCE upon the drug's sedative effects can develop. The hallucinations, excitement, and euphoria that toxic doses of the drug produce might be sought by some users of other hallucinogenic drugs; however, these effects are quite often frightening and unpleasant in the extreme, and so it is doubtful that anyone would wish to repeat them.

> Recent reports on the impressions of patients treated with *scopolamine,* the active principle of henbane, supply more information. They experience a feeling of pressure in the head as if a heavy body rested on it. At the same time an invisible force seems to close their eyelids. Sight becomes vague and all objects seem to be stretched lengthwise. All kind of visual hallucinations are produced while the eyes are open. For instance, a black circle on a silver background or a green circle on a golden background appears. The eyes then close and sleep sets in. The senses of taste and smell are also frequently affected. When sleeping the individual is surrounded by fantastic apparitions.
>
> —Louis Lewin, *Phantastica: Narcotic and Stimulating Drugs* (1964)

score. [from (?) *score dough,* the price of a BUNDLE of narcotics; the proceeds of a theft; money; among American drug addicts *the score* means "sufficient money to purchase narcotics; since around 1930—*EP*] *1.* to purchase narcotics.

I was living near 145th and Broadway at that time and I was *scoring* up there. I'd get my six bags, 11 o'clock at night go to work, and the same routine all day. —addict, quoted in Jeremy Larner and Ralph Tefferteller, *The Addict in the Street* (1964)

2. purchase of narcotics. *3.* acquisition of money by an illegal transaction.

scratch (scratching). [description of addict's compulsion to scratch himself] being an addict.

script. [contraction of *prescription*] a narcotics prescription. Compare READER.

scrubwoman's kick. naphtha, sometimes used as a cleaning preparation, emits intoxicatory fumes, which produce giddiness, loss of coordination, and sometimes euphoria; scrubwomen are supposed to have enjoyed the practice of inhaling the fumes until they were mildly intoxicated.

seccy. SECONAL, a BARBITURATE.

Seconal. [secobarbital, Eli Lilly and Company.] a short-acting, fast-onset BARBITURATE hypnotic and sedative. The hypnotic dosage is 100 milligrams. Excessive long-term use will result in PSYCHIC DEPENDENCE and PHYSICAL DEPENDENCE with severe WITHDRAWAL SYMPTOMS if use is abruptly ceased. Overdosage results in central nervous system depression, respiratory depression, constriction of the pupils slightly (though in severe poisoning they may dilate), decreased urine formation, lowered body temperature, and coma; death comes from cessation of the respiratory reflex. Supplied in bright red 32-milligram capsules. Slang names: red birds, red devils, reds.

seed. the butt of a MARIJUANA cigarette. Compare ROACH.

seggy. SECONAL, a BARBITURATE.

serotonin. also called 5-hydroxytryptamine, enteramine, and 5-HT. A neurohormone found in the nervous system, small intestine, and brain. Neurohormones are chemical messengers which transmit nerve impulses across the synapses between the neuron and the muscle cell, thus activating the muscle. Other neurohormones are ADRENALIN (epinephrine) and acetylcholine.

Serotonin is known to activate the smooth muscle of the small intestine, raise blood pressure, and constrict small blood vessels. Its function in the brain is only dimly understood but is thought to be important, even though less than 1 percent of the body's total supply of serotonin resides there.

Because of its chemical similarity to the indole ring in hallucinogenic drugs such as BUFOTENINE, LSD-25, PSILOCYBIN, and MESCALINE, it is thought to be intimately related with their action, although precisely how is not certain. LSD-25, for example, seems to block the action of serotonin. When the two are placed together on a slice of smooth muscle tissue, nothing happens, although serotonin alone (or LSD alone) causes the muscle to contract. This suggests an analogous action in the brain.

According to one theory, LSD in the brain may compete with serotonin for the monoamine oxidase enzymes (see MONOAMINE OXIDASE INHIBITORS), which normally act upon serotonin to produce metabolites. When serotonin does not metabolize normally, as a result of LSD's monopolizing the necessary enzymes, it may throw off abnormal by-products, one of which could be bufotenine, which has hallucinatory effects when injected. A similar derangement of serotonin caused by chemicals produced within the body rather than the hallucinogenic drugs may possibly be a cause of schizophrenia. This chemical theory of schizophrenia has yet to be demonstrated. (For another theory see ADRENOCHROME.)

Another theory of the relationship between serotonin and the effects of LSD postulates that serotonin acts as a mediator or inhibitor of nerve messages within the brain, serving to channel them in an orderly manner; that LSD replaces serotonin but is a weaker inhibitor and thus, more messages are transmitted. According to this theory, the brain's regulatory center becomes overloaded, like a telephone switchboard suddenly jammed with incoming calls and lighting up on every circuit, and the illusions, pseudo hallucinations, distortions of normal perception, inflow of subconscious, repressed materials, etc., caused by hallucinogenic drugs are explained as dislocations of the usual orderly patterns of brain function, a figurative storm of suddenly unleashed material beating against the consciousness in sheets and waves.

Another theory holds that by blocking serotonin LSD induces temporary starvation of message transmissions; into this vacuum flow subconscious materials, disoriented perceptions of the surrounding environment, and so on, which take over the individual's consciousness.

It is interesting to note that MORPHINE and the TRANQUILIZER CHLORPROMAZINE, often used to reverse the LSD experience, also inhibit the action of serotonin, while RESERPINE, another tranquilizer, acts to stimulate it. All these explanations still have to be demonstrated by experiment.

set. *1.* [term proposed by Timothy Leary] the mental state of a person about to take a drug, encompassing both his state at the time and his deep psychological tendencies. Some LSD theoreticians hold that the set, and the SETTING determine the quality of the psychedelic experience, including any adverse reactions. Anyone harboring a latent psychosis (part of his set) might emerge from the LSD with a chronic long-term psychosis; or a novice, frightened, ill at ease in his surroundings, and distrustful of his companions, might have a temporary, acute panic reaction to the drug. But even experienced LSD users with over a hundred favorable LSD TRIPS under their belts can experience adverse results. Still, it seems incontrovertible that the person's intelligence, background, imagination, emotional state, and response to suggestion by others will color and provide the content of the hallucinations and emotions he experiences while under the influence of a hallucinogenic drug. By the same token, there are always unpredictables in an individual's makeup at a given point in time, which makes a certain prediction of his reaction to experimental drugs like LSD impossible.

2. [from (?) stage *set*] a drug-selling and drug-taking locale; a place where a group of addicts and pushers habitually congregate and are known to each other and where drugs are available. Compare LEAVING-THE-SET WALK, SCENE.

> The *set* is on the fifth floor and the floor is creaking an' groaning under the weight of all the coolies that are swinging. You dig the open door of the roof and smell burning pot.
> —Piri Thomas, *Down These Mean Streets* (1967)

setting. the total environment in which the hallucinogenic-drug user undergoes his drug experience. A supportive, friendly environment in which the user is supervised by a trusted person and is surrounded by pleasing objects, colors, and music, rich in associational content and interacting with a favorable SET is considered most conducive to a favorable experience. In a favorable setting in a therapeutic atmosphere a patient counseled by a psychiatrist may achieve a positive, therapeutic experience. A supportive setting, however, is no guarantee against an adverse reaction.

set up. *1.* to entrap a narcotics user by having an informant sell him drugs in the presence of narcotics officers. *2.* to conceal drugs in a drug user's residence and then raid it, as in "the cops *set* him *up* for a bust." Compare PLANT.

seventeen-fifty-one. [from the number of the New York State statute] felonious possession of drugs, i.e., in amounts above a statutory minimum which establishes a legal presumption that drugs are being held for purposes of sale.

seventeen-forty-seven B. possession of BARBITURATES, a misdemeanor under New York state law.

shit. [from (?) a deprecation of the quality of diluted heroin on the market, in comparison with that available in the 1920s; see JUNK; or using a socially proscribed word, see CRAP] HEROIN. Nonnarcotics users have taken over the term to some extent and use it to refer to HASHISH, PAREGORIC, and LSD.

> Lysergic shit
> —R. Fariña, *Been Down So Long Looks Like Up to Me* (1966)

Shiva. SIVA.

shlook. a puff of a MARIJUANA cigarette. Compare POKE, TOAK.

shooting gallery. *1.* a place where addicts regularly go to inject themselves with their purchases. Some addicts rent out their apartments for this purpose. *2.* the place in a hospital where addicts in withdrawal (or on maintenance therapy) are given their shots or oral doses.

shooting gravy. injecting "cooked" blood. Sometimes the addict's blood, drawn back up in the needle while he is injecting, coagulates and clogs the needle. He pours the mixture of blood and NARCOTICS back into his COOKER, heats it until the blood dissolves, and reinjects. Compare BOOTING, GRAVY.

shoot up. inject HEROIN.

> I began mainlining about 3 years ago—maybe 4—after I lost my job, and then I began *shooting up* pretty regular.
> —addict, quoted in Dr. Donald B. Louria, *Nightmare Drugs* (1966)

short. [since around 1930—*EP*] a car. Compare CRACKING SHORTS.

short con. a petty confidence game. Compare LONG CON.

short count. a short weight of a drug given by a supplier to a PUSHER for resale to the addict, the object being to cheat the pusher.

short go. *1.* a shortage. *2.* short weight from the PUSHER'S supplier. Compare PANIC, SHORT COUNT.

> Everything was going as good as could be expected, till the panic hit. There was a *short go* on heroin on account of some big wheeler-dealer with millions of dollars worth of the stuff had gotten himself busted and this caused a bad shortage.
> —Piri Thomas, *Down These Mean Streets* (1967)

shying. the technique of cooking OPIUM pills—*MM*, 1946. *Obsolete?*

sick. suffering WITHDRAWAL SYMPTOMS.

sickie. [from (?) SICK in the drug addict's sense, or from (?) mentally *sick*] a college student who uses NARCOTICS.

> For students who use heroin are referred to as *sickies* by even the most Bohemian students. More important, they suddenly become "square." They have allowed the body to dominate, and they have exhibited vulnerability and dependence; cool people do not depend. Most important, with their glazed faces and drug obsession they scare even the habitual marijuana users or "potheads."
> —Richard Goldstein, *One in Seven: Drugs on Campus* (1966)

Siva. the mahadevi, or great god, of the Hindu trinity, who brought CANNABIS to mankind. Taking BHANG or CHARAS often accompanies ceremonies of worship to Siva.

sixteenth. one-sixteenth ounce of diluted HEROIN, a measure for purposes of sale to the addict. Compare PIECE.

sizzle. NARCOTICS carried on the person.

skid bag. [from *skid row,* gathering place of derelicts; the bottom of the heap] a BAG containing highly diluted HEROIN.

skin. cigarette paper for rolling MARIJUANA cigarettes.

skinning. SKIN POPPING.

skin popping. [perhaps from *pop,* to burst or break; or from *pop,* to fire a pistol; leading to *shoot,* and *to shoot,* i.e., inject, drugs; compare BANG; since the 1920s—*EP*] injecting a narcotic subcutaneously or intramuscularly. The onset of the drug's effects is not so immediate as it is with MAINLINING (injecting intravenously). Neophytes often pass through three modes of taking the drug on their way to addiction: SNIFFING or snorting, skin popping, and mainlining. The practice of skin popping is also resorted to by old addicts whose veins are "used up." Skin popping often results in sores and boils on the body, through which tetanus bacillus enters. In New York City, 75 percent of all tetanus cases are addicts; 50 percent of these cases are fatal. Compare INFECTION.

sleepwalker. HEROIN addict.

slogans. college users of nonnarcotic drugs, often using puns, coin slogans to call for the legalization of hallucinogenic drugs or simply signal to each other their underground bonds.

> Keep off the Grass
> Be Ahead
> Support Your Local Travel Agent [reference to the LSD TRIP and the
>   LSD PUSHER]
> This Trip Is Necessary [LSD trip]
> Let's Legalize Pot
> End Marijuana Prohibition
> Be Aware [i.e., keep alert for federal narcotics officers—Berkeley
>   poster on which American flag is basic design]

smack. [corruption of *schmeck*] SCHMECK.

smashed. intoxicated on drugs.

smeck. SCHMECK.

snakeroot. RAUWOLFIA SERPENTINA.

snappers. [the glass vials are snapped open so that the contents can be inhaled] AMYS.

sniffing. inhaling HEROIN or COCAINE in powdered form through the nostrils. Compare SCHMECK, SNORT.

> Looking dead at Alfredo, I inhaled, first through one nostril, then
> through the other. Then turning quickly, away I went into the cold,
> cold street. Almost immediately I felt a burning sensation in my
> nose, like a sneeze coming. I pulled out my handkerchief and had
> barely enough time to put it to my nose when the blood came pour-

ing out. *Man, I thought, this cap has blown out the insides of my nose.* But in a few seconds the bleeding stopped just as it started.

Now the night lights seemed to get duller, my awareness of things delayed. But the music was clearer and I felt no pain, nothing at all. I seemed sort of detached. I felt a little sick in my belly, but the good-o feeling was better. I saw Trina coming to meet me and I crossed the street and walked toward her, walking real light, real dreamy and slow, so she would have to meet me more than halfway. Sometimes I'd make her walk all the way to me, but tonight I felt good. —Piri Thomas, *Down These Mean Streets* (1967)

snop. MARIJUANA or a marijuana cigarette.

snort. *1.* to inhale HEROIN or COCAINE through the nose. *2.* an inhalation of heroin or cocaine.

When you SNORT heroin, you know, it got a bad, bitter taste, like a taste that would turn your stomach inside out. It got some way-out taste. I couldn't SNORT because I couldn't take that taste; so I started shooting up.
—addict, quoted in Jeremy Larner and Ralph Tefferteller
The Addict in the Street (1964)

snow. [from the white, flaky appearance, since around 1900] COCAINE crystals.

sodium succinate. MESCALINE antagonist; it reverses the hallucinogenic effects of the drug.

soma. an intoxicating beverage made from the juices exuded from stems of an unknown plant (possibly *Asclepias acida* or CANNABIS) and used ceremonially by priests and nobles in ancient India. Legend says that after drinking soma the god Indra was inspired to create the universe. Because restrictions were placed upon the drug's use in ancient times and it was replaced by yoga as a religious technique, its certain identity has been lost.

Sominex. See SCOPOLAMINE entry and quotation.

source, the. a supplier of drugs; frequently of pharmaceutical but non-narcotic drugs such as HALLUCINOGENS, AMPHETAMINES, or BARBITURATES. The source may synthesize the drugs himself in a home laboratory or obtain them illicitly from manufacturers or pharmacists.

spaced. [perhaps from a sensation of floating in space, the dislocation of the time sense caused by hallucinogenic drugs] *1.* in a state of altered consciousness induced by a drug, usually a HALLUCINOGEN, such as MARIJUANA, HASHISH, or LSD. *2.* out of communication; in a state of pent-up inarticulateness as one undergoes the mental effects of a hallucinogenic drug; HIGH.

spaced out. SPACED.

sparkle plenties. [after *Sparkle Plenty,* a character in "Dick Tracy"] AMPHETAMINES.

speed. [from SPEEDBALL; or from the stimulant effects of the drug] *1.* AMPHETAMINES, usually METHEDRINE. *2.* speedball.

speedball. HEROIN and COCAINE or AMPHETAMINE (DESOXYN is most common) injected as a mixture. The cocaine or amphetamine enhances the RUSH, while the heroin tempers the unpleasant extremes of the cocaine exhilaration and perhaps prolongs the KICK. Compare BOMBITA, FLASH.

> The reason for a *speed* is you get this tremendous girl [cocaine] kick that lasts only about one-half hour, and after it sort of starts dying off you have this almost buzzing sensation in all of your body and everything. But it becomes definitely sensuous, you know, all of a sudden and then after that it is just beginning to wear off, then wham, it's just like you made the boy [heroin] *then.* It comes on with this flash and everything. It's as though it holds off, you know, until the girl can operate.
> —Helen Macgill Hughes (ed.), *The Fantastic Lodge* (1961)

spike. hypodermic needle.

splash. AMPHETAMINES.

split. [SYNANON term] to run away, leave, break off treatment.

splits. probably a TRANQUILIZER, identity unknown.

> *Splits* were common [in prison]. They're round white pills with a groove across the middle, some sort of tranquilizer. If you swallow one with a glass of hot water, you get a gone high that's almost like heroin. . . .
> "That damn fool, he got some splits and it's bad enough to swallow them like he does, three or four at a gulp, but he went and crushed them and copped some works, an eye dropper and a needle, and shot himself up. His heart stopped."
> —Piri Thomas, *Down These Mean Streets* (1967)

spoon. *1.* [from the tiny *spoons* used to ladle out the HEROIN] *2.* a measure of pure heroin, about 1/16 ounce, i.e., the unit by which the wholesaler often sells it to the PUSHER, who then cuts it and puts it in bags. There are, very roughly, seven bags to a spoon. *3.* an ordinary teaspoon (usually with handle bent) used for dissolving heroin over heat prior to injecting it. Compare BAG, CUTTING, PIECE, SIXTEENTH.

square. *1.* anyone who does not use drugs. Compare STRAIGHT. *2.* a conventional cigarette.

S.S. a suspended sentence.

> Remember I said in the Automat that when a junkie gets busted he rats on a couple of connections to get an *SS*—a suspended sentence?
> —narcotics detective in James Mills, *The Panic in Needle Park* (1966)

star dust. COCAINE.

stash. a hiding place for drugs and drug-taking equipment. Taping to the side of a toilet tank is a common stash. See HOLD, HOLDING.

> There are essentially two schools of thought. The first is the extreme one-up method of *stashing in the most obvious place*. On the coffee table labeled in plain sight. This is the preferred style in your upper socio-economic circles. The opposite point of view is the place *where it cannot be*. Inside the cubes or within brick walls, for example. Both obviously unsuitable due to the preparations involved. A third viewpoint does exist: this is the reactionary non-holder, his thesis being *never hold* [keep drugs on the premises]. A fourth view, not worthy of prime attention, is the *off-pad* scheme. On the roof the roof stash, or the clothesline stash. The object here is to avoid direct holding. If you smoke you must hold sometime. Stash in your own home. Avoid unnecessary losses that can result from accidental stash uncovery. A cause for great paranoia.
> —*The Marijuana Newsletter No. 2* (March 15, 1965)

steamboat. [from the resemblance to a steamboat smokestack] to inhale the butt of a MARIJUANA cigarette stuck in a hole in a toilet roll, the hand enclosing one end, the mouth on the other end. Since the butt is too short and hot to hold in the fingers, it is inserted in the roll, which traps the smoke to be inhaled. Thus none of the smoke escapes, and it is cooled. Marijuana users believe that the concentration inhaled mixed with air, or "hyperventilated," is greater in potency.

stick. *1.* [from *stick of tea,* a thinly rolled cigarette—*MM,* 1946] MARIJUANA cigarette purchased already rolled. *2.* [from Yiddish *schtick,* a technique, especially a characteristic bit of theatrical business] a favored criminal technique or mode of con; a style of life or criminal's *modus operandi.*

> Way down he was tickled that I wanted to imitate his *stick* of being.
> —Piri Thomas, *Down These Mean Streets* (1967)

sting. [from *sting,* to rob or defraud; verb since the 1800s; noun since around 1920— *EP*] a robbery, theft, illegal obtaining of money from a victim.

> I could uh . . . use uh my particular accent and have them believin'
> one thing . . . and the others was—would be takin' the *sting* off, you
> know?   —addict in Seymour Fiddle,
> *Portraits from a Shooting Gallery* (1967)

stone. [from STONED, high on a drug; also, a stone is smooth, hard, solid, final] completely, finally, ultimately (good).

> . . . so cold it [a Coca-Cola] hurt my throat clear round to the back
> of my neck. But it was *stone* good.
>   She was really a good-looking blip, stone-smooth.
> —Piri Thomas, *Down These Mean Streets* (1967)

stone addict. [see STONE; one becomes completely, fully stoned quickly; also (?) the idea of finality, of being ultimately stoned, completely achieving the goal of drug use] an addict who has rapidly acquired a strong habit.

stoned. in a state of drug-induced intoxication, elation, or euphoria, in a pleasant stupor.

stool. [from *stool pigeon,* police informer] *1.* to give information to police on illicit narcotics activities. *2.* to cooperate with police in trapping narcotics users.

STP. [DOM (4-methyl-2,5-dimethoxy-α-methylphenethylamine), Dow Chemical Company; probably from the brand name of a motor oil additive, "scientifically treated petroleum," which promises added power] a synthetic hallucinogenic drug chemically related to AMPHETAMINE and MESCALINE, STP achieved notoriety in the summer of 1967, when hospitals began receiving cases marked by psychotic reactions to the drug. Ten such cases were admitted in eleven days in San Francisco; one chronic psychosis and a possible death were also reported. It was believed that several thousand capsules containing the drug had been distributed free at a San Francisco be-in in April or May. The capsules were described by police as white with blue spots (later a New York biweekly described them as orange).

Use of the initials was variously attributed to members of the Hells Angels motorcycle gang (the motor-oil additive) and to Timothy Leary ("serenity, tranquillity, and peace"). At any rate, the drug was undoubtedly real, and its effects were said to be both more dramatic and longer lasting than those of LSD, three to four days as opposed to eight to twelve hours, although it was less potent on a weight-for-weight basis.

The tranquilizing drug CHLORPROMAZINE, frequently administered to calm an LSD taker who has had a panic psychotic reaction, was found to intensify and worsen adverse reactions to STP, leading some doctors to believe that STP, like chlorpromazine, resembled ATROPINE and hence one POTENTIATED the other. Another report called the drug BZ, a top-secret "nerve gas" being experimented on by the Army. When at last the Food and Drug Administration BUREAU OF DRUG ABUSE CONTROL obtained samples and analyzed them, they announced it was a mescaline derivative (and hence subject to the DRUG ABUSE CONTROL AMENDMENT OF 1965).

A BDAC chemist then noticed the similarity of the drug's formula to that of an experimental drug, DOM, upon which Dow Chemical had applied for a patent. A check with the company revealed that the formulas were in fact identical. Whether STP represented the theft of Dow's formula, a leak of supplies of the actual drug (it had been sent to some scientific investigators and was being proposed for use in mental illness), or the independent discovery of some underground chemist, could not be determined. Although some experienced users of HALLUCINOGENS praise it, others say that it carries more risk of a psychotic reaction than any other drugs; one writer said the odds were sixty to forty against a good TRIP.

Another writer, close to the drug underground, reported that the "manufacturer" was distributing the drug free of charge.

> All veterans concur on the overwhelming power of *STP*. They speak of a maelstrom of relentless energy. "A feeling," said [Richard] Alpert "that it's going to do it to you whether you like it or not." The energy seems to manifest itself physically. "You feel like your body

is a conductor for tens of thousands of volts," said a user. "I was desperate for a ground." People tripping on STP physically tremble with the energy sensation. It is a stretching, quivering, shaking experience. Many have emerged from STP with a sudden concern for physical health. "We have need to be strong," said one. "We need protein. The macrobiotic diet is bad news."

The relentless rush of energy is often a frightening experience. "Acid is like being let out of a cage," explained one user. "STP is like being shot out of a gun. There's no slowing down or backing up. You feel like your brakes have given out.". . .

A key to survival in the STP experience seems to be an ability to surrender to the energy flow of the drug. Resisting the rush or holding back can lead, many report, to an incredibly frustrating up-tight experience.

STP seems to lack the disorientation of acid. Although the audio and visual hallucinations are vivid, a girl explained, "Everything looks like it does when you're straight. It's like being on the other side of a glass wall." There also seems to be less identity confusion than under LSD. "You know who you are," she said. Many have found that they could easily function—make telephone calls, find cabs,—shortly after the peak of the STP experience. These things can be difficult to do after an intense LSD experience.

Another recurring report about STP is a sensation of timelessness. Alpert calls it "a totally NOW orientation." Past and future seem to dissolve in an electric present. As time was lost, Alpert recalled, "I felt that I had lost something human. I felt that I had lost my humanity."

But the most enticing, and clearly the most disturbing aspect of STP is that, unlike LSD, it seems to have a cumulative effect. It is a long trip to begin with. The direct effects last about 14 hours, and a stoned aftermath may continue until sleep.

The next morning, many STP initiates have discovered that they still felt high, or at least "different." It is a mild feeling, but a persistent one. Generally rated a "good" feeling, it seems to last indefinitely. . . .

Some people claim to have discovered intense telepathic powers in STP. Another curious aspect of STP, a user explained, is that at the peak of the experience you tend to think that everyone else has taken the drug. He described his experience:

"I got out of the cab on St. Mark's Place. It was three in the morning and the street was full of people, standing around. The sky was glowing, like it was flaming. I thought it was the Second Coming or something. I was absolutely convinced that It had just happened

or would happen in seconds. And I thought everyone else knew it. How do you react when you're convinced? I was completely stoned."
—Don McNeill, *The Village Voice* (April 13, 1967)

straight. [from *getting straight,* getting one's affairs straightened out; also, perhaps, from *straight,* in the sense of being sexually normal] *1.* in a state of narcotics-induced euphoria with concomitant forestalling of WITHDRAWAL SYMPTOMS, as in "I need a shot to get *straight.*" *2.* not using drugs. *3.* not possessing drugs on the person. *4.* SQUARE, middle-class. *5.* a nonmarijuana cigarette.

straighten out. *1.* to prevent WITHDRAWAL SYMPTOMS. *2.* to restore the HEROIN addict to a normal, anxiety-free state of mind. Compare STRAIGHT.

> Like I might find old Joe Schmo today and buy three bags from him and find that one bag *straightens* me *out.* Now, okay, so I'll time my shots and get away with fifteen dollars today. Tomorrow I can't find Joe Schmo so I go find Larry the Jerk, and I buy three off him and one won't straighten me out, and maybe three won't straighten me out.   —addict, quoted by James Mills, in *The Drug Takers* (1965)

stramonium. an alkaloid (occurring in jimsonweed, DATURA STRAMOMIUM, a plant of the same family as BELLADONNA and henbane), which is actually the alkaloids ATROPINE and HYOSCYAMINE. Stramonium can cause mental confusion and sluggish thinking or make the user preternaturally excited with accompanying hallucinations. In large doses, it produces narcosis, coma, stupefaction, convulsions, and death. It is sometimes used in asthma remedies. Compare DATURA, ASTHMADOR.

street, on the. the addict's milieu; by extension, to be using drugs.

street, the. [from the addict's necessity of constantly searching (HUSTLING) for drugs, purchasing on street corners, committing petty thefts to get money for drugs, etc.; similar to *pounding the pavements*] where the addict spends much of his time; hence, the addict's life, in which he devotes his time to finding drugs and is incapable of working at a regular job.

> It seems that addicts in general find it difficult to tolerate prolonged interpersonal contacts when there is no means of running away from them. . . . It is no accident that our patients refer to the world outside [of the U.S. Public Health Service Hospital, Lexington, Ken-

tucky] as *"the street";* they cherish their mobility, the opportunity to escape difficult relationships very highly.
—psychiatrist in James Mills, *The Panic in Needle Park* (1966)

strung. STRUNG OUT.

strung out. [from (?) *stringy,* reflective of the addict's emaciated appearance, or from (?) the sense of stringing something along, drawing it out, stringing along with something; since the 1950s] *1.* badly addicted to a drug. *2.* thin and sick looking because of long-term addiction. Compare EMBALAO. *3.* unable to obtain sufficient drugs to keep comfortable.

stuff. narcotics, usually HEROIN.

superpot. MARIJUANA which has been soaked in alcohol, dried, then smoked. Another method is to inject the alcohol into a marijuana cigarette with a hypodermic needle. The resulting cigarette is said to be more potent in its hallucinogenic effects.

sweet lucy. MARIJUANA.

swingman. PUSHER, peddler, connection.

Synalgos-DC. [Drocode (DYHYDROCODEINE) bitartrate and other ingredients, Ives Laboratories] a CODEINE derivative used to relieve mild to moderate pain. Supplied in blue and gray capsules containing 16 milligrams of dyhydrocodeine. Manufacturer's recommended dosage is two capsules initially, then one or two capsules, two or three times daily. A CLASS B NARCOTIC.

Synanon. [from an addict's mispronunciation of *seminar*] a communal-living program for the rehabilitation of drug addicts, in which the addicts help cure each other, through group therapy, mutual reinforcement, companionship, and social pressure. The members of each Synanon house are all addicts or former addicts; they stay as long as they like but are discouraged from leaving until they are judged capable of remaining off drugs—it is hoped permanently, though no "cures" are claimed. The stages of therapy are as follows:

1. Withdrawal from drugs; confinement to the house. No outside contacts.
2. When withdrawn from drugs and apparently off them, the member continues to live in the house but can work at an outside job.
3. Working and living outside the house; "cured."

There are no statistics available on the number of cures wrought by

Synanon. Apparently very few have progressed to phase 3, except those who have stayed in the movement and set up new branches of Synanon or work at Daytop Lodge, a similar program located in Staten Island, New York. Like members of Alcoholics Anonymous, Synanon addicts are "cured" by replacing their drug addiction with an addiction to the "movement."

> We haven't been at this long enough to know for sure about cures. I won't pronounce anybody cured for at least five or six years. Not until some of our graduates go out there and come up against the things an adult must face—like losing a house, or a job or a child— without using drugs.   —Chuck Diederich, founder of *Synanon*, in
> Richard B. Stolley, in *The Drug Takers* (1965)

synhexyl. PYRAHEXYL.

synthetic opiates. the class of synthetic MORPHINE substitutes (opioids) which resemble morphine in many of their actions and sometimes their chemical structures yet also differ in their actions, depending upon the synthetic. All induce some degree of PHYSICAL DEPENDENCE, though with many the WITHDRAWAL SYMPTOMS are less severe than those of morphine addiction. By the same token, many are of greater analgesic potency than morphine. The principal chemical types of synthetics are:

1. meperidine (pethidine) and such related drugs as alphaprodine, anileridine, and piminodine.
2. substituted morphinans, of which levorphanol is the most potent and important.
3. diphenylheptane derivatives such as methadone.

system, the. an addict's TOLERANCE, as in "he took too much heroin for the *system* and o.d.-ed."

T t

tabs. capsules containing LSD-25.

taken off. to be robbed of money or drugs, as in "I was standing in the hall about to shoot up, but I got *taken off* by three men from the neighborhood."

take off. *1.* to get high. *2.* to inject narcotics.

take-off artist. an addict who supports his habit by robbing (TAKING OFF) other addicts or pushers.

taking off. robbing.

tall. [from the idea of high] in a drug-induced state of euphoria; HIGH.

tapita. [from diminutive of Spanish *tapa,* cork, plug cap, meaning little cap] a bottle cap used for cooking HEROIN.

Taractan. [chlorprothixene, Roche Laboratories] a MAJOR TRANQUIL-IZER structurally similar to the phenothiazines. Used in severe mental and emotional disorders arising out of psychotic or neurotic states. Manufacturer's recommended dosages are from 10 milligrams three times a day (mild to moderate neuroses) up to 25 to 50 milligrams three to four times daily (maximum 600 milligrams) in severe neurotic and psychotic states. Supplied in red coated tablets with "ROCHE" inscribed on them in 10-, 25-, 50-, and 100-milligram sizes.

tar beach. a roof used for sleeping by HIPPIES.

taste. small amount of HEROIN proffered as a gift.

tea. [from the physical resemblance to marijuana leaves chopped up for smoking; since the 1930s—*EP*] MARIJUANA.

> Watch your gums on that stick of *tea*
> and get high with me.
> It sends me gate and I can't wait
> I'm viper mad. —marijuana song, around the 1940s

tea bag. smoking MARIJUANA, as in "in the *tea bag.*"

tea head. [see HEAD] a frequent, often heavy, habitual MARIJUANA smoker.

tea pad. rooms in apartments or pup tents on the roof in Harlem where MARIJUANA was sold and users gathered and smoked marijuana communally in the 1930s and 1940s.

tecata. HEROIN.

telepathine. HARMINE.

ten-cent pistol. a HEROIN bag that actually contains poison.

tens. ten-milligram AMPHETAMINE tablets.

teonanactl. [Nahuatl, God's flesh] Aztec name for hallucinogenic mushrooms. See MUSHROOMS, SACRED.

tetrahydrocannabinol. the euphorically ACTIVE PRINCIPLE in CANNABIS. When cannabis is smoked, it is believed that tetrahydrocannabinol is changed less than any of the other resinous materials found in the hemp leaves and thus is more highly concentrated in the smoke. In experiments, however, natural HASHISH given to animals had more potency than the sublimate remaining after smoking. Nearly eighty derivatives of natural tetrahydrocannabinol have been compounded, but it was not reproduced synthetically until 1966. Compare PYRAHEXYL. Subject to the DRUG ABUSE CONTROL AMENDMENT OF 1965.

Texas tea. MARIJUANA.

THC. TETRAHYDROCANNABINOL.

Theo-Nar. [contains NOSCAPINE, Key Pharmaceuticals, Inc.] a cough-reflex depressant containing an alkaloid of OPIUM. Each delayed-release tablet contains 30 milligrams of noscapine, a non-addicting alkaloid of opium. Recommended for symptoms of bronchial asthma and emphysema. A CLASS M NARCOTIC.

third eye. in the psychedelic drug cult, the inward-looking eye, the new vision into self that drugs provide.

thirty-three-oh-five. [from the number of the statute] under New York state law, possession of narcotics, a misdemeanor when the amount held is below the minimum required for presumption of holding for purpose of sale, a felony.

Thorazine. [CHLORPROMAZINE hydrochloride, Smith Kline & French Laboratories] a MAJOR TRANQUILIZER. Recommended in anxiety, tension states, and for control of acutely agitated or disturbed mental patients. Usual recommended dosage is 25 milligrams. The drug is an LSD antagonist (reverses that drug's effects) and is the most popular prescription in cases of LSD-induced panic reactions.

throwing rocks. committing crimes.

thrupence bag. [from *pound,* five dollars, or nickel, five dollars] a bag of MARIJUANA costing $2.50 (local).

> At Columbia, marijuana is sometimes given as a Christmas present (one pusher revealed that he specially packages $2.50 doses of marijuana—which he calls a *"thrupence bag"*—for purchases by Columbia students around Christmas time).
> —Richard Goldstein, *One in Seven: Drugs on Campus* (1966)

thrusters. AMPHETAMINE pills.

thumb. a fat MARIJUANA cigarette.

ticket, the. LSD-25.

tiger drug, the. AYAHUASCA (yage), a HALLUCINOGEN.

tighten somebody's wig. to give him some MARIJUANA to smoke —*MM,* 1946. *Obsolete.*

tin. a small amount of OPIUM—*MM,* 1946. *Obsolete?* Compare LID.

tingle. a RUSH, or onset, of HEROIN's effects felt immediately in the abdomen or across the chest.

TJ. Tijuana, Mexico; popular rendezvous for American tourists purchasing MARIJUANA.

tlitliltzen. [Nahuatl, black] Aztec word for the black hallucinogenic morning glory seeds. See MORNING GLORY SEEDS.

TMA. [3,4,5-trimethoxyphenyl-β-aminopropane] a synthetic HALLUCINOGEN of greater potency than MESCALINE but less than LSD-25.

toak. also toke. *1.* a puff of a MARIJUANA cigarette. *2.* smoking the entire cigarette, as in "a few *toaks* and he was high." Compare POKE.

toast. addicts' song.

> A ballad about "the life," the underworld and gray world through which the addicted pass for a period of time; generally handed down in prisons and hospitals.
> —Seymour Fiddle, *Portraits from a Shooting Gallery* (1967)

toke. TOAK.

toke pipes. tiny short-stemmed pipes in which MARIJUANA is smoked.

toke up. [from *toke*] to light up a MARIJUANA cigarette.

tolerance. the cumulative resistance to the pharmacological effects of a drug, gradually increased as use continues and the system adapts to its, sometimes selective as to the effects tolerated. Tolerance has set in when repeated administration of a given dose produces a decreasing effect, or increasingly larger doses must be administered in order to obtain the effects of the original dose. Compare ADDICTION, BARBITURATES, HEROIN, PHYSICAL DEPENDENCE.

tooies. TUINAL capsules.

tools. equipment for injecting drugs, mainly HEROIN. Compare GIMMICKS, WORKS.

Top. a brand of wheat-straw cigarette paper, impregnated with different flavors, in which loose MARIJUANA is rolled for smoking.

topi. PEYOTE.

torn up. intoxicated by a drug.

tossed. searched for drugs.

> I don't get *tossed* too often. One time I got tossed three days in a row. . . . But they never find anything on me. Not because I'm clean. I'm never clean. I've almost always got works or pills or something. But they can't look where I carry the things. And when they're tossing me I start crying and screaming and making a scene and they get nervous.
> —addict in James Mills, *The Panic in Needle Park* (1966)

toss out. to feign WITHDRAWAL SYMPTOMS in order to obtain narcotics from a doctor. Compare WINGDING.

tracked up. [from TRACKS, needle scars caused by repeated injec-

tions] covered with blue healed and semihealed scars from a hypodermic needle.

> I shot up every day and I was pleased in a funny way that my arm
> wasn't *tracked up* like a trolley-car run.
> —Piri Thomas, *Down These Mean Streets* (1967)

tracks. [from (?) the appearance, and in the sense of *traces*] *1.*
veins collapsed from too frequent narcotics injections. *2.* needle scars
from frequent injections in the form of blue or black spots with a
tattooed appearance.

> *Tracks* are marks, like a long black streak coming down your arm
> directly over your vein; that comes from hitting in the same place
> so much. Now when you skin-pop you hit all over your body; you
> can't keep up with the tracks. You lose them. They just keep falling
> off.   —addict, quoted in Jeremy Larner and Ralph Tefferteller,
> *The Addict in the Street* (1964)

tranquilizers. term for a number of drugs which have a depressant
effect on the central nervous system, relieve anxiety and tension,
and sometimes relax the skeletal muscles. Unlike hypnotic-sedative
drugs, such as BARBITURATES, tranquilizers generally do not cause
hypnosis, drowsiness, or loss of alertness (except in amounts larger
than necessary for therapy). However, there are many exceptions
to this rule, and frequently the tranquilizers offer little to recommend
them over barbiturate sedatives in calming anxiety and tension (and
are usually higher priced). Tranquilizers are usually classified both
pharmacologically and chemically as MAJOR TRANQUILIZERS and
MINOR TRANQUILIZERS, terms which reflect their therapeutic use.

trap. a hiding place for drugs. Compare STASH.

travel agent. [suggested by the LSD TRIP; since the 1950s] *1.* LSD-25.
2. an LSD PUSHER.

trey. a $3 BAG of HEROIN. Compare DECK, THRUPENCE BAG.

trip. *1.* to take a hallucinogenic drug. *2.* the hallucinogenic drug
experience.

trips. LSD.

tripsville. San Francisco.

tryptamine. nonhallucinogenic chemical from which the hallucinogenic drugs DMT, LSD, BUFOTENINE, and PSILOCYBIN can be derived.

Tuinal. [amobarbital sodium and secobarbital sodium, Eli Lilly and Company] a short- to intermediate-acting BARBITURATE hypnotic and sedative, combining in equal amounts AMYTAL and SECONAL. Recommended dosages: for sedation 3/4 grain (50 milligrams); for hypnosis 1 1/2 to 3 grains (100 to 200 milligrams). The lethal dose is approximately twelve times the hypnotic dose. Tuinal is sold in 3/4-grain (50-milligrams), 1/2-grain (100-milligrams), and 3-grain (200-milligrams) capsules with blue body and orange cap. Slang names: tooies, rainbows, red and blues.

turned out. introduced to the fast life, or drugs.

turn on. [from (?) the mechanical sense of turn on a light, machine, etc.; since the 1950s] *1.* to introduce someone else to drugs, as in "I *turned* him *on.*" *2.* to take drugs oneself, as in "We copped some pot and *turned on.*" *3.* to become intoxicated from drugs as in "he was *turned on.*" *4.* by extension, any exhilarating experience.

Tussanil-DH. [DIHYDROCODEINE bitartrate and other ingredients, Misemer Pharmaceuticals] a cough syrup containing a CODEINE derivative. Each 5 cubic centimeters (1 teaspoonful) of the syrup contains 1.66 milligrams of dihydrocodeine bitartrate. In sufficiently large dosages it can produce PSYCHIC DEPENDENCE and PHYSICAL DEPENDENCE. A CLASS X NARCOTIC. No prescription.

twenty-five. LSD-25.

twist. MARIJUANA.

twisted. *1.* suffering WITHDRAWAL SYMPTOMS. *2.* under the influence of drugs. Compare BENT.

tying up. wrapping a cord, necktie, belt, etc., around the upper arm so as to distend the vein, preparatory to an intravenous shot of HEROIN.

U u

up. in a state of intoxication from some drug, especially an AMPHETAMINE or LSD-25.

upper. an AMPHETAMINE pill.

uppie. an AMPHETAMINE pill.

ups. AMPHETAMINE pills.

uptight. [in the sense of being hemmed in, back against the wall] *1.* objectively in a tight situation with the law: the evidence is against you. *2.* tense, worried, feeling hemmed in. *3.* touchy, defensive, flaring up with hostility. Compare PARANOIA.

using. taking drugs.

V v

Valium. [diazepam, Roche Laboratories] a MINOR TRANQUILIZER and skeletal-muscle relaxant. Used in alleviating neurotic tension and anxiety states and in controlling muscle spasms (as in cerebral palsy). Manufacturer's recommend dosages: 2 to 5 milligrams, two or three times daily, in mild to moderate neuroses; up to 5 to 10 milligrams three or four times daily in severe neurotic reactions. Prolonged, heavy dosage can result in PHYSICAL DEPENDENCE with severe WITHDRAWAL SYMPTOMS (convulsions, tremor, abdominal and muscle cramps, and sweating) if drug is abruptly ceased. Supplied in white 2-milligram and yellow 5-milligram tablets inscribed with "ROCHE."

Valmid. [ETHINAMATE, Eli Lilly and Company] a nonbarbiturate hypnotic. According to the manufacturer, the hypnotic dose is 500 milligrams at bedtime, which can be repeated as late as three to four hours before arising, in the event the patient wakes up, without residual sedation ("drug hangover"). Massive doses of Valmid can cause death through depression of the respiratory center. The drug has a euphoric effect on some persons, especially former alcoholics or disturbed persons, who may develop a PSYCHIC DEPENDENCE upon it. Prolonged, heavy use produces PHYSICAL DEPENDENCE and severe WITHDRAWAL SYMPTOMS upon abrupt cessation of the drug. Supplied in 0.5-gram (7 1/2-grain) peach-colored tablets with "DISC-KETS" inscribed upon them. Subject to the DRUG ABUSE CONTROL AMENDMENT OF 1965.

vendedor. [Spanish, seller, salesman] a PUSHER, narcotics peddler.

Veronal. See BARBITURATES.

vinho de jurumena. a narcotic beverage prepared from the seeds of *Mimosa hostilis* by the Pancaru Indians of Brazil. A closely related genus is PIPTADENIA. It is a HALLUCINOGEN and is used by the Indians in religious ceremonies and magical rites. Contains an alkaloid first named nigerine but later identified as DMT, a hallucinogen and the ACTIVE PRINCIPLE of the plant.

violated. arrested for a parole violation, as in "I stopped seeing my P.O. [parole officer] and started back on drugs and then I got *violated* again and went in for three months."

vipe. [from *viper*] to smoke MARIJUANA. *Obsolete.*

viper. [from the sense that marijuana renders one as dangerous and unpredictable as a viper; since the 1930s—*EP*] a MARIJUANA smoker. *Obsolete.*

> When your pipes get dry
> Then you know you're high
> Everything is dandy
> You truck on down to the candy store.
> But you don't get no peppermint candy
> Then you know your body's sent
> You don't care if you don't pay rent.
> Light a tea and let it be
> If you're a viper.   —"If You're a Viper" (around 1940)

Virola. a genus of tree belonging to the NUTMEG family (Myristicaceae) whose resin is used by Indians of the Colombian Amazon to make an intoxicating snuff, which they call *yakee* or *parica*. Species include *Virola colophylla, V. calophylloidea,* and perhaps *V. elongata*. The ACTIVE PRINCIPLE is believed to be MYRISTICIN (ELEMICIN), which is also found in nutmeg and is responsible for its hallucinogenic effect. The resin is collected by stripping the bark before the sun is up, scraping it off, and boiling to a thick paste which is dried, pulverized, sifted, and mixed with ashes of wild coca stems.

> I took about one-third of a teaspoonful [of the snuff] in two inhalations using the characteristic V-shaped bird-bone snuffing tube. This represents about one-quarter the dose that a diagnosing medicine man will take to bring on an eventful state of unconsciousness. . . . Within fifteen minutes, a drawing sensation was felt over the eyes followed very shortly by a strong tingling in fingers and toes. The drawing sensation in the forehead gave way to a strong and constant headache. Within a half hour, the feet and hands were numb and sensitivity of the fingertips had disappeared. . . . Shortly after eight, I lay down in my hammock, overcome with a drowsiness, which, however, seemed to be accompanied by a muscular excitation except in the hands and feet. About nine-thirty, I fell into a fitful sleep which continued, with frequent awakenings, until morning. . . . The witchdoctors see visions in color, but I was able to experience neither visual hallucinations, nor color sensations. The large dose used by the witch-doctor is enough to put him into a deep but disturbed sleep, during which he sees visions and has dreams which, through the wild shouts emitted in his delirium, are interpreted by an assistant. That it is a dangerous practice is acknowledged by the witchdoctors themselves. They report the death, about 15 years ago, of one of their number . . . during a yakee intoxication.
>
> —Richard E. Schultes, *Psychedelic Review* (1964)

vol. VOLUNTEER.

volunteer. at the U.S. Public Health Service (Narcotics) Hospital, Lexington, Kentucky, one who commits himself for treatment of narcotics or BARBITURATE addiction and is free to leave any time.

voyager. person under the influence of LSD-25.

wake-up. the addict's first morning injection.

waste. to destroy, pulverize, hit hard, obliterate.

> Indio pushed another stick [marijuana cigarette] in my hand. I *wasted* it down to nothing.
> —Piri Thomas, *Down These Mean Streets* (1967)

wasted. *1.* passed out from acute drug intoxication. *2.* see WASTE.

weed. MARIJUANA.

weeding out. smoking MARIJUANA.

weight. a supply of, measure of drugs. Compare PIECE.

> Give her her *weight* for the week. . . . He said that these were the people into all the cocaine *weight* and that he was going to cut me into them. —Claude Brown, *Manchild in the Promised Land* (1965)

wheat. [probably from the wheat-straw paper used in rolling the cigarette] MARIJUANA.

wheel. a car. Compare CRACKING SHORTS.

whistling (I came in). [from the idea of the wind whistling through an old house; the addict's clothes are threadbare, and the wind is whistling through him in this manner—Seymour Fiddle, *The Language of Addiction*] entering a hospital very sick, run down, and impoverished.

white lady, the. HEROIN. Compare WHITE STUFF.

white light. a hallucination of a blinding white light, accompanied by a feeling of omniscience, said to be produced by STP.

> Within forty minutes I was peaking, experiencing what I can only describe as *white light,* whatever that might be.
> —editorial, *Innerspace* (1967)

whites. BENZEDRINE pills.

white stuff. [since the 1920s] COCAINE, MORPHINE, or (usually) HEROIN.

wig. [from *hair, head* extended to mean the mind, and *wig out,* lose one's wig, i.e., mind; "*wig,* head or hair; wig-trig, idea"—*MM,* 1946] *1.* the mind. *2.* to be upset, excited, panicky. *3.* to WIG OUT, to be crazy.

> So I says, "What's with you? You *wig* already?"
> —William Burroughs, *Naked Lunch* (1959)

wig out. abrupt, usually euphoric, dramatic alteration of subjective mood under the influence of a drug. Compare BLOW YOUR MIND, FREAK OUT, FLIP OUT.

wild Geronimo. [around the 1940s] a drink consisting of barbiturates dissolved in an alcoholic beverage.

winder. a VOLUNTEER for treatment at U.S. Public Health Service (Narcotics) Hospital, Lexington, Kentucky, one who can leave at any time, and thus who *winds* in and out.

wingding (throw a). feigned WITHDRAWAL SYMPTOMS to get a doctor to give one narcotics. Compare TOSS OUT.

wings. *1.* the first MAINLINE shot. *2.* learning how to take narcotics in this way.

> He gave me my *wings*—my first mainline shot.
> —James Mills, in *The Drug Takers* (1965)

withdrawal symptoms or syndrome. a cluster of characteristic reactions and behavior, of varying intensity, depending on the amounts of the drug taken and the length of time used, sometimes fatally severe, which ensue upon abrupt cessation of a drug upon which the body has PHYSICAL DEPENDENCE. The withdrawal syndrome varies with the drug. An antagonist drug, which acts to reverse the effect of the addictive drug, will precipitate withdrawal symptoms when it is administered; however, not all drugs to which physical dependence develops have antagonist drugs. These symptoms often can be controlled only by carefully spaced dosages of the drug upon which there is dependence or a related drug.

CHARACTERISTIC WITHDRAWAL SYNDROMES

drug dependence of the morphine, opiate type: appears within a few hours of last dose. Reaches peak intensity in twenty-four to forty-eight hours. Subsides spontaneously. Symptoms: anxiety, restlessness, generalized body aches, insomnia, yawning, tears, running nose, perspiration, contraction of the pupils, gooseflesh, hot flushes, nausea, release of the bowels, diarrhea, rise in body temperature, rise in respiratory rate, rise in systolic blood pressure, abdominal cramps, seminal ejaculations, muscle cramps, dehydration, and loss of body weight. Nalline and levallorphan will precipate these symptoms.

drug dependence of the barbiturate type: appears within sixteen to twenty-four hours of cessation of drug-taking. Reaches peak intensity in two or three days. Subsides slowly. There is no antagonist which will precipitate the withdrawal syndrome. Symptoms: anxiety, involuntary twitching of muscles, tremor of hands and fingers, progressive weakness, dizziness, distortion in visual perception, nausea, vomiting, insomnia, weight loss, sudden drop in blood pressure when addict stands, epileptic type of seizure and severe convulsions (possible death from exhaustion or heart failure) delirium tremens, and, later, a major psychotic episode accompanied by paranoid reactions, schizophrenic reactions with delusions and hallucinations, withdrawn semistuporous state, and/or disorganized panic, depending upon the individual. Alcohol will at least partially suppress the withdrawal syndrome.

drug dependence of the alcoholic type: appears with the following symptoms: tremors, sweating, nausea, rapid heart beat, rise in temperature, jerky reflexes, and, in severe cases (where the consumption has been in large amounts over a long period), convulsions, and delirium tremens (confusion, disorientation, delusions, and vivid visual hallucinations). The withdrawal syndrome can be suppressed by barbiturates. Compare COCAINE, ETHYL ALCOHOL, OPIUM, TRANQUILIZERS.

works. equipment for injecting HEROIN, consisting of needle; bottle cap or spoon (COOKER) for dissolving heroin over heat; eyedropper bulb or baby's pacifier; eyedropper; paper collar packed around the junction of the dropper and the needle; belt, string, or cord (for wrapping tightly around the arm to distend the vein); small bottle of distilled water in which to dissolve the heroin and cook it. Compare FIX, GIMMICKS.

wrap. innocuous-looking covering of a package of marijuana or other bulky drug in which it is transported or shipped in the mail. Compare STASH.

Beware of a smelly stash. This might be scented by trained POT-HEAD HOUNDS which are occasionally toured through bus depots and similar baggage scenes, sniffing out stashes poorly packaged. *A bad wrap can burn you.* . . . Important things to remember about packaging are: Use no identifying or implicating containers, wrap in both foil and plastic film. Another layer of brown paper might help especially if you plan to stash under the kitty-litter, a very good spot where a good wrap really makes a difference.

—*The Marijuana Newsletter No. 2* (March 15, 1965)

yage. AYAHUASCA.

yaje. AYAHUASCA.

yakee. hallucinatory snuff prepared by Yekwana Indians from the VIROLA plant.

yellow jackets. [from the color] NEMBUTAL capsules. Also called yellow.

yen. [from Chinese *yen-yen* or *inyun fun,* OPIUM habit; one suffering with *inyun;* hence a strong need; since the 1880s—*EP*] now, any craving. Compare COP SICKNESS, YENNING.

> I felt my throat blend in and out with the *yen.* The taste that takes place even before you get the junk in your system. All of a sudden, I felt like nothing mattered, like if all the promises in the world didn't mean a damn, like all that mattered was that the stuff is there, the needle is there, the yen is there and your veins have always been there.   —Piri Thomas, *Down These Mean Streets* (1967)

yen hok. [since the 1880s—*EP*] needle used to cook OPIUM pellets. *Obsolete?*

yenning. [from YEN] experiencing WITHDRAWAL SYMPTOMS.

yen pok. [since the 1880s—*EP*] pellet of OPIUM prepared for smoking. *Obsolete?*

yerba. [from Spanish, *hierba,* grass, weed, herb, and *mala hierba,* weed, bad character, marijuana] MARIJUANA. Compare GRASS, HERB, WEED.

yopo. hallucinogenic snuff made by Otomac Indians of the Orinoco Valley from PIPTADENIA.

Z z

zap. [from the noise made by the ray gun in "Buck Rogers," a science-fiction comic strip and radio series] *1.* to (symbolically) defeat someone, as in "I *zapped* him with love." *2.* to (literally) kill, hurt, or overpower someone with violence or a weapon.

zigzag. a brand of wheat-straw cigarette paper, impregnated with different flavors, in which loose MARIJUANA is rolled for smoking.

ZNA. mixture of dill weed and monosodium glutinate, smoked for an alleged hallucinogenic effect.

zonked. highly intoxicated from a drug.

Appendix I

Nonsynthetic derivatives of opium, morphine, and cocaine. *Source: Federal Bureau of Narcotics,* 1967.

Opium, powdered, granulated, or deodorized, or tinctures or extracts of opium.
Mixed alkaloids of opium and their salts.
Morphine and its salts.
Codeine and its salts.
Thebaine and its salts.
Noscapine and its salts.
Papaverine and its salts.
Cotarnine and its salts.
Narceine and its salts.
Ethylmorphine and its salts.
Apomorphine and its salts.
Nalorphine (N-allylnormorphine) and its salts.
Hydromorphone (dihydromorphinone) and its salts.
Metopon (methyldihydromorphinone) and its salts.
Dihydrocodeine and its salts.
Hydrocodone (dihydrocodeinone) and its salts.
Oxycodone (dihydrohydroxycodeinone) and its salts.
Cocaine and its salts.
Ecgonine and its salts.
Levorphan and racemorphan (3-hydroxy-N-methylmorphinan) and their salts.
Levomethorphan and racemethorphan (3-methoxy-N-methylmorphinan) and their salts.
Dihydromorphine (3,6-dihydroxy-N-methyl-4,5-epoxymorphinan) and its salts.
Oxymorphone (14-hydroxy-dihydromorphinone) and its salts.
Pholcodine (morpholinylethylmorphine) and its salts.

Appendix II

Generic names of synthetic opiates. *Source: Federal Bureau of Narcotics,* 1967.

ACETYLMETHADOL
ALLYLPRODINE
ALPHACETYLMETHADOL
ALPHAMEPRODINE or NU–1932
ALPHAMETHADOL

ALPHAPRODINE or NU–1196

ANILERIDINE

BENZETHIDINE

BETACETYLMETHADOL

BETHAMEPRODINE or NU–1932

BETAMETHADOL

BETAPRODINE or NU–1779

CLONITAZENE

DEXTROMORAMIDE

DIAMPROMIDE

DIETHYLTHIAMBUTENE

DIMENOXADOL

DIMEPHEPTANOL

DIMETHYLTHIAMBUTENE

DIOXAPHETYL BUTYRATE

DIPHENOXYLATE

DIPIPANONE

ETHYLMETHYLTHIAMBUTENE

ETONITAZENE

ETOXERIDINE

FENTANYL

FURETHIDINE

HYDROXYPETHIDINE

ISOMETHADONE

KETOBEMIDONE

LEVOMETHORPHAN, RACEMETHORPHAN (its racemic and levorotatory forms
and their salts, but excepting its dextrorotatory form and its salts)

LEVOMORAMIDE

LEVOPHENACYLMORPHAN

LEVORPHANOL, DEXTRORPHAN, RACEMORPHAN, NU–2206

METAZOCINE

METHADONE

METHADONE-INTERMEDIATE

MORAMIDE-INTERMEDIATE

MORPHERIDINE

NORACYMETHADOL

NORLEVORPHANOL

NORMETHADONE

NORPIPANONE

PETHIDINE

PETHIDINE-INTERMEDIATE-A

PETHIDINE-INTERMEDIATE-B

PETHIDINE-INTERMEDIATE-C

PHENADOXONE or CB–11

PHENAMPROMIDE

PHENAZOCINE

PHENOMORPHAN (its racemic and levorotatory forms, but excepting its dextrorotatory form and its salts)

PHENOPERIDINE
PIMINODINE
PIRITRAMIDE
PROHEPTAZINE
PROPERIDINE
RACEMORAMIDE
TRIMEPERIDINE

Appendix III

Generic and trade names of barbiturate, amphetamine, and combination drugs regulated by the Drug Abuse Control Amendment of 1965 (Public Law 89–74). *Source: Journal of the American Pharmaceutical Association*, May, 1968.

A-884 (Methamphetamine)
Abactal (Massengill)
Abadex No. 1, 2 and 3 (ABA)
Abate (Cambridge)
A.C.A.P. (Halsom)
Acotal (Prof. Drug Service)
Actemin
Adetate (M.S. and D.)
Adipan (Amphetamine Sulfate)
Adiparthrol (Amphetamine Sulfate)
Adipex (Methamphetamine)
Adjudet Troches (Ives)
Ad-Nil No. 2 (Medics)
Ad-Nil (Medics)
Adrizine
Afatin (d-Amphetamine Sulfate)
Afettine (d-Amphetamine Sulfate)
Agrypnal (Phenobarbital)
Aironol (Airhart)
Airo-Sed (Airhart)
Airotal (Airhart)
Aktedron
Aladrine Tablets (Table Rock)
Aladrine Tablets and Liquid (Merit)
Aladrine Liquid (Table Rock)
Alafed (Crest)
Albemap (d-Amphetamine Sulfate)
Albutal (Medical Arts)

Alentol (Amphetamine Sulfate)
Alepsal (Fougera)
Aliasis No. 2 (Superior)
Alka-Nux (MacEslin)
Allobarbital
Allobarbitone
Allodene (Amphetamine Sulfate)
Allonal Tablets (Roche)
Allylbarbituric Acid
Allylisobutylbarbituric Acid
Allylisopropylbarbituric Acid
Allylisopropylmalonylurea
Allylisopropylmethylbarbituric Acid
Allypropymal
Al-Nal-Capsules (Cumberland)
Alphetamine Capsules (Alpha)
Alphetamine 10 Capsules (Alpha)
Alprine (Ulmer)
Alubarb Elixir (Approved)
Alurate (Hoffmann-LaRoche)
Alurate Sodium (Hoffmann-La-
    Roche)
Alurate Verdum Elixir (Hoffmann-
    LaRoche)
Aluro (Foy)
Alutricol (Tutag)
Amagesic (Caldwell and Bloor)
Amaphen Tablets (Trimen)

Amba-Dex-TD (Moffet)
Amba-Dex (Moffet)
Ambar (Robins)
Ambar No.1 and 2 (Robins)
Ambarb Capsules (Manne)
Ambi-Dex (Buffalo)
Ambodex (Testagar)
Ambrol (Smith Miller and Patch)
Amcobarb Dakaps (Amco)
Amcodex Dakaps (Amco)
Am-Dex (Superior)
Amedrine (Methamphetamine)
Amerital (Merit)
Amex Tablets (Pasadena)
Amfadiol (Philips Roxane)
Amfebarbs (Gold Leaf)
Amfet-Oxy-20 (Studebaker)
Amfetamine (Amphetamine Sulfate)
Amgesic (Deseret)
Amitrene (Normand)
Ammonium Chloride Compound Capsules (Elder)
Amobarbital
Amobarbital Sodium
Amobese (Cole)
Amodex-Timed (Testagar)
Amodex (Testagar)
Amo-Dextro (Rocky Mountain)
Amo-Dextrosule Jr. and Sr. (Storck)
Amo-Dextrosule Sr. Timesule (Arnar-Stone)¹
Amo-Dexules Capsules (Recsei)
Amo-Dexules No. 1 and 2 (Recsei)
Amodril (North American)
Amo-Dureide (Goodrich-Wright)
Amondex Timed Capsules (Testagar)
Amo-Pellcaps No. 1 and 2 (Kirkman)
Amordex (Palmedico)
Amorex Injection (Mallard)
Amosec Capsules No. 2 (Penhurst)
Amosene (Ferndale)
Amospan (B.S. and L.)
Amo-Tran (Superior)
Amotrax Capsules (Jamieson-Mc-Kames)
Amozar (North American)
Ampelose Tablets (Blue-Line)
Ampha-Cel Plus (Paramount)
Amphamed (Amphetamine Sulfate)
Amphamine Tablets (Naman)
Ampha-Mix Tablets (Sonnenberg)
Amphaplex (Palmedico)
Ampharb (Harvey)

Amphatamin (Amphetamine Sulfate)
Amphate (Arnar-Stone)
Amphate (Storck)
Amphcaps (Manne)
Amphebarb Tablets (Jabert)
Amphecell (Allan)
Amphedase (Parke-Davis)
Amphedex (Royce)
Amphedex-TDC (Canfield)
Amphedex-15 (Tilden-Yates)
Amphedrine (Vanpelt Brown)
Amphedrine-M (Vanpelt Brown)
Amphedroxyn (Lilly)
Amphe-Gum (Prof. Drug Service)
Amphelose (Prof. Drug Service)
Amphemine Tablets (Prof. Drug Service)
Am-Phet Capsules (M.J.)
Am-Phet Capsules (Pharmich)
Am-Phet Unoday PH 758
Am-Phet (Lemmon)
Am-Phet (Paul Maney)
Ampherex (Royce)
Amphet-A-Barb Extendos No. 1 (Archer-Taylor)
Amphet-A-Barb Forte No. 2 (Archer-Taylor)
Amphetamine
Amphetamine and Methylcellulose (Bariatric)
Amphetamine Dextro and Amobarbital (Vitarine)
Amphetamine HCl-l
Amphetamine l-Glutamate-l
Amphetamine Maleate-d
Amphetamine Mucate Monobasic-l
Amphetamine Para Aminobenzoate-l
Amphetamine Potassium Saccharate-dl
Amphetamine Reducing Capsules No. 1 (Davis-Edwards)
Amphetamine Reducing Capsules No. 2 (Davis-Edwards)
Amphetamine Reducing Capsules No. 3 (Davis-Edwards)
Amphetamine w/Amobarbital (West-Ward)
Amphetamine-10 (Alpha)
Amphetamine-20 (Alpha)
Amphetaminum (Amphetamine Sulfate)
Amphetavite Tablets (Len-Tag)

Amphetidisin-10 (Allan)
Amphetidisin (Allan)
Amphetocel (Lemmon)
Amphet-O-Phen Tablets (Ruckstuhl)
Amphet-O-Phen Tablets (Wolins)
Amphetoplex (Vitamix)
Amphetoplex Injectable (Penhurst)
Amphetose Tablets (Jabert)
Amphex (Algro)
Amphezamin (Amphetamine Sulfate)
Amphezine Tablets (Royce)
Ampho-Bese Tablets (Rugby)
Amphobarb (CMC)
Amphocaps (Jabert)
Amphocel (Metropolitan)
Amphocel Tablets (Pharmich)
Amphoids-S (Gold Leaf)
Amphocell Tablets (Wolins)
Amphone (Elder)
Amphovite (Tri-State)
Amphovite Improved Capsules (Tri-State)
Am Plus (Roerig)
Ampsu Capsules (Manne)
Am-Sul Barb Capsules (M.J.)
Am-Sul Jr. Capsules (M.J.)
Amsustain (Key)
Amvicel (Stuart)
Amvicel-X10 (Stuart)
Amvicel-X15 (Stuart)
Amvidex Timecaps (Caldwell and Bloor)
Am-Vite (Drug Industries)
Amwatrol (Goodrich-Wright)
Amyaldex (Hiss)
Amylobarbitone
Amylofene Sodium (First Texas)
Amytal (Lilly)
Amytal and Aspirin (Lilly)
Amytal Sodium
Analgesic Ovals (Lampert)
Analstat (Bush)
Analval (Vale)
Anara (Amphetamine Sulfate)
An-Du-Hist (Philips Roxane)
Anfetamina (Amphetamine Sulfate)
Angesic Tablets (Edwards)
Anox Capsules (Winston)
A-N Rectorettes (Oak Ridge)
A-N Rectorettes-Infant (Oak Ridge)
Ans (Kenwood)
Ante-Mens (Haberle)
Antibesity Tablets (Dumas-Wilson)

Antibesity (Mallinkrodt)
Anti-Nausea Children's Suppository (Webster)
Anti-Nausea No. 1 Suppository (Webster)
Anti-Nausea No. 2 Suppository (Webster)
Antussal (Vale)
Apadex (Franklin)
Apadex (Sherry)
Apalon Tablets (Kessel)
Apamine (Stillco)
A.P.C. and Butabarbital (Park)
A.P.C. w/Isobutylallylbarbituric Acid (Davis-Edwards)
Apeco (AGM)
Apetain Granutabs (Tutag)
Apetain w/Amobarbital (Tutag)
Appetabs (Saron)
Appetrol Tablets (Wallace)
Appetrol-SR Capsules (Wallace)
Aprobarbital
Aprobarbital Sodium
Aprotal Elixir (Grail)
Aprozal
Apyrilene-Deoxie (Foy)
Aquachloral (Webster)
Arbatal (Kay)
Arcodex (Arcum)
Arcodex No. 2 (Arcum)
Arda Timed Capsules (Testagar)
Ardex 10 and 15 (Arden)
Armide No. 2 (Warren)
Armadex 1 and 2 (Arden)
Armodex (Arden)
Arnetrim Tablets (Arnell)
Ar-Sed Tablets (Arden)
Arvynol (Pfizer)
A-Sec No. 1 Suppository (Webster)
A-Sec No. 3 Suppository (Webster)
A-Sec No. 5 Suppository (Webster)
Asper-Sed (Beach)
Asphenhy (Lynn)
Aspirin Phenobarbital (Sutliff and Case)
Aspirin w/Phenobarbital (Barrows)
Aspirin 5gr Phenobarbital ½ gr (Davis-Edwards)
Aspirin-Phenobarbital (Table Rock)
Aspir-Phen Tablets (Wolins)
Astedin (Amphetamine Sulfate)
Astrobute Tablets (GP Labs)
At-1053 Hysobel No. 3 (Zemmer)

Atblake Formula No. 252 Capsules (Hiss)
Atblake Formula 276 (Hiss)
Auraplex w/ Amphetamine (Bernhoft)
Auraplex w/ Phenobarb (Bernhoft)
A. V. M. (Luke)

Bakersed Green (W. F. Baker)
Bamadex (Lederle)
Bamadex Sequels (Lederle)
Bamite (First Texas)
Bandyne (Blaine Parker)
Bar-Dex (Barre)
Bar-Dex TD (Barre)
Bar-It (Lanpar)
Bar-Jam (Superior)
Bar-Pax Tablets (Bowman)
Barba-Key Capsules (Key)
Barba-Key Slocaps (Key)
Barba-Niacin (Cole)
Barba-Niacin Forte (Cole)
Barbadex (Kirkman)
Barbamil
Barbamyl
Barbatose No. 2 Tablets (Vale)
Barbeldonna (Lima)
Barbelixir (MacEslin)
Barbenyl
Barbicaine (Cutter)
Barbiclin (Taylor)
Barbico (Jenkins)
Barbicoid (Moore Kirk)
Barbidex (Davis and Sly)
Barbidex TDC (Canfield)
Barbidon Elixir (Supreme)
Barbikote Tablets (MacEslin)
Barbinal (Phillips)
Barbine Tablets (Davis and Sly)
Barbinux (Physicians Supply)
Barbinux w/ Rhubarb (Physicians Supply)
Barbiphenyl
Barbipill (Chicago)
Barbisec (Kay)
Barbita (Chicago)
Barbitab Plus (Barre)
Barbital
Barbital Compound (Boyer)
Barb-Sul Capsules (M.J.)
Barbital Hyoscyamus Passiflora Compound (Zemmer)
Barbital Sodium

Barbitidisin (Allan)
Barbiton Sodium
Barbitone
Barbitwin (Paul Maney)
Barbivis (Chicago)
Barbosec (Rowell)
Barbulen (Len-Tag)
Barcole (Haag)
Barcon-3 Tablets (Tutag)
Bardex Capsules (Wayne)
Bardex No. 1, 2 and 3 (Coast)
Bardex Timcaps (Wayne)
Barfeine (Bill Moss)
Bariatric Formula No. SS2 (Bariatric)
Bariatric Formula No. SS3 (Bariatric)
Bariatric Formula No. SS5 (Bariatric)
Bariatric Formula No. 37 (Table Rock)
Bariatric Formula No. 38 (Table Rock)
Bariatric Formula No. 75A (Bariatric)
Bariatric Formula No. 75B (Bariatric)
Bariatric Formula No. 75D (Bariatric)
Bariatric Formula No. 75F (Bariatric)
Baritab Plus (Barre)
Barmine Tablets (Tutag)
Barpental
Barplex (Massengill)
Barprin (Cenci)
Barsec Capsules (MacEslin)
Bartime (Barrows)
Barturate (Davis and Sly)
Bartwo (Ulmer)
Barval No. 1 Tablets (Durst)
Barval No. 2 Tablets (Durst)
B-Barb (Foy)
BBS Tablets (AGM)
B-Bromoallyl Sec-Amylbarbituric Acid
Bebital (Wilfred)
Bebadol (Ives-Cameron)
Beedex Capsules (Greens Pharm)
Beladryl Injectable (Bellevue)
Belap No. 2 Tablets (Haack)
Belatol No. 2 (Cenci)
Bellachar (Queen City)

Bellachar Flavored Coated Tablets (Lustgarten)
Belladonna Leaves Extract and Phenobarbital No. 1 (Rexall)
Bel-Phen No. 2 Tablets (Stanlabs)
Beminal w/ Phenobarbital (Ayerst)
Benecycles Capsules (Bernhoft)
Benzafinyl (Amphetamine Sulfate)
Benzamphetamine (Amphetamine Sulfate)
Benzebar (Smith Kline and French)
Benzedrine (Smith Kline and French)
Benzedryna (Amphetamine Sulfate)
Benzpropamine (Amphetamine Sulfate)
Beplete (Wyeth)
Berla-Dexatal (Berkeley)
Berla-Sed (Berkeley)
Besertal Tablets (Central)
Beta-B Liquid (Comboceuticals)
Betabarb Tablets (Evron)
Beta-Chlor (Mead Johnson)
Betafen (Amphetamine Sulfate)
Betaphen (Amphetamine Sulfate)
Bevital (Key)
Bexaphed Capsules (Bexar)
Biatal Tablets (Kendall)
Bifran Tablets (Strasenburgh)
Bioxyphen Injection (Invenex)
Biphetamine-T 12 ½ Capsules (Strasenburgh)
Biphetamine-T 20 Capsules (Strasenburgh)
Biphetamine (Strasenburgh)
Bised (Bryant)
Bisedalan (Allan)
Bisosed (Buck)
Blairserp (Blair)
Blue-Phen (Lemmon)
Bluzedrin (Amphetamine Sulfate)
Bontril (Carnrick)
Bontril No. 1 and No. 2 (Carnrick)
B-Phen Elixir (Wolins)
B-Pheno (Superior)
Bromi-Chlor Solution (Bowman)
Bromides and Chloral Compound Liquasol (Vitamix)
Bromides w/ Sodium Phenobarbital Elixir (Vale)
Bromides-Phenobarbital Special Formula 4140 (Drug Products)
Bromionyl w/ Barbital (Upjohn)

Bromiphen (McNeil)
Bromital (Moffet)
Bromobarb (Hart)
Broncohist (Sutliff and Case)
Bro-Sed (Superior)
Brothane Solution (Cole)
Bubartal Sodium (Columbus)
Bubartal TT (Columbus)
Buethanasia Veterinary Injection (Burns)
Bufeta Compound (Burrough Bros.)
Bufotenine
Burbartal (Columbus)
Burrizem No. 2 (Zemmer)
Busotran Tablets (Klug)
Butabarb (Hiss)
Butabarb Elixir (Barre)
Butabarb Elixir (Hiss)
Butabarb Elixir (Penhurst)
Butabarb Unicelles (Hiss)
Butabarbital
Butabarbital Sodium
Butabarpal Injection (Philadelphia)
Butacalm No. 1 (Wesley)
Butacalm No. 2 (Wesley)
Butacex (Paul Maney)
Buta-Dexsules (Normal)
Butacyl (Queen City)
Butak (Haack)
Butalix (Vale)
Butallylonal
Butalynn (Lynn)
Butalynn-GR (Lynn)
Butamed-Elixir (Medics)
Butamin Tablets (Mallard)
Butapal (Philadelphia)
Butaparbal (Philadelphia)
Butaphed Tablets (Wendt-Bristol)
Butaphen Elixir (Veltex)
Butaphen Sodium (Veltex)
Butapin No. 1 (Wendt-Bristol)
Butapin No. 2 (Wendt-Bristol)
Butapro (Prof. Drug Service)
Butapro Elixir (Approved)
Butarb (Arden)
Butasaron Tablets (Saron)
Butasec (Hiss)
Butased-30 (Schlicksup)
Butaserp (Queen City)
Butatab (Palmedico)
Butatal Elixir (Grail)
Butatin Tablets (Winston)
Butatrax (Sutliff)

Buta-Trol (Pacer)
Butazem No. 1, 2 and 3 (Zemmer)
Butesco (Bowman)
Butethal
Butex (C.B.S.)
Butex ¼ and ½ (C.B.S.)
Butibarbital Elixir (Vita-Fore)
Buticaps (McNeil)
Butiserpazide-25 Tablets (McNeil)
Butiserpazide-50 Tablets (McNeil)
Butiserpine Liquid (McNeil)
Butiserpine-RA Tablets (McNeil)
Butiserpine Tablets (McNeil)
Butisol (McNeil)
Butisol-Hyoscyamus Compound Tablets (McNeil)
Butisol Sodium (McNeil)
Butisol-RA (McNeil)
Butizide-25 Tablets (McNeil)
Butizide-50 Tablets (McNeil)
Butobarbital
Butobarbitone
Butodex (Paul Maney)
Butrate (Kay)

C and B Tonic (Caldwell and Bloor)
Cafaryl (Elder)
Calaformula w/ Amphetamine Sulfate (Eric Kirk)
Calate (Marsin)
Calmate Tablets (Henry Schein)
Calpental (P. J. Noyes)
Cal-Sed (Philips Roxane)
Caltrol (Lanpar)
Cambrised Elixir and Tablets (Cambridge)
Cambrised Jr. Tablets (Cambridge)
Cap-O-Sed (Croyden-Browne)
Capsule No. 2-AGF (Davis and Sly)
Carbadex Capsules (Stanford)
Carbadex Tablets (Stanford)
Carboxyphen
Carbrital (Parke Davis)
Carbrital Half Strength (Parke-Davis)
Carbropent (Blue Line)
Carcell (Garde)
Carcell (Physicians Supply)
Carcell-Ten (Garde)
Cardia Sedative Compound (Wendt-Bristol)
Carnusen (Queen City)
Carrbutabarb (Carrtone)

Carrtime (Carrtone)
Cav-Caps (Kare)
Cedital (Franklin)
Cekophen (Veltex)
Cel-Am-Vite Capsules (Nysco)
Celdex (Rocky Mountain)
Cel Obese (Paramount)
Cel-O-Rex No. 2 Tablets (Ruckstuhl)
Ceilamine (Echos)
Cell O-B (Ruckstuhl)
Cello-Bese (Halsom)
Cellodex Tablets (Dumas-Wilson)
Cellodex Tablets (Hiss)
Cell-O-Dex Tablets (Fellows Testagar)
Cell-O-Rex No. 2 (Ruckstuhl)
Cellomine (Kenyon)
Celludex (Royce)
Celludex Tablets (Jabert)
Celludex-Plus (North American)
Celludrine (Gotham)
Cellukraft Special (Kraft)
Cellulet Tablets (Cumberland)
Cellulet Tablets (Nysco)
Cellutabs (Kraft)
Celu-Len (Len-Tag)
Cendex Cenule (Dadex)
Cendexal (Central)
Cendexal (Daderal)
Centra-Sed (Southern)
Centramina (Amphetamine Sulfate)
Cephalgia (Crest)
Ceretol-B (Barre)
Charbel (Delavau)
Charbell (H. Sonnenberg)
Charbelphen (Modern)
Charbophen (Tricounty)
Charcoal w/ Bellophen Tablets No. 2775 (Richlyn)
Chardonna Tablets (Rorer)
Char-Hal (Halsom)
Char-Ken Tablets (Approved)
Charloid (Wesley)
Charlynn (Lynn)
Charspast (Truxton)
Chloral
Chloral Betaine
Chloral Bromide Compound (Davis and Sly)
Chloral Hydrate
Chloral Hydrate and Hyoscine (Durst)
Chloral-Ten (Mid-Atlantic)

Chloraldurat (Chloral Hydrate)
Chlor-Caps (Paramed)
Chlordex (Pharmaceutical Distributing)
Chlorhexadol
Chlorprophenpyridamine w/ Dextro Amphetamine Sulfate (Coral)
Chlor-Stron Tablets and Liquid (Edom)
Co-Entero Tablets (Coast)
Cole-Inel (Pharmacole)
Comad (Bush)
Combisede Elixir (Sherry)
Combital (Rand)
Combogel-B (Comboceuticals)
Comfex (Bush)
Complagesic Tablets (Coast)
Compobarb Capsules (Vitarine)
Cona-Forte No. 2 Liquid (Crystal)
Continucaps (Davis and Sly)
Corel (Moffet)
Corparex Meta-Kaps (Sutliff and Case)
Corparid (Sutliff and Case)
Corvitin (Methamphetamine)
Cough-Eaze (Foy)
Cradex (Craig)
Cradex B No. 1 and 2 (Craig)
Crystodex (Crystal)
C.T. Blue No. 1-CVK (Durst)
C.T. Gray No. 1-DCQ (Harvey)
C.T. Green (Blaine)
C.T. Green No. 1-CMR (Carr)
C.T. Green No. 1-CSE (Harvey)
C.T. Green No. 1-CTE (Durst)
C.T. Green No. 1-CYK (Durst)
C.T. Green No. 1-DAV (Schuemann)
C.T. Green No. 1-DDU (Durst)
C.T. Green No. 1-14422 (Caldwell and Bloor)
C.T. Green No. 1-14807 (Caldwell and Bloor)
C.T. Green No. 1-15058 (Caldwell and Bloor)
C.T. Mottled Pink No. 1-CDO (Arrow)
C.T. Natural No. 1-BAV (Lyons)
C.T. Natural No. 1-CNV (Lynwood)
C.T. Natural No. 1-CWP (Raymer)
C.T. Natural No. 1-CYL (Durst)
C.T. Natural No. 1-DBK (Durst)
C.T. Natural No. 1-DBL (Caldwell and Bloor)

C.T. Natural No. 1-14966 (Caldwell and Bloor)
C.T. Natural No. 2-AGG (Hiss)
C.T. Pink No. 1-CTJ (Caldwell and Bloor)
C.T. Pink No. 1-CVL (Durst)
C.T. Pink No. 1-CVW (Harvey)
C.T. Purple No. 1-CVN (Durst)
C.T. Red No. 1-AYJ (Caldwell and Bloor)
C.T. Rose-Pink No. 1-CWT (Durst)
C.T. Tan No. 1-DDL (MacEslin)
C.T. White No. 1-BSC (Wendt-Bristol)
C.T. White No. 1-CAS (Lafayette)
C.T. White No. 1-CBU (Arrow)
C.T. White No. 1-CER (Pan American)
C.T. White No. 1-CQO (Davis and Sly)
C.T. Yellow No. 1-ARE (Schuemann)
C.T. Yellow No. 1-BMP (Caldwell and Bloor)
C.T. Yellow No. 1-CTF (Harvey)
C.T. Yellow No. 1-CVM (Durst)
Curban No. 1 (Pasadena)
Curban ½ Capsules (Pasadena)
Curban-P (Pasadena)
Curbetite-La (Amfre-Grant)
Curral
Cyclobarbital
Cyclobarbital Calcium
Cyclobarbitone
Cyclohexenylethylbarbituric Acid
Cyclonal Sodium
Cyclopal (Upjohn)
Cyclopen (Massengill)
Cyclopentenyl-Allylbarbituric Acid
Cyclopentenylallylbarbituric Acid
Cycotin (Reed and Carnrick)
Cydril
Cymital Tablets (Haack)

D-8-Desamine (Starr)
D-9-Desophen (Starr)
DA-10 Timcaps (Vanol)
D-A-Cap No. 1, 2 and 3 (Kenyon)
Dadex (d-Amphetamine Sulfate)
Dadex (Mar)
d-Amphetamine Amobarbital No. 1 (Vitec)
d-Amfetasul (Pitman-Moore)

d-Amitrene (Normand)
d-Ampel-Kaps No. 1 and 2 (Grail)
d-Amphetamine Sulfate
d-Amphetamine Carboxymethylcellu-
lose Salt
d-Amphetamine HCl
d-Amphetamine l-Glutamate
d-Amphetamine Methylcellulose and
Di-Calcium Phosphate (Inter-
state)
d-Amphetamine Phosphate
d-Amphetamine Phosphate Dibasic
d-Amphetamine Tannate
D-Ampho-Caps 10 and 15 (Kare)
D-Ampho-Sed 10 and 15 (Kare)
Dantal Tablets (Daniels)
Dapco-S (Schlicksup)
Daprisal (Smith Kline and French)
Daro (Fellows Testagar)
Daropervamin (Methamphetamine)
D.A.S. Timecaps 10 and 15mg
(Allen)
D.A.S. 10 and 15 (Wayne)
D.A.S. (Dextroamphetamine Sulfate)
D.A.S. (Stayner)
D.A.S. (Wayne)
DAS w/ Methocell (Plymouth)
DAS-Amobarb Timcap II (Coral)
Dasa-C (Lynn)
Daspan Tablets (Naman)
D-Ate Capsules (Pharmich)
D-Ate Unoday (Paul Maney)
Davit Capsules (PRL)
Daycap-Am (Brooke)
Daycap-B (Ethical)
Daycap w/ Am (Owen)
Daycap (Ethical)
Daysed (New England)
D-Betaphedrine (Dextroamphetamine
Sulfate)
D-Cap (Kenyon)
D-Citramine (Preston)
d-Desoxyephedrine HCl
D-Dextro Tablets (Firks)
De-Amo Timed Capsules (Spartan)
Deamsu Capsules (Hanlon)
Deba
De-Em Timed Capsules (Naman)
Delatropin (Eastern Research)
Del-Caps (Organd)
Deledex Capsules (Lynn)
Delfeta-Sed Plus T (Eastern Re-
search)

Delfetamine (Eastern Research)
Delobese Injectable (Delco)
Delsox No. 4 (Queen City)
Deltolate (Mallard)
Delvinal
Delvinal Sodium (M.S. and D.)
Delvinal-Aspirin (M.S. and D.)
Delvinal-Diethylstilbestrol (M.S. and
D.)
Delysid (Sandoz)
Deofed (Drug Products)
Deoxie Injection and Tablets (Foy)
Dephadren (d-Amphetamine Sul-
fate)
Depoxin (Methamphetamine)
Desamine Capsules No. 10 and 15
(Starr)
Desamine-TD (Starr)
Descolate Syrup (Vita-Fore)
Desephine Tablets (Studebaker)
Desfedran (Methamphetamine)
Desobarb (Tilden-Yates)
Desobarb ½ Strength (Tilden-
Yates)
Desobarb Tablets (MacEslin)
Des-O-E Tablets (Wendt-Bristol)
Desodrin (Tri-State)
Desonine Tablets (Jabert)
Desophen (Starr)
Desophen No. 1 and No. 3 (Starr)
Desoroids Tablets (Tracy)
Des-Oxa-D (Walker)
Desoxamin (High)
Desoxedrine (Testagar)
Desoxo-5 (Sutliff and Case)
Desoxy-Phen (Lemmon)
Desoxy-Plex (Bush)
Desoxyephedrine Adipate Mono-
basic-d
Desoxyephedrine Mucate-d
Desoxyephedrine (Upjohn)
Desoxyets (Abbott)
Desoxyfed (Methamphetamine)
Desoxyn (Abbott)
Desoxynorephedrine
Desoxyphed (Methamphetamine)
Destim (Methamphetamine)
Desyphed (Winthrop)
Desyphen (Methamphetamine)
D.E.T.
Detrex (Mallard)
Dewux (Halsom)
Dex-A-Barb 10 and 15 (Bell)

Dex-Am-Fet Tablets (Moffet)
Dexabar No. 1 and 2 (Medco)
Dexabar Tablets (Myers-Carter)
Dexabar-15 Capsules (Paramed)
Dexabarb (Betan)
Dexabarb Capsules (Betan)
Dexabarb C.T. (Standex)
Dexabarb No. 1 and 2 (Bryant and Nysco)
Dexabarb No. 1, 2 and 3 Nyscaps (Cumberland)
Dexabarb No. 1, 2 and 3 (Hilly)
Dexabarb Stankaps (Standex)
Dexabarb Tablets (Cumberland)
Dexabarb Tablets (Wolins)
Dexabarb Timecaps (Allen)
Dexabese (Donley-Evans)
Dexacaps (Sherry)
Dexacaps (United)
Dexacaps w/ Amobarbital (United)
Dexacel Special Form No. 1229 (Westerfield)
Dexadan Capsules (Daniels)
Dexadur (Wynn)
Dexafet Tablets (Coast)
Dexagesic Tablets (Coast)
Dexahist (Tyler)
Dexa-Key Slocaps (Key)
Dexaline (d-Amphetamine Sulfate)
Dexalme (Meyer)
Dexalme-LA (Meyer)
Dexalme-S (Meyer)
Dexalone (Wynn)
Dexam (Mayrand)
Dex-Am-Bar Capsules (Naman)
Dex-Am-Caps (Naman)
Dexamed (d-Amphetamine Sulfate)
Dexa-Mine (Kay)
Dex-A-Mine 15 (Bell)
Dexamine (Arden)
Dexamine (Myers-Carter)
Dexamine-B (Kip)
Dex-Amo (Kenyon)
Dex-Amo 10 Tablets (Rasman)
Dex-Amo 15 Tablets (Rasman)
Dexamo No. 1 and 2 (Hamilton)
Dexamo (H. Sonnenberg)
Dexamo 10/60 (Vanol)
Dexamo 15/90 (Vanol)
Dexamo 5/30 (Vanol)
Dexamobarb Intervules No. 2 (Jan)
Dexamobarb No. 1 and 2 (Southern)
Dexamobarb Tablets (A.B.A.)

Dexamobarb Tablets (Barre)
Dexamobarb Tablets (Len-Tag)
Dexamobarb Tablets (Phillips)
Dexamobarb Tablets (Royce)
Dexamobarb Tablets (United)
Dexamobarb Tablets (Wolins)
Dexamobarb 1 and 2 (Southern)
Dexamobarb 2 and 3 (Sherry)
Dexamobarb (Hilly)
Dexamocaps (United)
Dexamosed-TD (Mayrand)
Dexamosed (Mayrand)
Dexamo-Tidisin (Allan)
Dexamphetamine
Dex-Am-Vite Capsules (Naman)
Dex-Am-Vite Capsules (Sherry)
Dexamyl (Smith Kline and French)
Dexaphet (Domed)
Dexaplex Capsules (Coast)
Dexaplus-TD 10-60 Capsules (Gateway)
Dexaplus-TD 15-60 Capsules (Gateway)
Dexaplus-TD 15-90 Capsules (Gateway)
Dexaplus 5-30 Tablets (Gateway)
Dexa-Pyramine (Vitamix)
Dexa-Pyramine Injection (Penhurst)
Dexa-Pyramine Injection (Vitamix)
Dexa-Pyramine Injection (Wayne)
Dexased Tablets (Midwest and Vitec)
Dexaslim (Domed)
Dexatal (Wynn)
Dexatal Tablets (Hartford)
Dexatal-TDC No. 1 and 2 (Hartford)
Dex-B-Plex (United Research)
Dex-Cel (Schlicksup)
Dexcel Tablets (Naman)
Dexedrina (d-Amphetamine Sulfate)
Dexedrine Sulfate (Smith Kline and French)
Dexibar (Barre)
Dexibar-B (Barre)
Dexigan Capsules (Arlo)
Dexime Timecaps (United)
Dexime w/ Amobarbital (United)
Dexital (Cenci)
Dexital Tablets (Metropolitan)
Dexital Tablets (Pharmich)
Dexivite Spaned-Cap (Indianapolis)
Dex-OB (Burroughs-Wellcome)

Dex-OB (Tully)
Dexobarb Fortis No. 2 (Jabert)
Dexobarb Fortis (Jabert)
Dexobarb No. 1 (Jabert)
Dexobarb (Jabert)
Dexobarbital-TR No. 1 and 2 (Rondex)
Dexobarbital (Rondex)
Dexocaps (Jabert)
Dexocel Capsules (United)
Dex-O-Cel (Airhart)
Dex-O-Phet Tablets (Laurel)
Dexol (Century)
Dexophate (Jabert)
Dexophrine (Methamphetamine)
Dexostan w/ Amobarbital (Stanlabs)
Dexosyn (Methamphetamine)
Dexotime (Hamilton)
Dexoval (Vale)
Dex-Sed No. 10 and 15 (Carnrick)
Dex-Sed (Carrtone)
Dexserpine 5 Tablets (Nysco)
Dexspan Capsules (Kip)
Dexspan-S Capsules (Kip)
Dex-Sule (d-Amphetamine Sulfate)
Dex-Sule (Normal)
Dex-Sules (Normal)
Dexstim (Central)
Dexten (d-Amphetamine Sulfate)
Dextenal (d-Amphetamine Sulfate)
Dextim (Methamphetamine)
Dextramose (Rupp and Bowman)
Dextrisal (Plymouth)
Dextro (Prof. Drug Service)
Dextro-Am-Bital No. 1 (Columbia)
Dextro-Am-Bital Tablets (Columbia)
Dextro-Amo No. 1, 2 and 3 Capsules (Tracy)
Dextro-Amobarb Tablets (Penhurst)
Dextro-Amobarb Tablets (Tracy)
Dextro-Amobarb-TD No. 2 (Penhurst)
Dextro-Amobarb-TD No. 1 (Penhurst)
Dextro-Amobarb (Coral)
Dextro Amphetamine w/ Amobarbital A (A.P.P.)
Dextro Amphetamine w/ Amobarbital B (A.P.P.)
Dextro-Amphetamine (H. Sonnenberg)
Dextroamphetamine Sulfate Compound Tablets No. 1 (Shaw)

Dextroamphetamine Sulfate Compound Tablets No. 2 (Shaw)
Dextrobar (Lannett)
Dextrobar (Naman)
Dextrobarb Capsules (Len-Tag)
Dextro-Barb-TD (Prof. Drug Service)
Dextrocaps (Len-Tag)
Dextro Carboxy Tablets (Richlyn)
Dextrocel (Lannett)
Dextro-Cel (Superior)
Dextro-Cel-Vite Capsules (Interstate)
Dextro-Cell (Lustgarten)
Dextro-Cell (United Research)
Dextrocell Tablets (Jones and Vaughan)
Dextrofate-TD (Prof. Drug Service)
Dextrofate-TD Capsules (Tracy)
Dextrofate-TD 15 (Prof. Drug Service)
Dextro-Fetamine Elixir (Vita-Fore)
Dextrolen (Len-Tag)
Dextrolett Tablets (Studebaker)
Dextrolett-B Tablets (Studebaker)
Dextroneed-T Capsules (Hanlon)
Dextro-Obicaps w/ Amobarbital (Gotham)
Dextro-Obitabs 15mg (Gotham)
Dextro-Obitabs 30 mg (Gotham)
Dextroplex Tablets (Naman)
Dextro-Profetamine (Clark and Clark)
Dextro-Profetamine (d-Amphetamine Sulfate)
Dextro-Prolongsules (Wolins)
Dextropyrin Tablets (Studebaker)
Dextrosule-7.5 (Storck)
Dextrosule (Arnar-Stone)
Dextrosule (Storck)
Dextro Teen-Tabs No. 3 15mg (Rugby)
Dextro-Timecaps 60 (Jabert)
Dextro-Timecaps 90 (Jabert)
Dextro Unicelles (Hiss)
Dextrulose (Evron)
Dexules Capsules (Recsei)
Dexules No. 1 and 2 (Reese)
Diadol (Buffington)
Dial (Ciba)
Diallylbarbituric Acid
Diamet (Lynn)

Diapep Tablets (K.L.R.)
Diatal C.T. (Prof. Drug Service)
Dietamine (Key)
Diethylbarbiturate Monosodium
Diethylbarbituric Acid
Diethylmalonylurea
Diethylmalonylurea Sodium
Diethyltryptamine
Digeratone (Direct)
Dimerin (Methyprylon)
Dimethylbarbituric Acid
Dimethylose C. T. (Veltex)
Dimethyltryptamine
Diocurb (Tutag)
Diphenoloid (Direct)
Diphetamine Tablets (Tutag)
Diphylets (Tutag)
Diphylets w/Amobarbital (Tutag)
Diphylets-T (Tutag)
Diphylets-T w/Amobarbital (Tutag)
Dipropylbarbituric Acid
Direcel (Direct)
Di-Tal (Academy)
Diurobese (Biber)
dl-Amphetamine HCl
dl-Amphetamine Phosphate
dl-Amphetamine Phosphate Dibasic
dl-Amphetamine Resin
dl-Amphetamine Sulfate
dl-Desoxyephedrine HCl
dl-Desoxyephedrine w/ Thyroid
    (Davis and Sly)
dl-Methamphetamine
dl-Methamphetamine HCl
DLsoxoid (Queen City)
d-Maphetamine Resin
d-Methamphetamine
d-Methamphetamine HCl
D.M.T.
Dobo (Klug)
Dobo-Sed (Klug)
Dobo-Sed-TD (Klug)
Dobo-TD Capsules (Klug)
Doffs-WT-Heavy (Dofs)
Doffs-WT-Light (Dofs)
D.O.E. (Tilden-Yates)
D-O-E Tablets (Tilden-Yates)
D-O-E (Breon)
D-O-X Tablets (Davis and Sly)
Doloal (Franklin)
Doloal (Superior)
Doloal (Zimmers)
DOM

Domafate (Haag)
Domapal (Haag)
Domapen (Haag)
Dopbese (Philadelphia)
Dorico Soluble
Doriden (Ciba)
Dormased Tablets (Crest)
Dorminal
Dormiral
Dormitol Compound (Buffington)
Dormonal
Dormytal
Dosarbital (Bowman)
Doxephin (Methamphetamine)
Doxitone (Haack)
Doxyfed (Raymer)
Doxyfed w/ Phenobarbital (Raymer)
Doxytal Elixir (Sherry)
Dramamine-D (Searle)
Dramphetamine Computabs (Dram)
Drex (Boyle)
Drinalfa (Squibb)
Drotamine Sulfate (Bush)
Ducevim (Bernhoft)
Ducevim-T (Bernhoft)
Ducevim-T Forte (Bernhoft)
Duenite (Superior)
Duo-Gesic (Frederick Trout)
Duoampho (Kenyon)
Duobarbital (Generix)
Duobarbital 1 and 2 Capsules
    (Tracy)
Duobarbital 1½ and 3 (Wolins)
Duobarbital 3 gr (Jan)
Duobarbital-HS (A.B.A.)
Duobrophen (Massengill)
Duocaps (Flatbush)
Duodon (Kirkman)
Du-Oria Tablets (Ascher)
Duoson 3 gr (H. Sonnenberg)
Duotal (Morton)
Duotal Capsules (Approved)
Dura-B-Sules Capsules (Tully)
Dura-Dex (Bonar)
Duradorm (Lincoln)
Duraduosules Capsules (Tully)
Duratabs (Wynn)
Durenosules Capsules (Tully)
Durophet (Amphetamine Sulfate)
Dusotal (G. F. Harvey)
DVB-10 (Norwood)
DVB-15 (Mayrand)

Dynaphenil (Amphetamine Phosphate)
Dynaphenyl (d-Amphetamine Sulfate)
Dys-Ban Capsules (Northwest)
Dysmengesic (Walden)

E.C. Green No. 4-AJE (Schuemann)
E.C. Green No. 4-AJT (Airhart)
Efroxine (Strasenburgh)
Elastonin (Amphetamine Sulfate)
Elastonon (d-Amphetamine Sulfate)
Eldertonic Elixir (Mayrand)
Eldoral
Elixsed (Chicago)
Elrodorm (Glutethimide)
Embinal
Embutal
Emebarb-TM (Elder)
Emesert No. 1 Suppository (Arnar-Stone)
Emesert No. 2 Suppository (Arnar-Stone)
Emesert No. 3 Suppository (Arnar-Stone)
Emesert Nos. 1, 2 and 3 (Storck)
En-Chlor (Ulmer)
Enhexymal
Ental Elixir and Tablets (Allison)
Enzobarb (K. and M.)
Ephadren (d-Amphetamine Sulfate)
Ephedrine and Nembutal 50 (Abbott)
Ephedrine and Phenobarbital Sodium (Massengill)
Ephedrine and Amytal (Lilly)
Ephedrine and Seconal (Lilly)
Ephedrine Sulfate w/ Sodium Seco-barbital (Davis-Edwards)
Ephedrotal Solu-Caps (Sutliff and Case)
Erasen (Davis-Edwards)
Erba (Methamphetamine)
Escodex 1 and 2 (Esco)
Escodex-A1 (Esco)
Escodex-A2 (Esco)
Eskabarb
Eskaphen-B (Smith Kline and French)
Eskatrol Spansules (Smith Kline and French)
Esperon (Table Rock)
Estimulex (Methamphetamine)
Estracorp (Sutliff and Case)

Ethalyl (Premo)
Ethalyl Sodium (Premo)
Ethchlorvynol
Ethinamate
Ethobral (Wyeth)
Etilfen (Phenobarbital)
Etoval
Eufodrin (Methamphetamine)
Eufodrinal (Methamphetamine)
Eunarcon
Euneryl
Euphased (Schenley)
Euphased-5 (Schenley)
Euphobine (Amphetamine Sulfate)
Euphodrinal (Methamphetamine)
Euphodyn (Amphetamine Sulfate)
Eurodex-Plus (Euron)
Euthanasia (Arnold)
Ev-Ren (Zimmers)
Evipal (Winthrop)
Evipal Sodium (Winthrop)
Evipan Soluble
Evrodex Tempules (Evron)
Evronal Sodium (Evron)
Expectomint (Research Staff)

Fabedrine (Amphetamine Sulfate)
Facaps (H. A. Pell)
Fedra-Thy (Cole)
Fello-Sed Elix (Fellows, Testagar)
Felsules (Fellows)
Fenamin (Amphetamine Sulfate)
Fenara (Amphetamine Sulfate)
Fenbane (Walker)
Fenbro (Cole)
Fenbutal Tablets (Tutag)
Fenedrin (Amphetamine Sulfate)
Fenobex (Strasenburgh)
Fenopromin (Amphetamine Sulfate)
Feridexate (U.S. Standard)
Feta Capsules (Misemer)
Fetabarb No. 1 and 2 (Misemer)
Fetamin (Mission)
Fiorinal (Sandoz)
Fiosal (Medco)
Flatutive Childtabs (Garde)
Floramine (Lemmon)
Floraphen-SCT (Prof. Drug Service)
Floranerval Tablets (Roger)
Florased (Caldwell and Bloor)
Floratal (Sherman)
Flornal Capsules (North American)
Flornal Tablets (North American)

Forbutol (Plymouth)
Forfetamine No. 3 (Cabot)
Formacaps (Plymouth)
Formula No. 12 (Spencer-Mead)
Formula No. 1720 (Jan)
Formula No. 1800 (Jan)
Formula No. 2 SF 1368 (Bariatric)
Formula No. 2 SF 1369 (Bariatric)
Formula No. 277 (Hiss)
Formula No. 3 SF 1362 (Bariatric)
Formula No. 3 SF 1363 (Bariatric)
Formula No. 37 (Bariatric)
Formula No. 38 (Bariatric)
Formula No. 39 (Bariatric)
Formula No. 5 SF 1365 (Bariatric)
Four Amphetamine Compound No. 751 (Darby)
Foy-Nux (Foy)
Fre-Tense Tablets (Kendall)
Fre-Tense Tablets (Westerfield)

Gabail (Fougera)
Galapose Capsules (Galen-Allison)
Galliadine (Astor)
Ganone (Endo)
Gardenal
Gardepanyl (Phenobarbital)
Genedex-5 Tablets (General)
Genetak Capsules (General)
Geralix (Ruckstuhl)
Gerisitone (Pharmacole)
Gerobit (Methamphetamine)
Gerone (Pittman-Moore)
Gerovit (Methamphetamine)
Gevrestin (Lederle)
Gimid (Glutehimide)
G.I. Tran (Westerfield)
Glutethimide
Gothotabs-CR (Gotham)
Green Deducing Formula (Kraft)
Green Reducing Formula Mild (Kraft)
Guianate (Wendt-Bristol)
Gyaphen (Durst)

Habgesic (Haberle)
Halabar Tablets (Carnrick)
Haltran (Haller)
Harmonyl-N (Abbott)
Harmonyl-N Half Strength (Abbott)
Haxsen (Haack)
Hebaral Sodium
Henbro Elixir (Bowman)

Henofor Elixir (Bowman)
Heprodyne Tablets (Westerfield)
Heropon (Methamphetamine)
Hetamine (Dumas-Wilson)
Hexanastab
Hexenal
Hexethal
Hexethal Soduim
Hexobarbital
Hexobarbital Sodium
Hexobarbitone
Hexobarbitone Sodium
Hexshortal (Sabra)
Hisdrin (Massengill)
Hist-Oxa-Mine (Walker)
Histamic-SR (Metro)
Histamic-SR SF. 670 (Net-Med)
Homaphine (C. D. Smith)
Hourdex No. 1 and 2 Capsules (Delta)
Hoursed Capsules (Delta)
H-P-A (Paine, Elder)
H.S. Cap (Luke)
H.S. Capsules Green No. 2-AKL (Hiss)
H.S. Capsules Clear No. 2-AKA (Hiss)
H.S. Capsules Clear No. 2-ALD (Caldwell and Bloor)
H.S. Capsules No. 3 Green No. 2-AFV (Hiss)
H.S. Capsules Red No. 2-AMD (Eric Kirk and Gary)
H.S. Capsules Yellow No. 2-AKJ (Pan American)
H.S. Need Capsules (Hanlon)
Hybar Tablets (Jenkins)
Hydex (Moore-Kirk)
Hy-Dex-Barb Capsules (High)
Hydra-Hal (Halsom)
Hydral Capsules (Person and Covey)
Hydrosoxy (Prof. Drug Service)
Hyobarb (Haberle)
Hyobarb (Indianapolis)
Hyonol (Durst)
Hyophen Tablets (Kendall)
Hyophen Tablets (Westerfield)
Hyophen-BB Tablets (Kendall)
Hyophen-BB Tablets (Westerfield)
Hyo-Sed (Bowman)
Hyoscyamus-Phenobarbital Tablets (Tilden-Yates)

Hyoscyamus-Phenobarbital (Davis and Sly)
Hypasen (Queen City)
Hyper-Sed (Sutliff and Case)
Hyphenal (Blaine)
Hypivals (Physicians Supply)
Hypnettes (Fleming)
Hypnodram Computabs (Dram)
Hypnogene
Hypno-Sed (Jenkins)
Hypocal (Benton)
Hypronate (Franklin)
Hyptran Tablet (Wampole)
Hy-Quad-Phed Tablets (High)
Hysobel (Zemmer)
Hysobel Forte (Zemmer)
Hysophen (Halsom)
Hyssen-AC (Canright)
Hytrobarb (Dalen-Kaemp)
Hy-Val-Flora w/ Phenobarb (Holland-Rantos)

Ibiozedrine (Amphetamine Sulfate)
Ibogaine
Idenal Tablets (Interstate)
Inazar (Indianapolis)
Indocybin (Psilocybin)
Indorex (Pasadena)
Indorex No. 1 and No. 2 (Pasadena)
Indorex-C (Pasadena)
Infadorm Drops (Reid-Provident)
Infaese (Tri-State)
Insolat Tablets (Denab)
Insomnital Tablets (Buffington)
Intraval Sodium
I-Pac (Spencer-Mead)
Ipral
Ipral Calcium (Squibb)
Ipral Sodium (Squibb)
Isamin (Amphetamine Sulfate)
Isoamyne (Amphetamine)
Isoamyne (Amphetamine Sulfate)
Isobarb (U.S. Standard)
Isobarb-APC Tablets (Richlyn)
Isobutal (Henry Schein)
Isobute-APC (Columbia)
Isobutylallylbarbituric Acid
Isollyl (Rugby)
Isomyn (Amphetamine Sulfate)
Isomytal
Isophan (Methamphetamine)
Isophen (Methamphetamine)
Isosed Tablets (Nysco)

Isothal (U.S. Standard)
Isothal 1½ (U.S. Standard)
Itobarbital

Jaydex Tablets (Mid-Atlantic)
Jensenex (Jenkins)
Juniors Phenobarbital (P. J. Noyes)
Jurasule Jr. and Sr. (Storck)

Kalicyanate (St. Louis)
Kaobarb (Bernhoft)
Kaophen (Vale)
Kelav (Halsom)
Kemodrin (Methamphetamine)
Kenital (Kendall)
Kessodrate (McKesson)
Kirkobee No. 3 (Kirk)
Knidex-TD (Knight)
Knidex-Ten Capsules (Knight)
Knised Tablets (Knight)
Kni-Tal (Knight)
K-N-S (King)
Kraftphenamide (Kraft)
Kraftoplex (Kraft)
Kraftquad No. 3 (Kraft)
Krodin (Kraft)
Kused Capsule (Kremers-Urban)
Kylobee Tablets (Kyle)

Laevomate-PM (Jabert)
Lamodex No. 1 and 2 (Tri-State)
l-Amphetamine
l-Amphetamine Succinate
Lanazine (Lannet)
Lasodex (Tri-State)
Latrodol w/ Phenobarbital (Physicians Products)
Lavabo (Superior)
Lavadex (Jabert)
Lavodrine Chroncaps (Cenci)
Lee-Sed (Rucker)
Lemo-FP Tablets (Pisgah)
Lentanet (d-Amphetamine Sulfate)
Leodrin (Amphetamine Sulfate)
Lestense (Sherry)
Lethol Injection (Pittman-Moore)
Levamphetamine
Levamphetamine Succinate
Levatrol (Pasadena)
Levetamine (Abbott)
Levoamphetamine Alginate
Levo-Ducevim (Bernhoft)
Levo-Trisules (Wilfred)

Levonor (Cooper-Tinsley)
Lifo-Dex Injection (New Mexico)
Linampheta (Lincoln)
Lipogen Trisules (Wilfred)
Lipogen-S Trisules (Wilfred)
Liquid No. 6-AAP (Stuart)
Liquid No. 6-AEG (Wendt-Bristol)
Liquid No. 6-AGM (Wendt-Bristol)
Liquid No. 6-AMT (Davis and Sly)
Liquid No. 6-ANU (Lyons)
Liquid No. 6-BAT (Durst)
Liquital (M.S. and D.)
List No. 1601 C.T. (Kirkman)
Lixophen (Massengill)
Lora (Wallace)
Lorinal (Arnar-Stone)
Loryl (Kremers-Urban)
Loubarb (Louisons)
Lowate Tablets (Key)
Lowebarb-CTR (Lowe)
Lowedex-CTR (Lowe)
LSD
LSD-25
Lull Tablets (Foy)
Lull-S Tablets (Foy)
Lumiflora (Buffingtons)
Luminal (Winthrop)
Luminal Sodium (Winthrop)
Luminal Sodium in Propylene Glycol
    Injection (Winthrop)
Lurline (Fielding)
Luxsul Capsules (Luly)
Lycoral (Fellows)
Lyn-TD Capsules (Lynwood)
Lynnbuserp (Lynn)
Lynnocell Tablets (Lynn)
Lynnprodex Injection (Lynn)
Lynnsed (Lynn)
Lysergic Acid
Lysergic Acid Amide
Lysergic Acid Diethyl Amide
Lytogen (Wilco)

M-A Barb (Medical Arts)
Mabutone (Reed and Carnrick)
Magalin Tablets (Westerfield)
Magnox (Bowman)
Maigret (Ferndale)
Malilum
Malobrom Sodium Elixir (P. J.
    Noyes)
Malonal
Mappine

Mardex 15-S (Mardale)
Margane (Northrup)
Marlibar-LA Capsules (Lexington)
Marlibar X-L (Lexington)
Marlibar-B Tablets (Lexington)
Marlibeph (Lexington)
Masobarb No. 1 and 2 (Mason)
Masopent Capsules (Mason)
Mauve (Superior)
Mavefred 2.5 and 5 (P.J. Noyes)
Maxiton (Amphetamine)
Maxiton (d-Amphetamine Sulfate)
M-Buta (Misemer)
M-Buta L.A. (Misemer)
M-Dex No. 1 and 2 (Misemer)
M-Dex No. 10 (Echos)
M-Dex No. 15 (Echos)
M-Dex No. 2 (Echos)
M-Dex 10 (Misemer)
M-Dex 15 (Misemer)
Mebaral (Winthrop)
Mebroin (Winthrop)
Mebusal-C (Ethical Specialties)
Mebutal (Medco)
Mecodrin (Amphetamine Sulfate)
Meda-Plex (Medco)
Medarsed (Medar)
Medex (Medco)
Medexin (Haberle)
Medinal (Warner)
Medomin (Geigy)
Menta-Bal (Walker)
Mephabarb Elixir (Mayrand)
Mephamosin (Oxford)
Mephenamide (Lynn)
Mephenesin w/ Pentabarbital MLT-
    TD (Nysco)
Mephesal (Garde)
Mephesal (Physicians Drug and Sup-
    ply)
Mepho-D (Walker)
Mephobarb Injection, Veterinary
    (Kay)
Mephobarbital
Mephonyl Tablets (Lynn)
Mescaline
Metalose (Tutag)
Metamine (Methamphetamine)
Metamsustac (Methamphetamine)
Methachlor Tablets (Jabert)
Metha-Dex (H. Sonnenberg)
Methadex (Nysco)
Methamphetamine Saccharate

Methamphetamine Sulfate

Methamphetamine w/ B-Complex (Franklin)

Methamphin (Rorer)

Methedrinal (Methamphetamine)

Methedrine HCl (Burroughs-Wellcome)

Methefed (Mid-Atlantic)

Methenexyl

Methenexyl Sodium

Methent-TD (Interstate)

Meth-OD Tablets (Trimen)

Methoserp Tablets (Nysco)

Methoxyn (Kenny)

Methylamphetamine (Methamphetamine)

Methylbenzedrin (Methamphetamine)

Methylisamin (Methamphetamine)

Methylisomin (Methamphetamine)

Methylisomyn (Methamphetamine)

Methylpropamine (Methamphetamine)

Methyprylon

Metrosed (Metro-Med)

Migesic (Thea-Medic)

Milatran Tablets (Milan)

Milidex (Bonar)

Mill-A-Sed (E. S. Miller)

Miller-Drine (Miller)

Mimetina (Amphetamine Sulfate)

Minabar (Minette)

Minukol (Elder)

Monetamine (Northwest)

Monophos Tablets (Tilden-Yates)

Monophos (Harvey)

Monsyl (Arcum)

M-Sed Liquid (Misemer)

M-Tablets (Winning-Peplau)

Multibarb-MLT (Hartford)

Multibarb (Cole)

Muslax (Cole)

Myalate (Grail)

Myosin (Caldwell and Bloor)

Myotal Injection, Veterinary (Warren-Teed)

Myothesia Injection, Veterinary (Massengill)

Nalertan (Neisler)

Namuron

NA-Pent (Mayrand)

NA-Pent Injection (Mayrand)

Nap-Tabs (Santa)

Napaphen w/ Chloral Hydrate Syrup (Vitamix)

Napental (Massengill)

Napental Injection, Veterinary (Massengill)

Naptabs (Santa)

Narcunomal

Narkine Syrup (Tilden-Yates)

Nascobarb (Maryland)

Nascobarb Ovalets (Mayrand)

Nascobarb-100 (Mayrand)

Naus-A-Tories (Table Rock)

Nebralin Tablets (Dorsey)

Nembu-Gesic (Abbott)

Nembu-Serpin (Abbott)

Nembu-Serpin Half Strength (Abbott)

Nembutal (Abbott)

Nembutal and Belladonna No. 1 (Abbott)

Nembutal Calcium (Abbott)

Nembutal Sodium (Abbott)

Neo-Artycal No. 2 (Queen City)

Neodrin (Methamphetamine)

Neo-Ducevim Tablets (Bernhoft)

Neodyne Tablets (Studebaker)

Neonal (Abbott)

Neopharmedrine (Methamphetamine)

Neoprobestine (Jabert)

Neo-Sedaphen (Smith Miller and Patch)

Neo-Slowten (Smith Miller and Patch)

Nevavan

Nesdonal

Nesdonal Sodium

Neulin (Walker)

Neurinase (Fougera)

Neurobarb

Neuronal

Neuronidia Elixir (Schieffelin)

Neurophen Elixir (Naman)

Neuroval (Vale)

Neuroval Elixir (Vale)

Neutrased (Mallard)

Nevrotose No. 2 (Vale)

Nevrotose No. 3 (Vale)

Nexorin Capsules (Dorsey)

Nicobarb (Modern)

Nicodex Tablets (R.E. Stanford)

Nicogesic Plus (Lemmon)

Nicotal-G (Hart)
Nicotal-G Elixir (Hart)
Nicotal No. 1 (Hart)
Nicotal No. 2 (Hart)
Nidar (Armour)
Nilorex (A.V.P.)
Nipirin (Massengill)
Niripase (Northrup)
Nisalco-Plus (Queen City)
Ni-Tabs (Bowman)
Nitensar (Armour)
Nitrital (Lemmon)
Nitrobar (McNeil)
N,N-Diethyltryptamine
N,N-Dimethyl-4-Hydroxytryptamine
N,N-Dimethylserotonin
Nobese Tablets (Edwards)
Noclon (Amphetamine Sulfate)
Noctal
Noctan (Methyprylon)
Noctec (Squibb)
Nodular (Methyprylon)
Noludar (Hoffmann-LaRoche)
Noptil
Noradrin (Methamphetamine)
Norephedrane (Amphetamine Sulfate)
Norexin (Smith-Dorsey)
Normadrine Solution (Van Pelt Brown)
Normin (De Leon)
Norodin (Endo)
Norodrin (Methamphetamine)
Nostal
Novadex (Perry)
Novydrine (Amphetamine Sulfate)
Noxyron (Glutethimide)
Nucleon and Amphetamine (Park)
Numal (United)
Nunol
Nurocam Tablets (Westerfield)
Nurodol (Buffington)
Nurokardiac Tablets (Rorer)
Nutrix Vitamin-Mineral Syrup (Wabash)
Nuxaphen (Durst)
Nuxi-Barb (Hazleton)
Nuxogen Tablets (Studebaker)
Nyomin-BA (Elder)

O-B8 Tablets (Wolins)
O-B13 Tablets (Wolins)
O-B15 Tablets (Wolins)

Obamide (Fisher)
O-B-C-T (Ruckstuhl)
Obecarb (Bush)
O-Bedex Lozenges (Lustgarten)
Obedex Lozenges (United Research)
Obedrill (B.L.B.)
Obedrin (Massengill)
Obedrin-LA (Massengill)
Obelones Tablets (Nejo)
Obesedrin (d-Amphetamine Sulfate)
Obesilin (Lincoln)
Obesonil (d-Amphetamine Sulfate)
Obesonil (Lincoln)
Obestrol (Crestmed)
Obetamine (Davis and Sly)
Obetrol (Obetrol)
Obeval (Vale)
O.B. Formula No. 15A (Kalmar)
Obi-Tri-Phet Injection (Gotham)
O.B.L. Lozenges (Yen-Tag)
Obocell (Neisler)
Obocell Complex (Neisler)
Obocell-TF (Neisler)
Obolip (Lakeside)
Obozet Capsules (Cenci)
Off-Tabs (Kare)
Oktedrin (Amphetamine Sulfate)
Omni-Sed Tablets (Delta)
Ondasil (Glutethimide)
Opidice (Boyle)
Oraldrina (Amphetamine Sulfate)
Orbital (Organd)
Ortal Sodium (Parke-Davis)
Ortedrine (Amphetamine Sulfate)
Ortenal (Amphetamine Sulfate)
Orthedrin (Amphetamine Sulfate)
Ortho-Phosphoryl-4-Hydroxy-n-Dimethyltryptamine
Ova-Bese (Harvey)
Owate (Paul Maney)
Oxabar (Durst)
Oxydess (Chimedic)
Oxydessin Tablets (Conal)
Oxydrene (Methamphetamine)
Oxydrin (Grant)
Oxyfed (Cole)

P. and B. (Schlicksup)
P. and H. No. 1 (Halsom)
P. and H. No. 1 (Moffet)
P. and H. No. 2 (Halsom)
P. and H. No. 2 (Moffet)
P-A-C w/ Cyclopal (Upjohn)

Pain-Tabs (Tracy)
Palagren Liquid (Westerfield)
Palagren (Kendall)
Palapent (Bristol)
Palgesic (Pan American)
Palinum
Palobese (Palmedico)
Pama (Conal)
Pambromal (Whittier)
Pamine-PB Drops (Upjohn)
Panbutal (Pan American)
Panbutal Elixir (Pan American)
Pannuxital (Airhart)
Panrexin-TP (Pan American)
Parabarb-3 Capsules (Paramed)
Paradex-10 Capsules (Paramed)
Paradex-15 Capsules (Paramed)
Paradexsets No. 3 (Paramount)
Paradol (Medics)
Paral (Fellows)
Paraldehyde
Parkoplex (Park)
Pasa-Flora (Indianapolis)
Pascotal List No. 384 (Bowman)
Pascotal List No.385 (Bowman)
Pasibar (Lima)
Pasijen Tablets (Jenkins)
Passi-Barb (Smith Miller and Patch)
Passibarbital (C. D. Smith)
Passi-Dyne Tablets (Tri-State)
Passilynn (Lynn)
Passimil (Superior)
Passiphen (McNeil)
Passital (Moffet)
Passitilla (Stuart, Elder)
Passobar (Arrow)
PB Tablets (Cenci)
PB-30 (Schlicksup)
PBR/12 Capsules (Scott-Allison)
P.C. Chocolate No. 9-AAQ (Davis & Sly)
Pedestal Capsules (Len-Tag)
Pelladex (Coast)
Pelladex-15 (Coast)
Pellbarb (Kirkman)
Pellcaps (Kirkman)
Pell-Sed Tablets (H. A. Pell)
Pembrin (Novocol)
Pembule (Novocol)
Pen-Phetamine (Clark and Clark)
Pentacine (Walker)
Pentaerythritol Chloral
Pental (Mallinkrodt)

Pental (Van Pelt and Brown)
Pentasom Tablets (Archer-Taylor)
Pentenal
Pentobarb-Caps (Wesley)
Pentobarbital
Pentobarbital-Aspirin Capsules (Bush)
Pentobarbital-Aspirin Capsules (Tilden-Yates)
Pentobarbital-Aspirin (Davis and Sly)
Pentobarbital Calcium
Pentobarbital Sodium
Pentobarbitol (Webb)
Pento-Del (Boyle)
Pentodyne (Tri-State)
Pentolen Capsules (Len-Tag)
Pentolixir (MacEslin)
Pento-Meph Injection (Foy)
Pentone
Pentoneed Capsules (Hanlon)
Pento-Pheno-Barb (Harvey)
Pentosal Capsules (Normand)
Pentotabs 1½ (Prof. Drug Service)
Pentothal Rectal Suspension (Abbott)
Pentothal Sodium (Abbott)
Pentyl
Pentymal
Pepsibarb Tablets (Tilden-Yates)
Pepsin Nux & Pheno (Dalen-Kaemp)
Peralga (Warner-Chilcott)
Percomon (Amphetamine Sulfate)
Perichlor (Ives-Cameron)
Peridyne (Queen City)
Perke-One (Ascher)
Perke-Two (Ascher)
Permadex 10 and 15 Capsules (Croyden-Browne)
Permadexal Capsules (Croyden-Browne)
Pernocton
Pernoston
Pervitin (Methamphetamine)
Petri-Chloral
Peyote
P.F. No. 109 (Table Rock)
P.F. No. 1103 (Winston)
P.F. No. 1263 (Winston)
P.F. No. 1466 (Table Rock)
P.F. No. 175 (Table Rock)
P.F. No. 287 Elixir (Winston)
P.F. No. 364 (Table Rock)
P.F. No. 708 (Table Rock)

P.F. No. 7777 (Moffet)
Phac (Cole)
Phanodorm
Phanodorm (Winthrop)
Phantosine-DLA Capsules (Cooper-Tinsley)
Pharb Liquid (Cole)
Pharmamedrine (Amphetamine Sulfate)
Phazyme w/ Phenobarbital (Reed and Carnrick)
Phedoxe-4B (Elder)
Phedrisox (Ascher)
Phemitone
Phenabee (Veltex)
Phenabee Liquid (Veltex)
Phenamine (Amphetamine Sulfate)
Phenaserp No. 1 (Bernhoft)
Phenaserp No. 2 (Bernhoft)
Phenedrine (Amphetamine Sulfate)
Phenedrine (MacAllister)
Phenital Sodium Capsules (Archer-Taylor)
Phenmetrazine HCl
Pheno-Amus (Bowman)
Pheno-Bell Tablets (Starr)
Pheno-Bepadol (Ives)
Phen-O-Brom (Tri-State)
Pheno-Brom (St. Louis)
Pheno-Bromide (Halsom)
Pheno-Nux (Vale)
Pheno-Nux and Pepsin (Wesley)
Phenobarb and Bromide Effervescent (Burroughs-Welcome)
Phenobarbital
Phenobarbital and Aspirin (Direct)
Phenobarbital and Aspirin (Medical Arts)
Phenobarbital and Belladonna Alkaloids (Direct)
Phenobarbital and Belladonna No. 1 (Upjohn)
Phenobarbital and Belladonna No. 1690 (Lilly)
Phenobarbital and Belladonna No. 1698 (Lilly)
Phenobarbital and Belladonna No. 2 1740 (Noyes)
Phenobarbital and Belladonna No. 638 (Bowman)
Phenobarbital and Belladonna (Halsom)

Phenobarbital and Belladonna (Superior)
Phenobarbital and Belladonna (Airhart)
Phenobarbital and Belladonna Tablets No. 1730 (Noyes)
Phenobarbital and Bromides Elixir (Moore Kirk)
Phenobarbital and Bromides Elixir (Philips Roxane)
Phenobarbital and Bromides Elixir (Tilden-Yates)
Phenobarbital and Bromides (Medical Arts)
Phenobarbital and Ephedrine Sulfate (Direct)
Phenobarbital and Hyoscyamus (Zimmers)
Phenobarbital and Hyoscyamus Formula No. 2 (Medical Arts)
Phenobarbital and Hyoscyamus No. 1 Zimmers)
Phenobarbital and Hyoscyamus $\frac{1}{2}$ (Superior)
Phenobarbital and Hyoscyamus $\frac{1}{4}$ (Superior)
Phenobarbital and Passiflora Compound (Blaine)
Phenobarbital Calcium
Phenobarbital Hyoscyamus and Passiflora (Briar)
Phenobarbital Hyoscyamus Compound P.F. No. 1576 (MacEslin)
Phenobarbital Hyoscyamus and Passiflora Compound (Medical Arts)
Phenobarbital Sodium
Phenobarbital, Sodium Citrate, Potassium Iodide (Blaine)
Phenobarbital Sodium in Propylene Glycol (Endo, Rorer)
Phenobarbital Stronger Elixir (Sutliff and Case)
Phenobarbital w/ Sodium Bromide Elixir (Zemmer)
Phenobarbital $\frac{1}{4}$ and Hyoscyamus $\frac{1}{4}$ (Caldwell and Bloor)
Phenobarbital $\frac{1}{4}$ and P.E. Hyoscyamus $\frac{1}{4}$ (Medco)
Phenobarbital $\frac{1}{4}$ gr w/Extract Hyoscyamus $\frac{1}{8}$ gr (Queen City)
Phenobarbital-Hyoscyamus Tablets (Westerfield)

Phenobarbital (Webb)
Phenobarbitone
Phenobella (Ferndale)
Phenobrom (Schuemann)
Phenobromal (Amco)
Phenobromide (Central)
Phenobromidine Elixir (Tilden-Yates)
Phenocaps (Jabert)
Phenocaps Fortis (Jabert)
Phenocyamus (Cole)
Phenodonna No. 2 (Modern)
Phenoflora (Philips Roxane)
Phenonyl
Phenopal
Phenosate Elixir (Bryant)
Phenosedophen Tablets (Studebaker)
Phenotropine (Moffet)
Phenoturic (Ethical)
Phenpromin (d-Amphetamine Sulfate)
Phenylethylbarbituric Acid
Phenylethylmalonylurea
Phenylmethylbarbituric Acid
Pheta 5, 10, and 15 Delacaps (Sig)
Phetabar (Moore-Kirk)
Phetabarb Delacaps (Sig)
Phetadex (d-Amphetamine Sulfate)
Phetabese (Cole)
Philopon (Methamphetamine)
Phob (Brewer)
Phy-Somol (Physicians Supply)
Placidyl (Abbott)
Plexamine Liquid (Naman)
Polybarb Capsules (Arnell)
Pomadex (Standex)
Pomadex-15 (Standex)
Pomatran (Standex)
Prednal Tablets (Nysco)
Prelital (PRL)
Prelu-Vite (Geigy)
Preludin (Geigy)
Premodrin (Premo)
Pre-Ob Tablets (Rasman)
Pretension (Quaker City)
Prevamodex 15 and 60 (Rand)
Previdex 10 and 15 (Rand)
Private Formula No. 1-DGN
Private Formula No. 1-DET (Harvey)
Private Formula No. 3-BCN (Jenkins)

Private Formula No. 4651 (Halsom)
Private Formula No. 9-AAM (Jenkins)
Private Formula No. 1-DHO (Mac-Eslin)
Private Formula No. 1-DGZ (Caldwell and Bloor)
Privenal
Probar (Allan)
Probarbital
Probarbital Calcium
Probarbital Sodium
Probestine (Jabert)
Probestine-TD (Jabert)
Profamina (Amphetamine Sulfate)
Profetamine (Amphetamine Sulfate)
Profetamine HCl (Archer-Taylor)
Profetamine Phosphate (Clark and Clark)
Prolaire (Stuart)
Prominal
Propallylonal
Propenyl (Amphetamine Sulfate)
Prospisamine (Amphetamine Sulfate)
Proponal
Proptane (d-Amphetamine Sulfate)
Providex Tablets (Provident)
Proxydrin (Professional Pharm)
Psilocibin
Psilocin
Psilocybin
Psilocyn
Psilotsin (Psilocin)
Psychedrine (Amphetamine Sulfate)
Psychedrinum (Amphetamine Sulfate)
Psychedryna (Amphetamine Sulfate)
Psychergine (Methamphetamine)
Psychoton (Amphetamine Sulfate)
Psykoton (Methamphetamine)
P.T.Z. (Franklin)
Pulsabarb (Physicians Supply)
Pulsaphen List No. 113 and 114 (Wesley)
Pulsobarb (Dalen-Kaemp)
Pymadex (Fellows, Testagar)
Pymadex Timed Capsule (Fellows, Testagar)
Pyramid (Barre)
Pyrdex Injection (Savage)
Pyriladex (Nysco)

Pyrilamine Maleate w/ Dextro-Amphetamine (United Research)

Q Caps (Testagar)
Quacharbell (Quaker City)
Quad-Set Tablets (Kenyon)
Quadamine (Tutag)
Quadra-Bar Tablets (Columbus)
Quadra-Barb (Moffet)
Quadra-Sed (Smith Miller and Patch)
Quadsed Capsules (Lynn)
Quakerdex Capsules (Quaker City)
Quartal Tablets (Tully)
Quasedate (Quaker City)
Quatra-Mak 20 TD (Jabert)
Qui-A-Zone (Walker)
Quiebar (Nevin)
Quiedrate Capsules (Luly)
Quiess (Durst)
Quinalbarbitone Sodium

R-239
R-3 Gray (Winning-Peplau)
R-3 Pink (Winning-Peplau)
R-3 Yellow (Winning-Peplau)
R/Amphetamine (Prof. Drug Service)
Rabudex (Lynn)
Rabudex-GR (Lynn)
Racemic Desoxynorephedrine
Racephen (Ives-Cameron)
Raldrate Syrup (Jones and Vaughan)
Ram-B-Phen (Northwest)
Raphetamine Phosphate (Strasenburgh)
R.A.S. (Stayner)
Ratiodrine (Metro-Med)
Raudilan-PB Tablets (Lannett)
Rectidon
Rectules (Fellows)
Red Expectorant (Wendt-Bristol)
Redex Jr. (Tri-State)
Reducap (Morton)
Reducaps (Werner)
Reducell (Bush)
Reducing Capsules 10 mg-No. 2 sf. 1234 (Davis-Edwards)
Reducing Capsules 10 mg-No. 3 sf. 1235 (Davis-Edwards)
Reducing-Tabs 10 mg-No. 1 Grey (Davis-Edwards)
Reducing-Tabs 10 mg-No. 2 White (Davis-Edwards)

Reducing-Tabs 10 mg-No. 3 Pink (Davis-Edwards)
Reducing-Tabs 15 mg-No. 3 Blue (Davis-Edwards)
Reducing-Tabs 15 mg-No. 3 Pink (Davis-Edwards)
Reducto (Arcum)
Redutab (Morton)
Relaxan (Pitman-Moore)
Relaxinal (Success Chemical)
Releas-Obese (Vanguard)
Reme (Caldwell and Bloor)
Reniphen (Winston)
Reniphen No. 2 (Winston)
Reoxyn Injection (Pasadena)
Reposans (Physicians Prod.)
Resedex (Cenci)
Reserbutal (Lustgarten)
Reserbutal No. 2 (Lustgarten)
Reserpal (Garde)
Reserpine and Phenobarbital (Direct)
Reserpine w/Mebaral (Winthrop)
Reserpodex Tablets (Teemar)
Resitab ½ (Arnell)
Resital Elixir (Arnell)
Respazem (Zemmer)
Respazem No. 2 (Zemmer)
Restinal Tablets (Sanford)
Restophen (Kay)
Restophen Half-Strength (Noyes)
Revamodex 15 and 60 (Rand)
Revicaps (Lederle)
Revidex (Rand)
Rhinalator (Amphetamine Sulfate)
Rhinodex Tablets (Stanford)
Ro-Dex (Rowell)
Rogesic (Rocky Mountain)
Rohist-Plus (Rocky Mountain)
Rotase (Northrup)
Rotase-Mitte (Northrup)
Rotran (Rocky Mountain)
Roxyn (Rocky Mountain)
R-S-Tabs (Kare)
Rubarsin (Rupp and Bowman)
Ruck-Sed (Rucker)
Ru-Ludin (Rudy Klein)
Rutanol
Rx No. 4087 (Zemmer)
Rx No. 4100 (Zemmer)
Rx No. 4109 (Zemmer)
Rx No. 4135 (Zemmer)
Rx No. 4148 (Zemmer)
Rx No. 4156 (Zemmer)

Rx No. 4176 (Zemmer)
Rx No. 644 (Kirkman)
Rx No. 822 (Kirkman)
Rx No. 988 (Kirkman)
Rx No. 989 (Kirkman)

S. No. 5 Tablets (Starr)
Sagatal
Salipral (Lustgarten)
Salipral (Kenyon)
Salipral (Wynn)
Salisil w/Phenobarbital (Elder)
Sal-Meph Improved (Fisher)
Sandoptal (Sandoz)
Santalgesic Tablets (Santa)
Sarodormin (Glutethimide)
S.B.P. (Lemmon)
S.C. Blue No. 3-AXF (Harvey)
S.C. Blue No. 3-BAF (Durst)
S.C. Cream No. 3-AJP (Fox)
S.C. Gray No. 3-APY (Davis and Sly)
S.C. Gray No. 3-ATC (Caldwell and Bloor)
S.C. Green No. 3-AVR (Raymer)
S.C. Green No. 3-AYL (J. Allan Shaw)
S.C. Green No. 3-14826 (Caldwell and Bloor)
S.C. Lavender No. 3-AXQ (Harvey)
S.C. Lavender No. 3-BBH (Mac-Eslin)
S.C. Pink (Caldwell and Bloor)
S.C. Pink No. 3-AVJ (Raymer)
S.C. Pink No. 3-13310 (Scheumann)
S.C. Purple No. 3-ATG (Sherwood)
S.C. Purple No. 3-AXV (Caldwell and Bloor)
S.C. Red No. 3-AXO (Lampert)
S.C. Red No. 3-AYE (Durst)
S.C. T. Passitilla Yellow (Stuart)
S.C. Violet No. 3-AZW (Caldwell and Bloor)
S.C. White No. 3-ASB (Physicians Supply)
S.C. Yellow No. 3-AVG (Scheumann)
Scophenesin (Nelson-Boyer)
Schlickative (Schlicksup)
Schlickinol 100 Capsules (Schlicksup)
Sebephen (Haag)
Sebutal (Tilden-Yates)

Sec-Am-Bital Capsules (Columbia)
Secamine Stankaps (Standex)
Secbutobarbitone
Seco-8 Capsules (Fleming)
Secobar Capsules (Naman)
Secobarbital Sodium
Secobarbital Soluble
Secobarbital (Webb)
Secobarbitol
Secocaps (Hiss)
Secodex (Hart)
Secodex Capsules (Cumberland)
Secodrin (Premo)
Secodrin Encore (Hart)
Secolen Capsules (Len-Tag)
Secolynn Sodium Capsules (Lynn)
Secomob Capsules (Allen)
Seconal (Lilly)
Seconal Sodium (Lilly)
Seconeed Capsules (Hanlon)
Seconesin (Crookes-Barnes)
Seco-Pro 1½ (Prof. Drug Service)
Seco-Synatan (Neisler)
Secotress (Wampole)
Sectal (St. Louis)
Sectal Capsules (United)
Seda-Bute (Cole)
Seda-Symtol Temsules (Veltex)
Sedabar Tablets (Klug)
Sedabarb No. 2 Tablets (Tilden-Yates)
Sedacaps (Dumas-Wilson)
Sedacil (MacEslin)
Sedacil Coated Tablets
Sedadex (Novocol)
Sedadrops (Walker)
Sedafax (Eastern Research)
Sedaflora (Philips Roxane)
Sedagesic (Kay)
Sedalgesic (Table Rock)
Sedalgesic Inserts (Table Rock)
Sedalixir (Walker)
Sedalones Tablets (Nejo)
Sedalyn (Lynwood)
Sedamine (Boody)
Sedamine-1 (Modern)
Sed-A-Nat (National)
Sedapav (Moore Kirk)
Sed-A-Ped Liquid (Steven)
Sedaphen (Smith Miller and Patch)
Sed-A-Plex Tablets (Austin)
Sedaplex (Walker)

Sedapro-TD (Prof. Drug Service)
Sedaserpine (Oxford)
Sedatal (Medco)
Sedative No. 1 (Lampert)
Sedative No. 2164 (Borneman)
Sedative No. 6 (Philips Roxane)
Sedavin (Wendt-Bristol)
Sedavol (Wendt-Bristol)
Sedelixir (MacEslin)
Sedeval
Sedex (Nysco)
Sedex Nyscaps (Cumberland)
Sedinyl (Smith Miller and Patch)
Sedital (Halsom)
Sedital (United Research)
Sedital Tablets (Wolins)
Sedital Tablets No. 4614 (Richlyn)
Sedobarb (Whittier)
Sedobarb No. 2 (Whittier)
Sedo-Bee Tablets (Southern)
Sed-O-Et (Drug Products)
Sedogel (Medical Arts)
Sedolin (Amphetamine Sulfate)
Sedotane (Wendt-Bristol)
Sedoval Tablets (Westerfield)
Sedovas (Massengill)
Sedpane (Freeport)
Semoxydrine (Massengill)
Sendex Delay-Caps (American)
Senigesic (Caldwell and Bloor)
Senostim Liquid and Tablets (Lynn)
Serbuta (Freeport)
Ser-Doma (Haag)
Serpabarb Tablets (Misemer)
Serp-Ex-5 Tablets (Scott-Tussin)
Sertal (Medical Arts)
Sertec-M Tablets (Arnell)
Sertrim Tablets (Arnell)
Sertrim-RA (Arnell)
Setaflem (Rupp and Bowman)
Setared (Rupp and Bowman)
Sevital (Academy)
Sevocol (Wendt-Bristol)
S-F-D-1 (Riders)
Sigmodal
Silbar (Haack)
Simpamine (Amphetamine Sulfate)
Simpatedrin (Amphetamine Sulfate)
Sistol Elixir and Tablets (Studebaker)
Slodex Tablets (Mid-Atlantic)
Slo-Jaydex (Mid-Atlantic)
Sodital (Arnar-Stone)

Sodium Phenobarbital w/Sodium Bromide Solution (Durst)
Sodium Phenylethylbarbiturate
Sodium 5-Allyl-5-(1-Methyl-Butyl)-2-Thiobarbiturate
Sodium 5-Ethyl-5-(1-Methylbutyl)-2-Thiobarbiturate
Sodium 5-Ethyl-5-Hexylbarbiturate
Soduben (Arcum)
Solfo-Serpine (Poythress)
Solfoton (Poythress)
Solsed (Jackson-Mitchell)
Solu-Barb (Fellows Testagar)
Solu-Barb Tablets (Pediatric)
Soluble Pentobarbital
Soluble Phenobarbital
Soluble Phenobarbitone
Somatal (Person and Covey)
Sombitol (Wesley)
Sombrul (Columbus)
Sombucaps (Riker)
Sombulex (Riker)
Sominal-PB (Flint-Eaton)
Sominal-Phenobarb (Davis and Sly)
Sominol Phenobarbital (Tilden-Yates)
Somlyn Tablets (Davis and Sly)
Somlyn-Phenobarbital (Davis and Sly)
Somnalar Tablets (Lardon)
Somnalert (Warren-Teed)
Somnesin Injection, Veterinary (Central)
Somnipron
Somni-Sed (Tutag)
Somnopentyl (Pittman-Moore)
Somnos (M.S. and D.)
Somonal
Somonal Capsules (Croyden-Browne)
Somorsed (Philips Roxane)
Somtrol (Philips Roxane)
Sonazar (Tutag)
Sondrate Elixir (Kenyon)
Soneryl
Sonnenberg Oblets (Sonnenberg)
Sopena-MRT (Thompson)
Sopental
Sopento (St. Louis)
Sotyl
Soxysympamine (Methamphetamine)
Spabelin No. 2 (Arcum)
Spandex-B (Bock)
Span-RD 12 (Metro-Med)

Span-RD (Metro-Med)
Spasmal (Franklin)
Spasmanol (Buffingtons)
Spasmosed (Lustgarten)
Spasmosed (Zimmers)
Special Amphetamine Formula (United)
Special Amphetamine Formula Capsules No. 351 (Rugby)
Special Dextro-Amphetamine Formula No. 182 (United)
Special Formula Capsules No. 1 (Halsey)
Special Formula Capsules No. 3 (Halsey)
Special Formula Capsules No. 6 (Halsey)
Special Formula Capsules No. 7 (Halsey)
Special Formula L-77 (Len-Tag)
Special Formula L-88 (Len-Tag)
Special Formula No. T-60 (Schlicksup)
Special Formula No. 00 Capsules SF 1290 (Pharmex)
Special Formula No. 1248 (Archer-Taylor)
Special Formula No. 1805 1-BJV (Wendt-Bristol)
Special Formula No. 51 (Penn State)
Special Formula Rx T-211 (Schlicksup)
Special Formula Rx T-214 (Schlicksup)
Special Formula SF No. 1291 (Bariatric)
Special Formula SF No. 1292 (Bariatric)
Special Formula T-208 (Schlicksup)
Special Formula T-209 (Schlicksup)
Special Formula T-210 (Schlicksup)
Special Formula Tab CM 6118 (Pharmich)
Special Formula Tablets (Davis-Edwards)
Special Formula Time Release SF No. 1293 (Bariatric)
Special Formula Time Release Tablets SF 766 (Amfre-Grant)
Special Formula Triangular Pink (Bariatric)
Special Formula 1-BRV (Blaine)
Special Nonau F (Wendt-Bristol)

Special Rx (Davis and Sly)
Special Rx 2247 (Spabelin No. 2) (APC, Arcum)
Special Rx 2295 (APC, McKesson)
Standex (Standex)
Stannitol No. 3 (Standex)
S-T-Barb (Scott-Tussin)
S-T-Desex-15 (Scott-Tussin)
Stedytabs-Delfeta-Sed (Eastern Research)
Stedytabs-Delfetamine 30 mg (Eastern Research)
Stental (Robins)
Stimalose (Irwin-Neisler)
Stimdex (Ulmer)
Stimdex Injection (New Mexico)
Stimulan (Amphetamine Sulfate)
STP
S-T-Pephedex (Scott-Tussin)
S-T-Secobarb (Scott-Tussin)
Sulfonal
Sulfondiethylmethane
Sulfonethylmethane
Sulfonmethane
Sulphet-AB Ovules No. 2 (Vita Elixir)
Sulphet-AB Ovules No. 3 (Vita Elixir)
Sulphet Ovules No. 2 (Vita Elixir)
Sybotan (Massengill)
Sympamina-D (d-Amphetamine Sulfate)
Sympatedrine (Amphetamine Sulfate)
Synacetyl (Airhart)
Synatan (Neisler)
Synatan Forte (Neisler)
Synate (Central)
Syndrox (McNeil)
Synorex (Schilling)
Synsatedrine (Amphetamine Sulfate)
Syntil (McNeil)

T-101 (Bell)
T-110 (Bell)
T-115 (Bell)
T-125 (Bell)
T-131 (Bell)
T-135 (Bell)
T-145 (Bell)
T-146 (Bell)
T-147 (Bell)
T-148 (Bell)

T-23 (Bell)
T-32 (Bell)
T-33 (Bell)
T-35 (Bell)
T-36 (Bell)
T-37 (Bell)
T-38 (Bell)
T-40 (Bell)
T-41 (Bell)
T-45 (Bell)
T-50 (Bell)
T-55 (Bell)
T-332 (St. Louis)
T-829 (Bush)
Tablet No. 1-ALK (Physicians Supply)
Tablet No. 1-BKK (Caldwell and Bloor)
Tablet No. 1-BLN (Davis and Sly)
Tablet No. 1-BND (Caldwell and Bloor)
Tablet No. 1-BRI (Lyons)
Tablet No. 1-BRQ (Davis and Sly)
Tablet No. 1-BVO (Davis and Sly)
Tablet No. 1-BZC (Caldwell and Bloor)
Tablet No. 1-13450 (Davis and Sly)
Tablet No. 3-AGC (Heyl)
Tablet No. 3-AJA (Sherwood)
Tablet No. 3-ASJ (Davis and Sly)
Tablet No. 3-ASK (Davis and Sly)
Tablet No. 312717 (Lyons)
Tablet No. 4-AIH (Caldwell and Bloor)
Tablet No. 4-AJE (Schuemann-Jones)
Takabarb No. 1 and 2 (Cenci)
Talalf Tablets (Tully)
Talamo (Merrell)
Talesco (Merrell)
Talpento (Merrell)
Talpheno (Merrell)
Tanphetamine
Tatol Tablets (Craig)
Taxite Capsules (Lancer)
T-Barb (Tennessee)
TD-10-60 (St. Louis)
T-D Caps A (Wendt-Bristol)
T.D. Caps 10 (St. Louis)
T-D Caps 10 (Wendt-Bristol)
T.D. Caps 15 (St. Louis)
T-D Caps 15 (Wendt-Bristol)
T.D. Caps 15-100 (Bush)

Tee-Dees Capsules (Pasadena)
Tee-Dees w/Amobarbital (Pasadena)
Teedex-LC Capusles (Teemar)
Teedexal Tablets (Teemar)
Teen-Tabs No. 3 15 mg (Rugby)
Teenette (Foy)
Tega-Dex-10 (Ortega)
Tega-Dex-15 (Ortega)
Tempo-Dex Tablets (Rasman)
Tempo-Dex 15 (Buffalo)
Tempodex (d-Amphetamine Sulfate)
Tempophene (Tutag)
Tempophene-H (Tutag)
Temsert No. 2 (Arnar-Stone)
Ten-Shun (Haberle)
Tensel (Foy)
Tense-Less (Medical Service)
Tensenal (Foy)
Tension Aid (Lit)
Tenstan (Standex)
Teolaxin (Paul Maney)
Teon (Winters)
Teon No. 1 Timecaps (Winters)
Teon No. 2 Timecaps (Winters)
Terp Cough Tabs (United Reesarch)
Terpi-Chlor (Richlyn)
Terpicol (Garde)
Terpi-Kal Tablets (Approved)
Terpin-Hy-Chlor (Darby)
Terponium (Medco)
Terpyamous (Lustgarten)
Tetrahydrophenobarbital
Tetronal
Thalmased (Kenyon)
Thenital (Ascher)
Theolaxin-Ph Unoday 748 (Paul Maney)
Theptine Elixir (Smith Kline and French)
Theratone (Day-Baldwin)
Theratone-B (Day-Baldwin)
Thiabarb (Caldwell and Bloor)
Thiamine-P (Vitamix)
Thiamital-CT (Standex)
Thibarb (Zemmer)
Thiopental
Thiopental Sodium
Thiopentone Sodium
Thiotal Sodium
Three Bromides Syrup (Lynwood)
Three in One (Rocky Mountain)
Thy-Obese No. 3 Jr. (TMCO)
Thyrex (Prof. Drug Service)

Tidex (Don Hall)
Tidex Tablets (Allison)
Timecaps 10 and 15 (Jabert)
Timed Tobie Capusles (Testagar)
T.M. 10 and 15 (TMCO)
T.M. 10-60 (TMCO)
T.M. 10-60 Capsules Special (TMCO)
T.M. 15-100 (TMCO)
T.M. 15-100 Capsules Special (TMCO)
TMCO Aprobarbital (TMCO)
TMCO Dextrobarb (TMCO)
TMCO Secobarbital Sodium (TMCO)
TMCO Sodium Pentobarbital (TMCO)
Tobaral Forte (Ascher)
Tolamine Tablets (Clark and Clark)
Tolaphen-Phenobarb (Invenex)
Tolbuzem (Zemmer)
Tolsamide w/Phenobarbital (Cenci)
Tolsom No. 2 (Superior)
Tonedom (Edom)
Tonedrin (Methamphetamine)
Tonedron (Methamphetamine)
Toni Ampho-Cellulose (TMCO)
Toni Barbital (TMCO)
Toni Dextrobarb (TMCO)
Toni Secobarbital (TMCO)
Toni-Tran (TMCO)
Tonodex Tablets (Key)
T-O-W Tablets (Kenyon)
Tragesin (Vale)
Tran-B (Byrne)
Tranbusol (Southern)
Trand (Buffingtons)
Trangic Tablets (Kenyon)
Tranizer (Wabash)
Tranquil (Detroit)
Tranquilans (Noyes)
Transed (Buffingtons)
Transen (Gateway)
Transibarb (Breon)
Trantab (Plymouth)
Trapanal (Thiopental Sodium)
Tred-Caps (Santa)
Trenket-Tabs (Lustgarten)
Tresodex (Midwest)
Triangle Reducing Tablets No. 1 (Davis-Edwards)
Triangle Reducing Tablets No. 2 (Davis-Edwards)

Triaxin (Mayrand)
Tri-Barbs (High)
Tribromatal Tablets (Parker)
Tri-Dex (Testagar)
Tridex (Testagar)
Tridex Timed (Testagar)
Tridex Jr. Timed (Testagar)
Tri-Dextro (Kenyon)
Trinotic (Testagar)
Triodex w/Amobarbital (Ruckstuhl)
Triofate Tablets (Hiss)
Trional
Trip-Notic (Ortega)
Triphenatol (Tri-State)
Tri-Phetamine Capsules (Wayne)
Triphex (Tennessee)
Triple-Barb (Moore-Kirk)
Trisobarb Tablets (Cenci)
Trisobarb w/Belladonna (Cenci)
Trital (Testagar)
Trivased Tablets (Wesley)
Tri-Zine Tablets (Virtal)
Tri-Zine G Tablets (Virtal)
T-Tonic (Tennessee)
Tuinal (Lilly)
T.V.D. Formula (Adams)
Twendex-PB (Allison)
Twin-Barb (Ascher)
Twin-Barb Improved (Ascher)
Twinital (TMCO)
Twinital 1 1/2 (TMCO)
Two-Bar (Key)
Two-Bar-HS Tablets (Key)
Two-Bar-Dex (Arden)
Two-Barbital Capsules (Supreme)
Tydex Capsules (Tyler)
Tydex-Plus (Tyler)
Tymafast (Mason)
Tymafast No. 1 Capsules (Mason)

Uni-Butamph-Dex (United Research)
Unicel Tablets (United)
Uni-Chlor-Dex TDC (United Research)
Uni-Haponal TDC (United Research)
Unitryl-S.A. Capsules (Myers-Carter)
Unitryl Tablets (Myers-Carter)
Uronal

Valaminetten (Ethinamate)

Valaspas (Moore-Kirk)
Valeripass (Standex)
Valmid (Lilly)
Valmidate (Ethinamate)
Valora (Superior)
Valtobarb (Valentine)
Vanaphen (Mallinkrodt)
Vanaphen (Van Pelt)
Vapedrine (Amphetamine Sulfate)
Vellada Tablets (Testagar)
Venesetic (Amobarbital Sodium)
Veraflex (Neisler)
Veralzem No. 2 (Zemmer)
Verbital Elixir (Burroughs Bros.)
Verdex Capsules (Lynn)
Veronal
Veronal Sodium
Vertavis-Phen (Neisler)
Vertens (Wabash)
Veruphen No. 2 (Zemmer)
Vesperal
Viatric (Dumas-Wilson)
Videxemin (Smith Kline and French)
Vinbarbital
Vinbarbital Sodium
Vio-Dex Capsules (Rowell)
Vio-Dex Timelets (Rowell)
Vio-Dexose Chewables (Rowell)

Vio-Lactal (Rowell)
Virtal-B Tablets (Virtal)
Vita-Dex Elixir (Vita-Fore)
Vita-Phen Elixir (Vita-Fore)
Vita-Sed Tablets (Krug)
Vitec Complex w/Desoxyphedrine (Vitec)
Vitobese (Detroit)
Volamin (Ethinamate)
Vonedrine (Methamphetamine)

Wans No. 1 and 2 (Webster)
Watrol Liquid (U.S. Vitamin)
Wefeta Capsules (Webb)
Wendased (Wendt-Bristol)
Wescophen-S (Wesley)
Wescophen-S List No. 109 (Wesley)
Wolgraine (Wolins)

X-Ameen Capsules (Xttrium)

Yelophen Tablets (Durst)

Zamine (d-Amphetamine Sulfate)
Zamitam (Marion)
Zamitol (Marion)
Zedrin (Amphetamine Sulfate)
Zil-A-Gen (Walker)

Appendix IV

Miscellaneous drugs regulated by the Drug Abuse Control Amendment of 1965 as having a potential for abuse because of their depressant, stimulant, or hallucinogenic effects (generic and trade names, where applicable). *Source: Federal Bureau of Drug Abuse Control,* February, 1966.

DEPRESSANTS

Chloral hydrate (Chloral)
Ethchlorvynol (Placidyl)
Ethinamate (Valmid)
Glutethimide (Doriden)
Methyprylon (Nodular)

Paraldehyde
Lysergic acid
Lysergic acid amide
Chloral betaine (Beta-Chlor)
Chlorhexadol (Lora)
Petrichloral (Periclor)
Sulfondiethylmethane (Tetronal)
Sulfonethylmethane (Trional)
Sulfonmethane (Sulfonal)

STIMULANTS

d-, dl-Methamphetamine (d-, dl-Desoxyephedrine)
    and their salts
Phenmetrazine and its salts (Preludin)

HALLUCINOGENS (*available only to qualified clinical investigators*)

DMT (Dimethyltryptamine)
LSD; LSD-25 (d-Lysergic acid diethylamide)
Mescaline and its salts
Peyote (Provisions of the law do not apply to non-
    drug use in bona fide religious ceremonies of the
    Native American Church)
Psilocybin; psilocibin
Psilocyn; psilocin